JAMES STEPHENS:

A Selection

JAMES STEPHENS:

A Selection

Selected and with an Introduction
by *LLOYD FRANKENBERG*

Preface by *PADRAIC COLUM*

London MACMILLAN & CO. LTD. 1962

MACMILLAN AND COMPANY LIMITED
London   Bombay   Calcutta   Madras   Melbourne

THE MACMILLAN COMPANY OF CANADA LIMITED
Toronto

First Printing

Printed in the United States of America

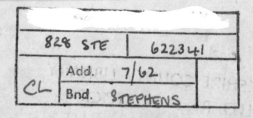

THE MAN WHO WISHES TO PUT A MOUNTAIN IN HIS POCKET CAN DO SO IF HIS POCKET AND HIS WISH BE OF THE REQUISITE MAGNITUDE.

(from *Here Are Ladies*)

Contents

Preface

James Stephens as a Prose Artist

By PADRAIC COLUM

The photograph I have of him shows James Stephens with a head resting on a hand. But resting is wrong; there is nothing passive in the long-wristed, knuckled hand, the mouth, the eyes. With intelligence and power there is combativeness in the face; strength and purpose are marked.

He brought into Irish literature (it was then at the stage of being a movement) a naturalism that was fresh as it was engaging:

> The driver rubbed at his nettly chin
> With a huge, loose forefinger, crooked and black.
> > (from "To the Four Courts, Please")

or:

> Her face was screwed and wrinkled tight
> Just like a nut—and, left and right,
> On either side she wagged her head
> And said a thing, and what she said
> Was desperate as any word
> That ever yet a person heard.
> > (from "Bessie Bobtail")

Into a poetry that was of the countryside or of a kingly past, James Stephens brought the streets of the town and the people of the streets.

"Writing is like fishing," Rudyard Kipling said, "you cast your hook in the stream—that's the story part; but to catch anything you must bait the hook; you must bait your hook with words, gaudy words." James Stephens had words of every kind—a whole thesaurus. Glance at any story of his and you will find one who can be prodigal with the right words:

The Ard-ri could look on all things with composure, and regard all things with a tranquil eye; but it should be known that there was one deed entirely hateful to him, and he would punish its commission with the very last rigour—this was, a transgression of the Sunday. During six days of the week all that could happen might happen, so far as Dermod was concerned, but on the seventh day nothing should happen at all if the High King could restrain it. Had it been possible he would have tethered the birds to their own green branches on that day, and forbidden the clouds to pack the upper world with stir and colour. These the king permitted, with a tight lip, perhaps, but all else that came under his hand felt his control.

(from "The Wooing of Becfola")

These words have rhythm: they are speech. James Stephens came out of the Dublin that delights in a story and is able to tell one with the right progression and the right timing; he could have made ballads that are sung on the Dublin streets, ballads that he sang with characteristic verve.

His first prose work, *The Charwoman's Daughter*, is, I take it, an idyll. And what is an idyll? It is (maybe) a piece of fiction, prose or poetry, in which a desirable life is always kept before us, in which the surroundings—landscape or metropolitan area—is given a glory, in which the main characters get and deserve our good wishes, and in which their actions and speeches have nobility. In their conduct there is innocence. Leave the poetry out, let there be a demand on our credulity rather than an appeal to our imagination (Oscar Wilde said of certain popular books of his time that they made a demand on our credulity without ever appealing to our imagination) and we have instead of the idyll, the sentimental story or poem. But make no mistake about it: the combination that makes the idyll is a rare thing in literature.

Well, James Stephens in his twenties made the combination and wrote *The Charwoman's Daughter*. The interior and exterior that Mary Makebelieve knows are equally memorable. The interior is the single room up five flights of stairs that she has always lived in with her mother. "She knew every crack in the ceiling, and they were numerous and of strange shapes. Every spot of mildew on the ancient wall-paper was familiar. She had, indeed, watched the growth of most from a grayish shade to a dark stain, from a spot to a great blob." But she knew the streets and the parks just as well as the room she lived in. The ducklings in the pond in Stephen's Green were seen through their babyhood by her. "They were quite fearless, and would dash to the water's edge where one was standing and pick up nothing with the greatest eagerness and swallow it with delight." Certain streets were her afternoon's promenade, and she knew them so intimately that she could tell her mother at bedtime "that the black dress with Spanish lace was taken out of Manning's window and a red gown with tucks at the shoulders and Irish lace at the wrists put in its place; or that the diamond ring in Johnson's marked One Hundred Pounds was gone from the case and that a slide of brooches of beaten silver and blue enamel was there instead." She took another outing after night fall, this time with her mother, when they made a round of the theatres— there were no cinemas then. They didn't actually witness any performances, but they had a view of the people going in and they took stock of the announcements on the big posters. "When they went home afterwards they had supper and used to try to make out the plots of the various plays from the pictures they had seen, so that generally they had lots to talk about before they went to bed."

It is over forty years ago since I first read *The Charwoman's Daughter* in the *Irish Review* of which I was one of the editors when the poet of *Insurrections* published it as his first prose work. I read it again with a sense of its singularity and its abiding charm. "Thus far the story of Mary Makebelieve" is the last line, indicating that more was to be told about that engaging young lady. But more has not been told. The charwoman is on the verge of obtaining a fortune when we hear the last of mother and daughter, and Mary who has dismissed an ogre of a suitor is on the point of falling in love with the young man who has become the next door neighbour's lodger. We don't know what happened to Mary and her mother in the years since. But of course they could not be the Makebelieves we were so happy with once they left "a small room at the very top of a big, dingy house in a Dublin back street," when Mary would have either a husband or a recognized suitor.

Still we cannot quench a longing to know if Mrs. Makebelieve when she had inherited her brother Patrick's dollars did any of the things she so earnestly decided to do when she was earning one shilling and sixpence a day. Her servants, for instance. Did she give them Ten Shillings per week and their board, with two nights free in the week while seeing they were well fed at all times? And did Mary acquire that heavy, wine-colored satin dress with a gold chain falling down in front of it, and that pretty white dress of the finest linen, having one red rose pinned at the waist, and that dress of crimson silk with a deep lace collar? And the young man who lodged in the room next theirs, he whose ally and stay was hunger—what adventures did he have? There is no better ally than hunger for a young man, his creator declared. "That satisfied and the game is up; for hunger is life, ambition, good-will and understanding, while fullness is all those negatives which culminate in greediness, stupidity and decay."

Since *The Charwoman's Daughter* appeared there have been memorable evocations of the Dublin scene—Joyce's *Ulysses,* Sean O'Casey's series of memoirs, and prior to it and to them there was George Moore's *Hail and Farwell.* But the Dublin Mary knew is the Dublin that one would feel most attached to. There were no rainy days there, it would seem. There were cloudy days that gave depth to the scene—"a beautiful gray day with a massy sky which seemed as if it never could move again or change . . . one of these days when a street is no longer a congery of houses huddling shamefully together and terrified lest anyone should look at them and laugh . . . the impress of a thousand memories, the historic visage becomes apparent . . . the great social beauty shines from the streets under this sky that broods like a thoughtful forehead." On such a day one would surely go through Stephen's Green, and crossing the bridge across the little lake one would look down and see hundreds of eels swimming about. "Some of the eels swam along very slowly, looking on this side and on that as if they were out of work or up from the country, and others whizzed by with incredible swiftness." From there one would walk along Grafton Street and past Trinity College, and so to Phoenix Park along the Quays, watching the seagulls hovering above or swimming on the dark waters of the Liffey, reaching the quiet alleys sheltered by trees and groves of hawthorn.

But the thing that *The Charwoman's Daughter* really gives us is a share in the happiness of the poor. Make no mistake about this: James Stephens was not one of those tender-minded people who idealize inexcusable conditions: he knew the misery and humiliation that the poor are condemned to; he wrote the terrible story "Hunger" and he shows us the starvation confronting Mary and her mother when sickness comes on the charwoman. But the poor have a happiness, and through James Stephens' gift Mary and her mother share it with us—their attachment to the few possessions that are theirs, their idealization of a world in which there seems to be security and ease, authority and abundance, their readiness for the simple enjoyment of common happenings, their reveries in which things are set right, their dreams of a more generous world.

The Crock of Gold is James Stephens' celebrated book: it has gone through edition after edition and reprinting after reprinting. The Leprecauns of Cloca Mora with their crock are at the centre of it, but there are other interesting beings. "There are whiskers on it," says the policeman who has taken hold of an obstreperous leprecaun on a dark road, "I never met whiskers so near the ground before." If a searching critic tells me there are incongruous elements in it I will have to agree; if he tells me further that a brand of transcendentalism is promulgated that is too modern for anyone who knows about leprecauns to know anything about, I will have to agree again. But what odds? "You would have a good time with us," says one of the leprecauns to the philosopher, "travelling on moonlit nights and seeing strange things, for we often go to visit the Shee of the Hills and they come to see us; there is always something to talk about, and we have dances in the caves and on the tops of the hills." And that is what *The Crock of Gold* is about—seeing strange things, finding something to talk about, visiting the Shee of the Hills, and getting out of our daily lives to such an extent that we can become intimate with donkeys, goats and cows. It has a procession of beings, mortal and immortal, an assembly out of the fields and streets, the raths and caves—leprecauns, philosophers and policemen, battered strollers in their quaintness and human wisdom, young girls, little girls and little boys, the alien god Pan and the native god Angus Óg. Why is this book more popular than any other of James Stephens' books? We all know that there is a world that is the other side of our day-by-day world: with all he has of intuition and reflection James Stephens in *The Crock of Gold* committed himself to this other side, and seeing him so wholeheartedly do this, we go wholeheartedly with him. This, I think, is the secret of *The Crock of Gold*'s appeal.

Mind you, the world at the other side of our day-by-day world has its struggles and triumphs, its hunger and love. It is the very same as our own world except for one thing: a pressure is lifted, the pressure of time. With that element out, or rather, with some of its density gone, the world has a fullness that was not known before. And the natural activities in that world are what the leprecaun recommends to the philosopher—"travelling on moonlit nights and seeing strange things. . . ."

The human entrants are refugees from Time. The leprecauns of course are, and have always been in that world. But the philosophers in *The Crock of Gold*, or at least the survivor of the pair, has a lien on it, too—else why should the leprecaun take it for granted he could come into it—for they are enemies of Time, and they talk day and night because they are talking against Time. The only villains in James Stephens' books of this genre are persons who have such an obsession about time that they interrupt and intercept the philosophers: they are the philosophers' wives. *The Demi-Gods*, a story about a seraph who is flung out of heaven and who rambles through Ireland with tinkers, deals with the same matters as *The Crock of Gold*. But it is not nearly so well known. This may be because, as a successor, it is overshadowed by the prestige of the first creation as sometimes happens with new genres. Or it may be because leprecauns are absent from *The Demi-Gods*.

To retell the stories from the old epics, the sagas, the court romances was a challenge to Irish writers in James Stephens' early days. That challenge he took up in *Irish Fairy Tales, Deirdre,* and *In the Land of Youth.* With his humour, poetry, fantasy, extravagance—the old storytellers combine these qualities, too—he made narratives out of them that have all his distinctiveness. Characteristically he makes shrewd use of the double time that is in the old stories—the time of the world of Faerie and the time of human computation. None except James Stephens could tell without hesitation or embarrassment how the wife of the King of Ireland leaves her husband one Sunday morning, enters on a series of adventures that take a couple of chapters to recount, and is back before he notices that she has left the conjugal domicile.

The problem of transferring imaginative creations from one literature to another is first of all the problem of penetrating what has to be transferred with one's own imagination and then of finding an idiom and a pattern that will represent what is characteristic in the original. James Stephens did all this in *Irish Fairy Tales, Deirdre,* and *In the Land of Youth.* He made himself at ease with the strange stories of Maeve's or of Cormac's Ireland, his own idiom with its combination of humour, poetry, fantasy and extravagance was in line with that of the old storytellers; he found a pattern which brings over to us the peculiarities of the originals. And he went beyond all this by creating a society and a land in which such things can happen. Certainly his personages live according to strange customs, but who are we to compare theirs with ours? Their manners are kind and majestic; they have endowments of beauty, pride and nobility. The Tara of these stories is a grander place than any archeological measurements show us for it is what the storytellers dreamed it to be, "the Lofty City, the Secret Place of the Road of Life," and whether it is possessed by Eochaid or Cormac or Dermod, has in it people who are natural even though their careers mingle with the careers of beings of another world.

Personally I think that *Irish Fairy Tales* is James Stephens' most fascinating book. It has never attained the popularity it should have come into and sustained. With "fairy tales" in the title the prospective reader, I imagine, thought of equivalents for Grimm and then found that what was in the book was at a long distance from Grimm's or from any other fairy tales he had ever read, or turning to it as a book for children found that to enjoy it one had to be adult. Its title landed it between two stools. What James Stephens gave us in this book are not fairy stories in the conventional sense though beings from another world move in and out of them. The originals belonged to the repertoire of the professional storytellers and reflected aristocratic and not folk life.

The two that are my favorites in *Irish Fairy Tales* are "Mongan's Frenzy" and "The Wooing of Becfola," and I think either would be hard to beat as a representative of the storyteller's art. It could be said that their originality is due to the peculiar pattern of the originals. Yes, but if one took the trouble to read the literal translations of these stories (they are given in a book published a few years ago, Dr. Myles Dillon's *The Cycles of the Kings*) one's admiration for James Stephens' art would be heightened. I have said that the pattern of these stories is peculiar. But the pattern of "Mongan's Frenzy" is so peculiar that one wonders how any storyteller could have related it without crazing his hearers.

There are white cows that are taken from a hag so that their meat might cure the sickness of a king. There is an invasion of a country to get compensation for the hag. There are venomous sheep that are loosed on the invader. There is a supernatural personage who offers the invading king a dog that will drive off the venomous sheep on condition that the king gives him the right to visit his wife. Then there is a love story that concerns Mongan, the child of the supernatural father. The lady he is betrothed to is taken away by the King of Leinster who, however, pledges himself not to become her husband for a year. The hag of the first part of the story reappears. Mongan, putting to use some of the sorcery he has learned, transforms her into a young beauty and brings her to an entertainment that the King of Leinster is giving for his marriage to Mongan's betrothed. The King of Leinster falls in love with her and takes her instead of Mongan's lady, and Mongan and his servant with their wives ride off, leaving the King of Leinster to waken up, the hag beside him, to the mockery of his servants. It is then casually mentioned that the hero Fionn was a re-incarnation of Mongan.

How could one make all this plausible enough for a story, find a centre for it and deliver it in a fashion that would be beguiling enough to hold us? If it hadn't been done I should be ready to assure the world that it couldn't be done. But there it is in *Irish Fairy Tales*, a brilliant and entertaining story. "Becuma of the

White Skin" and "The Wooing of Becfola" are fascinating stories, too. Indeed the story of King Dermod and the mysterious lady who was known at Tara as The Little-Dowered, Becfola, is to my mind, James Stephens at his best.

Here are examples of the humor and fantasy of *Irish Fairy Tales* both taken from "Mongan's Frenzy." The first is where the king, roosting precariously on a tree is given the hound:

Now if the sheep were venomous, this dog was more venomous still, for it was fearful to look at. In body it was not large, but its head was of a great size, and the mouth that was shaped in that head was able to open like the lid of a pot. It was not teeth which were in that head, but hooks and fangs and prongs. Dreadful was that mouth to look at, terrible to look into, woeful to think about; and from it, or from the broad, loose nose that waggled above it, there came a sound which no word of man could describe, for it was not a snarl, nor was it a howl, although it was both of these. It was neither a growl nor a grunt, although it was both of these; it was not a yowl nor a groan, although it was both of these: for it was one sound made up of these sounds, and there was in it, too, a whine and a yelp, and a long-drawn snoring noise, and a deep purring noise, and a noise that was like the squeal of a rusty hinge, and there were other noises in it also. . . . "There is nothing to frighten sheep like a dog," said Mananán, "and there is nothing to frighten these sheep like this dog."

The other passage is about the King of Leinster's awakening:

In the morning the servants came to waken the King of Leinster, and when they saw the face of the hag lying on the pillow beside the king, and her nose all covered with whiskers, and her big foot and little foot sticking away out at the end of the bed, they began to laugh, and poke one another in the stomachs and thump one another on the shoulders, so that the noise awakened the king, and he asked what was the matter with them at all. It was then he saw the hag lying beside him, and he gave a great screech and jumped out of the bed. "Aren't you the Hag of the Mill?" said he.
"I am indeed," she replied, "and I love you dearly."
"I wish I didn't see you," said Branduv.

The words are good and in their right place, but beyond that they are the words of a man who has entertained words and can let them crowd the doorway and the sills of his mind. In his talk he could go on to what in any other talker would be a superb invention, and then cap it with something extravagant, profound, or poetical, and this with a promptitude that one would remember as a feat. Few things in speech have stayed with me as vividly as something he said when James Joyce was speaking, as Joyce sometimes did, of persecutions. Suddenly James Stephens' hand shot out and he cried, "You are a king, and a king should have an eye to see and an arm to strike!" From anybody else this would have been an extravagance, but the energy that was of justice was behind the exclamation: it was what the occasion called for, it reminded a harassed man of what a great lineage he belonged to. I think after that they both sang ballads; I have a recollection of Stephens, his eyes closed, his hands folded singing "Cockles and mussels alive, alive O!" But my mind was on the rightness and readiness of his response.

Introduction

The Other End of the Rainbow

By LLOYD FRANKENBERG

Almost a generation has been missing out on the delight of James Stephens. It doesn't know what it's been missing. Apart from *The Crock of Gold* and *Collected Poems,* his gaiety has been out of print.

The trouble is, he never could be bothered to be dull. He can be fantastic. He can be sensible. He can be loving. He can be in a temper. He can be, he frequently is, all four things and more at once. He can even be, when he has a mind to, usually obliquely but sometimes head-on, realistic.

Not for long at a time. That would be not only dull, it would be pointless. Stephens' point with realism is to stare at it, to face it down, to make a sudden angry sound and bound away.

This is a trouble, a very real trouble for James Stephens and his readers. It is particularly disconcerting to his critics. Dullness confers weight; it can be hefted and tested in one hand, juggled to the other. So doubled, it can be compared.

What is one to do with lightness, with brightness, with air? All I can think to do is open my hands and hope the light will dance on them.

Real is an odd word. It reflects the queer worlds, so often at
odds, of realism and reality. The duplicity brings on curious
perplexities. Is this real? we ask ourselves anxiously, approaching
a work of fiction.

For centuries philosophers have brooded and mooted the question. It takes James Stephens to add his inspired three-penny-
piece. Reality, he says—you will find it in his double essay *On
Prose and Verse*—cannot be defined, not because we don't know
what it is, we don't know anything else.

While we're still catching our minds he slips in past our guard
with poetry too. The same thing goes, he says, for poetry. In fact
poetry, imagination, *is* reality. It may be just a little more real,
that's all.

What about that other side of reality, the so-called real side,
good old humdrum actuality? Stephens doesn't say so in so many
words, but the evidence is plain. He regards it as eccentric, a
sport, a form of imagination so extreme it's to be indulged in
sparingly, if at all, or it will take over. The lamp is real; so is the
hand that rubs it. Preposterous to go on rubbing the lamp after
the genie appears.

James Stephens was born, he thought, on February 2, 1882, in
Dublin, the same day (they sometimes said the same hour, six
o'clock in the morning) as his friend in later years, James Joyce.
There is some talk that that day and that hour were fixed upon
in honor of the friendship.

Far from evading reality, Stephens had to come quickly to
grips with it; which may account for some of his singular holds
and the low esteem in which he held facts. As we learn from
Birgit Bramsbäck's indispensable *James Stephens: A Literary and
Bibliographical Study* (1959, distributed here by the Harvard
University Press), the facts of his early life are few. A child of
the streets, he knew poverty perhaps grimmer than that surmounted in *The Charwoman's Daughter*. When he writes in his
poem "To the Four Courts, Please," "And the poor, when they're

old, have little of peace," it's not the pious remark of a sentimental onlooker, it's a plain statement of experience.

How many of his stories revolve about poverty and wishes, two sides of a coin. Money, largely fictitious, takes a prominent place. Never the same place twice. Between each story, Stephens casts the die into the Liffey. Or, for he worked there much, into the Seine.

In his first, *The Charwoman's Daughter*, published in 1912, the pervading imagination is a magic of wishing. The Make-believes wish so singlemindedly for their surroundings to alter that they are caught up in the wish, so delighted with all its prospects that it becomes real for them. The actual good fortune that befalls them is almost unnecessary. Almost. A more sentimental writer might have omitted it. But Stephens knows the potent fragility of wishing. He is too much the realist ever to think that wishing is enough. It is more than enough; but they should have some money too.

He never wrote the announced sequel. But he did not shirk the problem such a sequel poses. What happens when wishes come true? Whisking us off from city to magical countryside, *The Crock of Gold*, also in 1912, is a whirling dervish of wishes coming true all over the place.

As a child his mind must have fastened with fearful longing on the fabulous pot of gold buried by leprecauns (as he spells them) at the other end of the rainbow. Suppose one were to dig it up. What then?

Well of course, read the book and find out. It would be a deadly job to enumerate, in other than its own words, all the consequences of that act, or to catalogue the precise number of wishes and counterwishes that go whistling through. At least three levels of imagination are stirred and shaken, going one up on Coleridge who knew only two.

There are the leprecauns, little wishes, often spiteful, concerned with crocks and gold and stolen washboards, things that are apt to crowd the minds of the poor. There is Pan, strong desire, whose urgings and promptings even poverty cannot subdue. And there is Angus Óg, the divine, the overwhelming imagination.

They are all to some extent rewarded. The leprecauns get back what never belonged to them. Pan gets his wish too, he has the girl. Then Stephens goes Emersonian on us, just twisting and twitting the sage of Concord a bit. When gods arrive, the half-gods go.

Descending from his mountain fastness, Angus Óg calmly puts all to rights and appropriates the girl for himself. Not only are Ralph Waldo and Samuel Taylor possibly ribbed. The biggest and by no means most unkindly laugh of all is reserved for the Greeks. For Angus Óg is an Irishman.

And Stephens has a theme to be developed in *Deirdre* (1923) and *In the Land of Youth* (1924), written as he says to give modern Ireland "a new mythology to take the place of the threadbare mythology of Greece and Rome." Of course his tongue is in his cheek; where else is it ever? But it's a jest the more we laugh with, the more seriously we can take. The imagination doesn't die out with the Greeks and Romans. It may retire for a time, naturally to the top of a mountain, but it's ready to assert itself at any moment and with James Stephens it does.

By the way, whatever becomes of that gold? Nobody uses it; it's kept buried under a thorn bush, a meadowy Fort Knox, too fictitious for all its hard reality to compete with the full imagination. It is the *children* who return it to the leprecauns.

In the later books these levels, the three planes of imagination, will come to be replaced by ethereal interpenetrating spheres. A more complex geometry is evolved, which we might call The Solid Geometry of the Translucently Faceted Dimensions of Timescape. Picasso might have been inspired by it.

It sounds more complicated than it reads. On the page, on James Stephens' page, its most noticeable effect is the translucency. Only afterwards, coming to think of it, trying to keep up with it in retrospect, do we begin to realize how much more has been put before us than the eye has seen through.

As if to prepare himself for these realms Stephens wrote, evidently at top speed, the stories he collected in 1913 in *Here Are Ladies*. Now my peculiar problem begins.

Not to include something from each book would imply unwarranted preferences. I don't mean to suggest, by having *The Charwoman's Daughter* in full, that that is his best book. There are some who think it is. Others think *The Crock of Gold*. That is his best known, sometimes only known book. It's the one prose continuously in print. So I haven't made a selection from it. Any passage would be beautiful but unsatisfying; any complete episode would preempt too much else.

The stories in *Here Are Ladies* are so good that no matter what selection I made you would think I had chosen the best. They are about people who change or are changed. A number are linked in threesomes: "Three Heavy Husbands," "Three Women Who Wept," "Three Angry People."

Those three planes again, little wishes, strong desires, overmastering passions, have been upended and placed vertically among people whom anyone but Stephens might regard as ordinary. Except in one story, they have no overt traffic with super- or subnatural beings. Yet they are all, one way and another, bewitched.

What else is one to make of the father in the third of "Three Lovers Who Lost" (not included here) who hears that his daughter is having secret meetings with his clerk?

The spectacle of an elderly gentleman, side-whiskered, precise and grey, disguising himself with mufflers and a squash hat, and stalking with sombre fortitude the erratic wanderings of a pair of young featherheads, is one which mirth may be pleased to linger upon.

Tempers are continually rising. The same old boy at breakfast, arranging his vengeance, keeps letting out veiled hints which, since nobody gets them but himself, back up on him. "Here, growing suddenly furious, he gave an egg a clout."

This is the frame of mind normally reserved for a leprecaun.

To poverty and wishes, we must add another prevailing climate: tempers and rages.

Stephens' furies have force, point—no matter how sidelong—and wit. After all, he and his characters have real things to be rageful about. They don't as a rule get down on the floor and bite their feet. More often than not their rages are flung in the teeth of fortune, and sometimes outwit it.

Above all they have vast variety. Here is the ending of the third of "Three Angry People," another story not included. I'm now divulging the solution of a mystery. But this startling, this totally unexpected conclusion, without its fiercely logical clues, retains its mystery. I defy anybody to guess the beginning.

"If I happened to be you," I replied, "I would cut off my hair, I'd buy a man's clothes and wear them always. I'd call myself Harry or Tom; and then I'd go wherever I pleased, and meet whoever I wanted to meet."

She stared fixedly at herself in these garments, and under these denominations—

"They would know I was not a man," said she gravely.

I looked at her figure—

"No person in the world would ever guess it," said I.

She arose from her seat. She clutched her reticule to her breast—

"I'll do it," said she, and she stalked gauntly across the fields.

It's true that to get the full flavor of these simple astonishing words, you have to hear them. Though Stephens learned short-hand, he never could learn how to exclude sound from a sentence. Especially if that sentence involves somebody talking. All his sentences, of course, do.

The Demi-Gods, published the following year, grows directly out of, or rather around the one supernatural exception in *Here Are Ladies.* "The Threepenny-Piece" reverses the direction of *The Crock of Gold.* The imaginary wealth that might solve everything gives way to the possible small sum about which the lives of the poor agitate. By means of this hard-bitten entity, Stephens colonizes the celestial (and nether) regions with one

Irishman, whose unswerving demands for justice tyrannize both places and culminate by Gaelicizing a seraph.

Apparently Stephens came to feel that this episode, good as it is, is better surrounded by Ireland. We should never be too clear, between fantasy and reality, just which is which. Surrounding them by each other sharpens and brightens their imaginary distinctions. So he places "The Threepenny-Piece" (lost, of course) carefully in the middle of a group of tinkers, their ass and their guardian angels. (Characteristically, the angels are rather more in need of guarding than the tinkers.)

In so doing, in enclosing as he comes more and more to do in his later books, story within story, time within time, imagination within imagination, in what we shall now have to call the nest-of-translucent-boxes technique, he both complicates and simplifies my predicament.

He simplifies it to this extent. No single story or episode loses in isolation. You may read anything, that is to say, with full pleasure and the confidence that you're getting all of something. You need have no niggling feeling of digest or abridgment.

Who could put James Stephens in other words, or take a word from him anywhere? Despite his moment-to-moment seizures of inspiration, fits of glory you might call them, the result is never fitful, higgledy-piggledy or haphazard. However it comes about, and that's his secret, he achieves in his headstrong, apparently wayward forms straighter lines, more perfect arches, altogether sounder structures than many a writer who starts off like a surveyor, plotting the ground out from under your feet. He has a simple faith in complexity.

Occasionally a fact will rise to the stature and dignity of imagination. Then Stephens addresses himself to it with the utmost and most penetrating observation. So it is, in 1916, that he makes his instantaneous response, in *The Insurrection in Dublin,* to the day-by-day unfolding of the Easter Rising, of which the first day, the initial impact, is given here.

This fact is a dream coming true; the dream of the young man in *The Charwoman's Daughter*, believed in most fervently when he is hungriest. Although this dream, the regeneration of Ireland, is for the time being to be thwarted, there is a tremendous sense, in the telling, of its eventual realization.

If in his later books from the 1920 *Irish Fairy Tales* on, Stephens turns more and more to Irish myth and legend, it is no retreat into a Celtic Twilight. He plucks, from the wilder sources, their more cogent ferocity.

"Fairy tales" suggests children and I have seen this book listed as a juvenile. A child is, to be sure, more precocious than an age-group and easily captivated by these racy Court Romances. But their exuberance calls, to be fully enjoyed, for a youth that has survived maturity.

Padraic Colum, who knows this side of Stephens from the inside, speaks particularly of "Mongan's Frenzy." I have chosen, instead, "The Story of Tuan Mac Cairill." Not that I think it's better. In a very special way, what it relates could only have taken place in Ireland; all the more so for never having taken place.

Most Western countries have their mixtures of legend. In nearly all, except those touched by the most irate Puritanism, Christianity is a palimpsest of old and new myths, rites and gods. Usually, however, the pagan retainers have been fitted out with judicious disguises. Where but in Ireland, especially James Stephens' Ireland, would druidism, in the person of Tuan, and Christianity, in the shape of the Abbot Finnian, meet and while remaining unshakably, belligerently themselves, convert each other?

There is another, hidden motivation for making different choices. Padraic Colum gives sufficiently whetting hints to leave any reader in a state of burning curiosity. If I were to satisfy it, he might indeed think he was getting the best. By giving him others at least equally good, I hope so to incite the reader that he will rise up as one man and demand the rest.

At last poverty has all but left the scene. These are well-to-do heroes. Of course, some are better off than others. One of the new themes this entails is the vyings of generosity. "The Little Brawl at Allen" is the dire outcome of overostentatious giving. Even where all wishes can be carried out, they are the wishes of persons. And even where the persons are personages, they are Irish; they do not at all wish alike.

In these clashings, some real, some phantasmal, between legendary, sometimes multiple, personalities a most curious transformation comes to pass. Realms like subconscious, id, superego, ego are made bewilderingly simple. The Land of the Shí, of Faery, Stephens tells us in his book *In the Land of Youth* (Tir na n-Óg), rests in our world as an apple is contained within its skin. Inside this is another, the Land of Wonders; then still another, the Land of Promise; and then, after we have wished our way through all three, our own again.

You can see how easy it is for Stephens and his readers to commute. I have tried to pick episodes to convey this power of travel. No summary of the rest could hope to be helpful. Padraic Colum has shown how impossible the plots, boiled down, can be. It's even more impossible to indicate how skilfully, how blithely the plots overlay and play against each other. This knowledge can only be supplied by the books themselves as after too long an absence they return to us. Then we will begin to realize just how much the parts, which lose nothing alone, gain in proximity.

We may come to recognize, too, James Stephens as one of the masters of looking-glass reality. Unlike the mirror, which casts back images, a looking-glass invites submergence. Its diverse classics include Lewis Carroll's *Alice* and Samuel Butler's *Erewhon*, Dean Swift's *Gulliver's Travels* and Jean Cocteau's *Blood of a Poet*, the wit of Oscar Wilde, of James Thurber and of Aristophanes. Each has his special slant of reversal, turning life upside down or inside out, paying the world left-handed compliments.

The particular genius of Stephens is to believe with equal vehemence inside and out. He doesn't avoid the outside world; he just won't go chasing after it. Contrariwise, a native direction for him, he makes it follow him about.

Life is alive for him in the proportion and to the degree that it commands the power of imagination. It can do this any time, anywhere. The surprising, the melancholy fact is that it does not always do so. Struck by this incomprehensible inactivity, Stephens must every now and again stop short in his tracks to regard it, much as one might regard an obstinate donkey.

Stephens has more patience with the donkey. Some fantasy, however dim, is working in that close-set mind. But not in the mind of the man without imagination. Worse, or more puzzling than roguery or malefaction is the abiding lack of this power.

Consider his police force: that limb of the law that pays court to Mary in *The Charwoman's Daughter;* his bumpkin counterparts in *The Crock of Gold.* None of them is villainous in the sense of deliberately vindictive, malicious or cruel. They are simply obtuse; such realists indeed that were any of them ever by chance to read about himself in either of these books he'd say, "Well now, that was reasonably put. The man can't have anything much against me. He's given me the proper sound opinions such as that there is no such thing as a phoenix, probably never was, and that a park named for one could be more profitably utilized for grazing. If I've said that once, I've said it a thousand times. Maybe now I could sue him for plagiarism. He should write more about me and less about those vague, distressful characters, philosophers and tinkers, angels and asses, queer-behaving Gaelic heroes. Everybody knows they're all mythological.

"If he'd just keep his feet on the ground and get on with the story: how many miles I tramp on my beat, the rashers of bacon I consume, the pints of stout I put away, the number of the buttons I undo before turning in. That's what any man's after doing and what any man likes to hear about. But I suppose he's writing

mainly for children and such, like that dear near-loony Mary I
was almost marrying, the kind that likes nothing better to read
about than something unreal and marvelous."

Yet he can write as he must, he says, or die of it, "Hunger."
Only a master of fantasy could have distilled such a nightmare
of fact. "On some people misery comes unrelentingly." The re-
lentlessness is far more unremitting than the book of Job, which
after all has its ups and downs and a happy ending, new chattel,
new children and so on.

"Hunger," though it was written earlier, is in a collection of
nightmares, his last book of fiction in 1928, *Etched in Moonlight*.
The title story, patently a dream, is written with such insight that
for me its horror is more mounting than that of *The Turn of the
Screw*. Perhaps this is because, while I find it hard to believe in
ghosts, a dream is irresistible.

There could be no realer a dream than this shuddery, pellucid
examination of motives so deep they are seldom translated into
action. The dream is realer than waking reality; all its potential-
ities are realized. Reading it again I am inclined to feel, as so
often on re-reading James Stephens, "Here, above all, is his mas-
terpiece."

That's before reading *On Prose and Verse*. This little book, also
published in 1928, grew out of an introduction Stephens wrote
in French for *Mary Semblant*, the translation of his first novel.
In it he is less unkind than he might be to prose. He puts it in
its place with gentle violence. Prose, he says, must be invented
from comma to comma.

And he does invent it, he originates prose. He creates speech,
words that rise from the page like a steam of breath. True, they
are more flexible and high-spirited than prose has any need to be;
such absolutely right and delightful writing it seems effortless.
Now we come to know how strenuous the effortlessness has been.

He gives us too the themes pervading his writing. In his telling
they reduce to two, murder and philosophy. We have seen how

often he makes them one. The violence gets into the thinking; such a passion of talk and thought it becomes action.

Finally he draws us home to poetry, where it is natural for the imagination to be. That is where he started out and came back and where I first met him.

In the forties I began a book on modern poetry with James Stephens. It seems to me now as it did then that his poems provide a bridge from traditional forms.

At first sight his forms appear conventional enough, so much so they have seldom aroused antagonism. But a second glance shows him not quite content with these structures. He fiddles and tinkers with them, lets them out, pulls them in to make them fit his Irish rages, moods and high profundities.

Look what he does to their speed. Try reading "The Market" just for itself. Then think of a sonnet. See what Stephens makes of the sonnet, how he joggles it up and loosens it.

Think now of some old ballad. Read "The Market" again. See what Stephens makes of the ballad; how he steadies it up and tautens it.

You can place any number of verse forms, like stencils, over one of his poems till you find one that almost corresponds. You'll still have to adjust it, pushing it in or pulling it out like a slide rule. It's astonishing how true the new scale will figure out, mathematically and emotionally.

You don't have to do these things to enjoy the poems. They merely increase the enjoyment. They are useful, too, to allay any suspicion that because his poems fit so easily on the tongue, they are lacking in artifice. Compare, if you wish, his sleight-of-tongue with Herrick, with Cummings, with Marvell, with any other expert of delight. Match his savagery with Swift; his innocence, his sophistication with Blake.

Give over comparison; enjoy all. Each breaks and creates a mold, breathes a fire of life, restores and renews.

It's true, each poet does some one thing, at least, somewhat differently: some technical feat, some tone, some expansion of meaning. There is a constant effect, constantly varied, in Stephens' poems, not dissimilar to what he does in prose though more crystallized. I'd call it, just to keep tabs with it, a doubly ironical irony.

It consists not in saying the opposite of what he means but of meaning what he says at such a pitch, with such "excess" as he says of poetry, that it includes its opposite. It includes everything in and out of sight.

Take the six lines he calls "Washed in Silver":

> Gleaming in silver are the hills,
>   Blazing in silver is the sea,
> And a silvery radiance spills
>   Where the moon drives royally.
> Clad in silver tissue I
> March magnificently by.

This is too grand and sly and slyly grand to be called hyperbole. After all hyperbole, saying more than you should in order to express less than you mean, is a normal inflection in Irish speech. This raises it by several notches, broadens it, deepens it and turns it into something extraordinarily true, beyond any figure of speech. It is beautiful and funny, imbued with the proudest humility; gives itself the lie and thereby affirms itself with all the more passionate conviction.

What is it, more effectively than any paraphrase, saying? "I am my surroundings. I am nothing but my surroundings. My surroundings are me. My surroundings are dazzling. I'll dazzle you." No resort to symbolism, to arcane allusion, hardly any technical device whatever. Or is it a device, Stephens' unique device, so to interweave boast and deprecation that each multiplies the other to the nth?

When he came to collect his poems Stephens chose to arrange them by theme. You will find the selections here as they appear in the original books. This follows the chronological path of the prose. Sometimes too I prefer the earlier versions. Since you can have both, I hope no harm has been done. A poem, like any other life, is constantly changing.

Stephens holds to the belief that you can find poetry anywhere, in anything. In one of his unpublished broadcasts he shocks Dylan Thomas by suggesting you can find it in cracker-mottoes. "I think, Stephens, you must be pulling my (comparatively) young leg."

When these broadcasts are finally collected, we shall learn a deal more about how to read James Stephens. One already, issued by Spoken Arts, includes a number of the poems here. Once heard, Stephens' voice, nimble as a goat's foot, acts as living guide to all his poems. In deft and simple ways he tells us about them. When you read this poem about going up a mountain, he says, you should arrive there out of breath.

No symbol, no sublimation, the mountain, if you can climb it, is in the poem; the centaurs and the satyr, if you are not quick enough, have passed you by; the old man snarls by the fire; the lark sings up from the breezy land; the goats, if you follow warily, will lead you into the bright mystery of the sun.

❧ ❧
❧ ❧

A
JAMES
STEPHENS
READER

The Charwoman's Daughter
(Mary, Mary)

I

Mary Makebelieve lived with her mother in a small room at
the very top of a big, dingy house in a Dublin back street. As
long as she could remember she had lived in that top back room.
She knew every crack in the ceiling, and they were numerous
and of strange shapes. Every spot of mildew on the ancient wall-
paper was familiar. She had, indeed, watched the growth of most
from a grayish shade to a dark stain, from a spot to a great blob,
and the holes in the skirting of the walls, out of which at nighttime the cockroaches came rattling, she knew also. There was
but one window in the room, and when she wished to look out
of it she had to push the window up, because the grime of many
years had so encrusted the glass that it was of no more than the
demi-semi-transparency of thin horn. When she did look there
was nothing to see but a bulky array of chimney-pots crowning
a next-door house, and these continually hurled jays of soot
against her window; therefore, she did not care to look out
often, for each time that she did so she was forced to wash herself, and as water had to be carried from the very bottom of the
five-story house up hundreds and hundreds of stairs to her room,
she disliked having to use too much water.

1

Her mother seldom washed at all. She held that washing was very unhealthy and took the natural gloss off the face, and that, moreover, soap either tightened the skin or made it wrinkle. Her own face was very tight in some places and very loose in others, and Mary Makebelieve often thought that the tight places were spots which her mother used to wash when she was young, and the loose parts were those which had never been washed at all. She thought that she would prefer to be either loose all over her face or tight all over it, and therefore, when she washed she did it thoroughly, and when she abstained she allowed of no compromise.

Her mother's face was the color of old, old ivory. Her nose was like a great strong beak, and on it the skin was stretched very tightly, so that her nose shone dully when the candle was lit. Her eyes were big and as black as pools of ink and as bright as the eyes of a bird. Her hair also was black, it was as smooth as the finest silk, and when unloosened it hung straightly down, shining about her ivory face. Her lips were thin and scarcely colored at all, and her hands were sharp, quick hands, seeming all knuckle when she closed them and all fingers when they were opened again.

Mary Makebelieve loved her mother very dearly, and her mother returned her affection with an overwhelming passion that sometimes surged into physically painful caresses. When her mother hugged her for any length of time she soon wept, rocking herself and her daughter to and fro, and her clutch became then so frantic that poor Mary Makebelieve found it difficult to draw her breath; but she would not for the world have disturbed the career of her mother's love. Indeed she found some pleasure in the fierceness of those caresses, and welcomed the pain far more than she reprobated it.

Her mother went out early every morning to work, and seldom returned home until late at night. She was a charwoman, and her work was to scrub out rooms and wash down staircases. She also did cooking when she was asked, and needlework when she got any to do. She had made exquisite dresses which were worn by beautiful young girls at balls and picnics and fine, white shirts that great gentlemen wore when they were dining, and fanciful waistcoats for gay young men, and silk stockings for dancing in— but that was a long time ago, because these beautiful things used to make her very angry when they were taken from her, so that she cursed the people who came to take them away and sometimes tore up the dresses and danced on them and screamed.

She used often to cry because she was not rich. Sometimes, when she came home from work, she liked to pretend that she was rich; she would play at imagining that some one had died and left her a great fortune, or that her brother Patrick had come back from America with vast wealth, and then she would tell Mary Makebelieve of the things she intended to buy and do the very next day. Mary Makebelieve liked that. . . . They were to move the first thing in the morning to a big house with a garden behind it full of fruit trees and flowers and birds. There would be a wide lawn in front of the house to play lawn tennis in and to walk with delicately fine young men with fair faces and white hands, who would speak in the French language and bow often with their hats almost touching the ground. There were to be twelve servants—six of them men servants and six of them women servants—who would instantly do as they were bidden and would receive ten shillings each per week and their board; they would also have two nights free in the week, and would be very well fed. There were many wonderful dresses to be bought, dresses for walking in the streets and dresses for driving in a carriage, and others again for riding on horseback and for traveling in. There was a dress of crimson silk with a deep lace collar, and a heavy, wine-colored satin dress with a gold chain falling down in front of it, and there was a pretty white dress of the finest linen, having one red rose pinned at the waist. There were black silken stockings with quaint designs worked on them in red silk, and scarves of silver gauze, and others embroidered with flowers and little shapes of men and women.

When her mother was planning all these things she was very happy, but afterwards she used to cry bitterly and rock her daughter to and fro on her breast until she hurt her.

II

Every morning about six o'clock Mary Makebelieve left her bed and lit the fire. It was an ugly fire to light, because the chimney had never been swept, and there was no draught. Also they never had any sticks in the house, and scraps of paper twisted tightly into balls with the last night's cinders placed on them and a handful of small coals strewn on the top were used instead. Sometimes the fire blazed up quickly, and that made her happy, but at other times it went out three and four, and often half a dozen times; then the little bottle of paraffin oil had to be squandered—a few rags well steeped in the oil with a newspaper stretched over the grate seldom failed to coax enough fire to boil the saucepan of water; generally this method smoked the water and then the tea tasted so horrid that one only drank it for the sake of economy.

Mrs. Makebelieve liked to lie in bed until the last possible moment. As there was no table in the room, Mary used to bring the two cups of tea, the tin of condensed milk, and the quarter of a loaf over to the bed, and there she and her mother took their breakfast.

From the time she opened her eyes in the morning her mother never ceased to talk. It was then she went over all the things that had happened on the previous day and enumerated the places she would have to go to on the present day, and the chances for and against the making of a little money. At this meal she used to arrange also to have the room re-papered and the chimney swept and the rat-holes stopped up—there were three of these, one was on the left-hand side of the fire grate, the other two were under the bed, and Mary Makebelieve had lain awake many a night listening to the gnawing of teeth on the skirting and the scamper of little feet here and there on the floor. Her mother further arranged to have a Turkey carpet placed on the floor, although she admitted that oilcloth or linoleum was easier to clean, but they were not so nice to the feet or the eye. Into all these improvements her daughter entered with the greatest delight. There was to be a red mahogany chest of drawers against one wall and a rosewood piano against the wall opposite. A fender of shining brass with brazen furniture, a bright, copper kettle for boiling water in, and an iron pot for cooking potatoes and meat; there was to be a life-sized picture of Mary over the mantelpiece and a picture of her mother near the window in a golden frame, also a picture of a Newfoundland dog lying in a barrel and a little wee terrier crawling up to make friends with him, and a picture of a battle between black people and soldiers.

Her mother knew it was time to get out of bed when she heard a heavy step coming from the next room and going downstairs. A laboring man lived there with his wife and six children. When the door banged she jumped up, dressed quickly, and flew from the room in a panic of haste. Usually then, as there was nothing to do, Mary went back to bed for another couple of hours. After this she arose, made her bed and tidied the room, and went out to walk in the streets, or to sit in the St. Stephen's Green Park. She knew every bird in the Park, those that had chickens and those that had had chickens, and those that never had any chickens at all—these latter were usually drakes, and had reason on their side for an abstention which might otherwise have appeared remarkable, but they did not deserve the pity which Mary lavished on their childlessness, nor the extra pieces of bread with which she sought to recompense them. She loved to watch the ducklings swimming after their mothers: they were quite fearless, and would dash to the water's edge where one was standing and pick up nothing with the greatest eagerness and swallow it with delight. The mother duck swam placidly close to her brood and clucked in a low voice all kinds of warnings and advice and reproof to the little ones. Mary Make-believe thought it was very clever of the little ducklings to be able to swim so well. She loved them, and when nobody was looking she used to cluck at them like their mother, but she did not often do this because she did not know duck language really well, and feared that her cluck might mean the wrong things, and that she might be giving these innocents bad advice, and telling them to do something contrary to what their mother had just directed.

The bridge across the big lake was a fascinating place. On the sunny side lots of ducks were always standing on their heads searching for something in the water, so that they looked like only half ducks. On the shady side hundreds of eels were swimming about—they were most wonderful things; some of them were thin like ribbons, and others were round and plump like thick ropes. They never seemed to fight at all, and although the ducklings were so tiny the big eels never touched any of them, even when they dived right down amongst them. Some of the eels swam along very slowly, looking on this side and on that as if they were out of work or up from the country, and others whizzed by with incredible swiftness. Mary Makebelieve thought that the latter kind had just heard their babies crying; she wondered, when a little fish cried, could its mother see the tears where there was already so much water about, and then she thought that maybe they cried hard lumps of something that was easily visible.

After this she would go around the flower-beds and look at each; some of them were shaped like stars, and some were quite round, and others again were square. She liked the star-shaped flower-beds best, and next she liked the round ones, and last of all the square. But she loved all the flowers, and used to make up stories about them.

After that, growing hungry, she would go home for her lunch. She went home down Grafton Street and O'Connell Street. She always went along the right-hand side of the street going home, and looked in every shop window that she passed, and then, when she had eaten her lunch, she came out again and walked along the left-hand side of the road, looking at the shops on that side, and so she knew daily everything that was new in the city, and was able to tell her mother at nighttime that the black dress with Spanish lace was taken out of Manning's window and a red gown with tucks at the shoulders and Irish lace at the wrists put in its place; or that the diamond ring in Johnson's marked One Hundred Pounds was gone from the case and that a slide of brooches of beaten silver and blue enamel was there instead.

In the nighttime her mother and herself went round to each of the theaters in turn and watched the people going in and looked at the big posters. When they went home afterwards they had supper and used to try to make out the plots of the various plays from the pictures they had seen, so that generally they had lots to talk about before they went to bed. Mary Makebelieve used to talk most in the nighttime, but her mother talked most in the morning.

III

Her mother spoke sometimes of matrimony as a thing remote but very certain; the remoteness of this adventure rather shocked Mary Makebelieve; she knew that a girl had to get married, that a strange, beautiful man would come from somewhere looking for a wife and would retire again with his bride to that Somewhere which is the country of Romance. At times (and she could easily picture it) he rode in armor on a great bay horse, the plume of his helmet trailing among the high leaves of the forest. Or he came standing on the prow of a swift ship with the sunlight blazing back from his golden armor. Or on a grassy plain, fleet as the wind, he came running, leaping, laughing.

When the subject of matrimony was under discussion her mother planned minutely the person of the groom, his vast accomplishments, and yet vaster wealth, the magnificence of his person, and the love in which he was held by rich and poor alike. She also discussed, down to the smallest detail, the elaborate trousseau she would provide for her daughter, the extravagant presents the bridegroom would make to his bride and her maids, and those, yet more costly, which the bridegroom's family would send to the newly married pair. All these wonders could only concentrate in the person of a lord. Mary Makebelieve's questions as to the status and appurtenances of a lord were searching and minute, her mother's rejoinders were equally elaborate and particular.

At his birth a lord is cradled in silver, at his death he is laid in a golden casket, an oaken coffin, and a leaden outer coffin until, finally, a massy stone sarcophagus shrouds his remains forever. His life is a whirl of gayety and freedom. Around his castle there spread miles upon miles of sunny grass lands and ripened orchards and waving forests, and through these he hunts with his laughing companions—or walks gently with his lady. He has servants by the thousand, each anxious to die for him, and his wealth, prodigious beyond the computation of avarice, is stored in underground chambers, whose low, tortuous passages lead to labyrinths of vaults massy and impregnable.

Mary Makebelieve would have loved to wed a lord. If a lord had come to her when she paced softly through a forest, or stood alone on the seashore, or crouched among the long grass of a windy plain, she would have placed her hands in his and followed him and loved him truly forever. But she did not believe that these things happened nowadays, nor did her mother. Nowadays! her mother looked on these paltry times with an eye whose scorn was complicated by fury. Mean, ugly days, mean, ugly lives, and mean, ugly people, said her mother, that's all one can get nowadays, and then she spoke of the people whose houses she washed out and whose staircases she scrubbed down, and her old-ivory face flamed from her black hair and her deep, dark eyes whirled and became hard and motionless as points of jet, and her hands jumped alternately into knuckles and claws.

But it became increasingly evident to Mary Makebelieve that marriage was not a story but a fact, and, somehow, the romance of it did not drift away, although the very house wherein she lived was infested by these conjoints, and the streets wherein she walked were crowded with undistinguished couples. . . . Those gray-lived, dreary-natured people had a spark of fire smoldering somewhere in their poor economy. Six feet deep is scarcely deep enough to bury romance, and until that depth of clay has clogged our bones the fire can still smolder and be fanned, and, perhaps, blaze up and flare across a county or a country to warm the cold hands of many a shriveled person.

How did all these people come together? She did not yet understand the basic necessity that drives the male to the female. Sex was not yet to her a physiological distinction, it was only a differentiation of clothing, a matter of whiskers and no whiskers: but she had begun to take a new and peculiar interest in men. One of these hurrying or loitering strangers might be the husband whom fate had ordained for her. She would scarcely have been surprised if one of the men who looked at her casually in the street had suddenly halted and asked her to marry him. It came on her with something like assurance that that was the only business these men were there for, she could not discover any other reason or excuse for their existence, and if some man had been thus adventurous Mary Makebelieve would have been sadly perplexed to find an answer: she might, indeed, have replied, "Yes, thank you, sir," for when a man asks one to do a thing for him one does it gladly. There was an attraction about young men which she could not understand, something peculiarly dear and magnetic; she would have liked to shake hands with one to see how different he felt from a girl. They would, probably, shake hands quite hard and then hit one. She fancied she would not mind being hit by a man, and then, watching the vigor of their movements, she thought they could hit very hard, but still there was a terrible attraction about the idea of being hit by a man. She asked her mother (with apparent irrelevance) had a man ever struck her; her mother was silent for a few moments, and then burst into so violent a passion of weeping that Mary Makebelieve was frightened. She rushed into her mother's arms and was rocked fiercely against a heart almost bursting with bitter pride and recollection. But her mother did not then, nor did she ever afterwards, answer Mary Makebelieve's question.

IV

Every afternoon a troop of policemen marched in solemn and majestic single file from the College Green Police Station. At regular intervals, one by one, a policeman stepped sideways from the file, adjusted his belt, touched his moustache, looked up the street and down the street for stray criminals, and condescended to the duties of his beat.

At the crossing where Nassau and Suffolk streets intersect Grafton Street one of these superb creatures was wont to relinquish his companions, and there in the center of the road, a monument of solidity and law, he remained until the evening hour which released him again to the companionship of his peers.

Perhaps this point is the most interesting place in Dublin. Upon one vista Grafton Street with its glittering shops stretches, or rather winds, to the St. Stephen's Green Park, terminating at the gate known as the Fusiliers' Arch, but which local patriotism has rechristened the Traitors' Gate. On the left Nassau Street, broad and clean, and a trifle vulgar and bourgeois in its openness, runs away to Merrion Square, and on with a broad ease to Blackrock and Kingstown and the sea. On the right hand Suffolk Street, reserved and shy, twists up to St. Andrew's Church, touches gingerly the South City Markets, droops to George's Street, and is lost in mean and dingy intersections. At the back of the crossing Grafton Street continues again for a little distance down to Trinity College (at the gates whereof very intelligent young men flaunt very tattered gowns and smoke massive pipes with great skill for their years), skirting the Bank of Ireland,

and on to the River Liffey and the street which local patriotism defiantly speaks of as O'Connell Street, and alien patriotism, with equal defiance and pertinacity, knows as Sackville Street.

To the point where these places meet, and where the policeman stands, all the traffic of Dublin converges in a constant stream. The trams hurrying to Terenure, or Donnybrook, or Dalkey flash around this corner; the doctors who, in these degenerate days, concentrate in Merrion Square, fly up here in carriages and motor cars, the vans of the great firms in Grafton and O'Connell streets, or those outlying, never cease their exuberant progress. The ladies and gentlemen of leisure stroll here daily at four o'clock, and from all sides the vehicles and pedestrians, the bicycles and motor bicycles, the trams and the outside cars rush to the solitary policeman, who directs them all with his severe but tolerant eye. He knows all the tram-drivers who go by, and his nicely graduated wink rewards the glances of the rubicund, jolly drivers of the hackneys and the decayed Jehus with purple faces and dismal hopefulness who drive sepulchral cabs for some reason which has no acquaintance with profit; nor are the ladies and gentlemen who saunter past foreign to his encyclopedic eye. Constantly his great head swings a slow recognition, constantly his serene finger motions onwards a well-known undesirable, and his big, white teeth flash for an instant at young, laughing girls and the more matronly acquaintances who solicit the distinction of his glance.

To this place, and about this hour, Mary Makebelieve, returning from her solitary lunch, was wont to come. The figure of the massive policeman fascinated her. Surely everything desirable in manhood was concentrated in his tremendous body. What an immense, shattering blow that mighty fist could give! She could imagine it swinging vast as the buffet of a hero, high-thrown and then down irresistibly—a crashing, monumental hand. She delighted in his great, solid head as it swung slowly from side to side, and his calm, proud eye—a governing, compelling and determined eye. She had never met his glance yet: she withered away before it as a mouse withers and shrinks and falls to its den before a cat's huge glare. She used to look at him from the curbstone in front of the chemist's shop, or on the opposite side of the road, while pretending to wait for a tram; and at the pillar-box beside the optician's she found time for one furtive glance that shivered to his face and trembled away into the traffic. She did not think he noticed her, but there was nothing he did not notice. His business was noticing: he caught her in his mental policeman's notebook the very first day she came; he saw her each day beside, and at last looked for her coming and enjoyed her strategy. One day her shy, creeping glance was caught by his; it held her mesmerized for a few seconds, it looked down into her—for a moment the whole world seemed to have become one immense eye—she could scarcely get away from it.

When she remembered again she was standing by the pond in St. Stephen's Green Park, with a queer frightened exaltation lightening through her blood. She did not go home that night by Grafton Street, she did not dare venture within reach of that powerful organism, but went a long way round, and still the way seemed very short.

That night her mother, although very tired, was the more talkative of the two. She offered in exchange for her daughter's thoughts pennies that only existed in her imagination. Mary Makebelieve professed that it was sleep and not thought obsessed her, and exhibited voucher yawns which were as fictitious as her reply. When they went to bed that night it was a long time before she slept. She lay looking into the deep gloom of the chamber, and scarcely heard the fierce dreams of her mother, who was demanding from a sleep world the things she lacked in the wide-awake one.

V

This is the appearance of Mary Makebelieve at that time:— She had fair hair, and it was very soft and very thick; when she

unwound this it fell, or rather flowed, down to her waist, and
when she walked about the room with her hair unloosened it
curved beautifully about her head, snuggled into the hollow of
her neck, ruffled out broadly again upon her shoulders, and
swung into and out of her figure with every motion; surging
and shrinking and dancing; the ends of her hair were soft and
loose as foam, and it had the color and shining of pure, light
gold. Commonly in the house she wore her hair loose, because
her mother liked the appearance of youth imparted by hanging
hair, and would often desire her daughter to leave off her outer
skirt and walk only in her petticoats to heighten the illusion of
girlishness. Her head was shaped very tenderly and softly; it
was so small that when her hair was twisted up on it it seemed
much too delicate to bear so great a burden. Her eyes were
gray, limpidly tender and shy, drooping under weighty lids, so
that they seldom seemed more than half opened and commonly
sought the ground rather than the bolder excursions of straight-
forwardness; they seldom looked for longer than a glance, climbing and poising and eddying about the person at whom she
gazed, and then dived away again; and always when she looked
at any one she smiled a deprecation of her boldness. She had a
small white face, very like her mother's in some ways and at
some angles, but the tight beak which was her mother's nose
was absent in Mary; her nose withdrew timidly in the center
and only snatched a hurried courage to become visible at the
tip. It was a nose that seemed to have been snubbed almost out
of existence. Her mother loved it because it was so little, and
had tried so hard not to be a nose at all. They often stood together before the little glass that had a great crack running
drunkenly from the right-hand top corner down to the left-hand
bottom corner, and two small arm crosses, one a little above the
other, in the center. When one's face looked into this glass it
often appeared there as four faces with horrible aberrations; an
ear might be curving around a lip or an eye leering strangely
in the middle of a chin. But there were ways of looking into
the glass which practice had discovered, and usage had long

ago dulled the terrors of its vagaries. Looking into this glass Mrs. Makebelieve would comment minutely upon the two faces therein, and, pointing to her own triumphantly genuine nose and the fact that her husband's nose had been of quite discernible proportions, she would seek in labyrinths of pedigree for a reason to justify her daughter's lack; she passed all her sisters in this review, with an army of aunts and great-aunts, rifling the tombs of grandparents and their remoter blood, and making long-dead noses to live again. Mary Makebelieve used to lift her timidly curious eye and smile in deprecation of her nasal shortcomings, and then her mother would kiss the dejected button and vow it was the dearest, loveliest bit of a nose that had ever been seen.

"Big noses suit some people," said Mrs. Makebelieve, "but they do not suit others, and one would not suit you, dearie. They go well with black-haired people and very tall people, military gentlemen, judges and apothecaries; but small, fair folk cannot support great noses. I like my own nose," she continued. "At school, when I was a little girl, the other girls used to laugh at my nose, but I always liked it, and after a time other people came to like it also."

Mary Makebelieve had small, slim hands and feet: the palms of her hands were softer than anything in the world; there were five little, pink cushions on her palm: beginning at the little finger there was a very tiny cushion, the next one was bigger, and the next bigger again, until the largest ended a perfect harmony at the base of her thumb. Her mother used to kiss these little cushions at times, holding back the finger belonging to each, and naming it as she touched it. These are the names of Mary Makebelieve's fingers, beginning with the Thumb:—Tom Tumkins, Willie Winkles, Long Daniel, Bessie Bobtail and Little Dick-Dick.

Her slight, girlish figure was only beginning to creep to the deeper contours of womanhood, a half curve here and there, a sudden softness in the youthful lines, certain angles trembling on the slightest of rolls, a hint, a suggestion, the shadowy prophecy of circles and half hoops that could not yet roll: the trip of her movements was troubled sometimes to a sedater motion.

These things her mother's curiosity was continually recording, sometimes with happy pride, but oftener in a kind of anger to find that her little girl was becoming a big girl. If it had been possible she would have detained her daughter forever in the physique of a child; she feared the time when Mary would become too evidently a woman, when all kinds of equalities would come to hinder her spontaneous and active affection. A woman might object to be nursed, while a girl would not; Mrs. Makebelieve feared that objection, and, indeed, Mary, under the stimulus of an awakening body and a new, strange warmth, was not altogether satisfied by being nursed or by being the passive participant in these caresses. She sometimes thought that she would like to take her mother on her own breast and rock her to and fro, crooning soft made-up words and kissing the top of a head or the half-hidden curve of a cheek, but she did not dare to do so for fear her mother would strike her. Her mother was very jealous on that point, she loved her daughter to kiss her and stroke her hands and her face, but she never liked her to play at being the mother, nor had she ever encouraged her daughter in the occupations of a doll. She was the mother and Mary was the baby, and she could not bear to have her motherhood hindered even in play.

VI

Although Mary Makebelieve was sixteen years of age she had not yet gone to work; her mother did not like the idea of her little girl stooping to the drudgery of the only employment she could have aided her to obtain—that was, to assist herself in the humble and arduous toil of charing. She had arranged that Mary was to go into a shop, a drapery store, or some such other, but that was to be in a sometime which seemed infinitely remote.

"And then, too," said Mrs. Makebelieve, "all kinds of things may happen in a year or so if we wait. Your uncle Patrick, who went to America twenty years ago, may come home, and when he does you will not have to work, dearie, nor will I. Or again, some one going along the street may take a fancy to you and marry you; things often happen like that." There were a thousand schemes and accidents which, in her opinion, might occur to the establishment of her daughter's ease and the enlargement of her own dignity. And so Mary Makebelieve, when her mother was at work (which was sometimes every day in the week), had all the day to loiter in and spend as best she liked. Sometimes she did not go out at all. She stayed in the top back room sewing or knitting, mending holes in the sheets or the blankets, or reading books from the Free Library in Capel Street: but generally she preferred, after the few hours which served to put the room in order, to go out and walk along the streets, taking new turnings as often as she fancied, and striking down strange roads to see the shops and the people.

There were so many people whom she knew by sight; almost daily she saw these somewhere, and she often followed them for a short distance, with a feeling of friendship; for the loneliness of the long day often drew down upon her like a weight, so that even the distant companionship of these remembered faces that did not know her was comforting. She wished she could find out who some of them were.—There was a tall man with a sweeping brown beard, whose heavy overcoat looked as though it had been put on with a shovel; he wore spectacles, and his eyes were blue, and always seemed as if they were going to laugh; he, also, looked into the shops as he went along, and he seemed to know everybody. Every few paces people would halt and shake his hand, but these people never spoke because the big man with the brown beard would instantly burst into a fury of speech which had no intervals, and when there was no one with him at all he would talk to himself. On these occasions he did not see any one, and people had to jump out of his way

while he strode onwards swinging his big head from one side to
the other, and with his eyes fixed on some place a great distance
away. Once or twice, in passing, she heard him singing to himself the most lugubrious song in the world. There was another—
a long, thin, black man—who looked young and was always
smiling secretly to himself; his lips were never still for a moment,
and, passing Mary Makebelieve a few times, she heard him
buzzing like a great bee. He did not stop to shake hands with
any one, and although many people saluted him he took no
heed, but strode on smiling his secret smile and buzzing serenely.
There was a third man whom she often noticed: his clothing
seemed as if it had been put on him a long time ago and had
never been taken off again. He had a long, pale face, with a
dark moustache drooping over a most beautiful mouth. His eyes
were very big and lazy, and did not look quite human; they had
a trick of looking sidewards—a most intimate, personal look.
Sometimes he saw nothing in the world but the pavement, and
at other times he saw everything. He looked at Mary Makebelieve once and she got a fright; she had a queer idea that she
had known him well hundreds of years before and that he remembered her also. She was afraid of that man, but she liked
him because he looked so gentle and so—there was something
else he looked which as yet she could not put a name to, but
which her ancestry remembered dimly. There was a short, fair,
pale-faced man, who looked like the tiredest man in the world.
He was often preoccupied, but not in the singular way the others
were. He seemed to be always chewing the cud of remembrance,
and looked at people as if they reminded him of other people
who were dead a long time and whom he thought of but did
not regret. He was a detached man even in a crowd and carried
with him a cold atmosphere; even his smile was bleak and aloof.
Mary Makebelieve noticed that many people nudged each other
as he went by, and then they would turn and look after him and
go away whispering.

These and many others she saw almost daily, and used to look for with a feeling of friendship. At other times she walked up the long line of quays sentineling the Liffey, watching the swift boats of Guinness puffing down the river and the thousands of sea-gulls hovering above or swimming on the dark waters, until she came to the Phœnix Park, where there was always a cricket or football match being played, or some young men or girls playing hurley, or children playing tip-and-tig, running after one another, and dancing and screaming in the sunshine. Her mother liked very much to go with her to the Phœnix Park on days when there was no work to be done. Leaving the great, white main road, up which the bicycles and motor cars are continually whizzing, a few minutes' walk brings one to quiet alleys sheltered by trees and groves of hawthorn. In these passages one can walk for a long time without meeting a person, or lie on the grass in the shadow of a tree and watch the sunlight beating down on the green fields and shimmering between the trees. There is a deep silence to be found here, very strange and beautiful to one fresh from the city, and it is strange also to look about in the broad sunshine and see no person near at all, and no movement saving the roll and folding of the grass, the slow swinging of the branches of the trees or the noiseless flight of a bee, a butterfly, or a bird.

These things Mary Makebelieve liked, but her mother would pine for the dances of the little children, the gallant hurrying of the motor cars, and the movement to and fro of the people with gay dresses and colored parasols and all the circumstance of holiday.

VII

One morning Mary Makebelieve jumped out of bed and lit the fire. For a wonder it lit easily: the match was scarcely applied when the flames were leaping up the black chimney, and this made her feel at ease with the world. Her mother stayed in bed chatting with something more of gayety than usual. It was nearly

six o'clock, and the early summer sun was flooding against the
grimy window. The previous evening's post had brought a post-
card for Mrs. Makebelieve, requesting her to call on a Mrs.
O'Connor, who had a house off Harcourt Street. This, of course,
meant a day's work—it also meant a new client.

Mrs. Makebelieve's clients were always new. She could not
remain for any length of time in people's employment without
being troubled by the fact that these folk had houses of their
own and were actually employing her in a menial capacity. She
sometimes looked at their black silk aprons in a way which they
never failed to observe with anger, and on their attempting (as
they always termed it) to put her in her proper place, she would
discuss their appearance and morals with such power that they
at once dismissed her from their employment and incited their
husbands to assault her.

Mrs. Makebelieve's mind was exercised in finding out who
had recommended her to this new lady, and in what terms of
encomium such recommendation had been framed. She also de-
bated as to whether it would be wise to ask for one shilling and
ninepence per day instead of the customary one shilling and
sixpence. If the house was a big one she might be required by
this new customer oftener than once a week, and, perhaps, there
were others in the house besides the lady who would find small
jobs for her to do—needle-work or massages, or some such which
would bring in a little extra money; for she professed her willingness and ability to undertake with success any form of work
in which a woman could be eminent. In a house where she had
worked she had once been asked by a gentleman who lodged
there to order in two dozen bottles of stout, and, on returning
with the stout, the gentleman had thanked her and given her a
shilling. Incidents parallel to this had kept her faith in humanity
green. There must be plenty of these open-handed gentlemen
in houses such as she worked in, and, perhaps, in Mrs. O'Connor's house there might be more than one such person. There
were stingy people enough, heaven knew, people who would

get one to run messages and almost expect to be paid themselves for allowing one to work for them. Mrs. Makebelieve anathematized such skinflints with a vocabulary which was quite equal to the detailing of their misdeeds; but she refused to dwell on them: they were not really important in a world where the sun was shining. In the nighttime she would again believe in their horrible existences, but until then the world must be peopled with kind-hearted folk. She instanced many whom she knew, people who had advanced services and effects without exacting or indeed expecting any return.

When the tea was balanced insecurely on the bed, the two teacups on one side of her legs, the three-quarters of a loaf and the tin of condensed milk on the other, Mary sat down with great care, and all through the breakfast her mother culled from her capacious memory a list of kindnesses of which she had been the recipient or the witness. Mary supplemented the recital by incidents from her own observation. She had often seen a man in the street give a penny to an old woman. She had often seen old women give things to other old women. She knew many people who never looked for the halfpenny change from a newsboy. Mrs. Makebelieve applauded the justice of such transactions; they were, she admitted, the things she would do herself if she were in a position to be careless; but a person to whom the discovery of her daily bread is a daily problem, and who can scarcely keep pace with the ever-changing terms of the problem, is not in a position to be careless.—"Grind, grind, grind," said Mrs. Makebelieve, "that is life for me, and if I ceased to grind for an instant . . ." she flickered her thin hand into a nowhere of terror. Her attitude was that when one had enough one should give the residue to some one who had not enough. It was her woe, it stabbed her to the heart, to see desolate people dragging through the streets, standing to glare through the windows of bakeries and confectioners' shops, and little children in some of these helpless arms! Thinking of these, she said that every morsel she ate would choke her were it not for her own hunger. But maybe, said she, catching a providential glance of the golden-tinted window, maybe these poor people were not as poor as they seemed: surely they had ways of collecting a living which other people did not know anything about. It might be that they got lots of money from kind-hearted people, and food at hospitable doors, and here and there clothing and oddments which, if they did not wear, they knew how to dispose of advantageously. What extremes of ways and means such people must be acquainted with! No ditch was too low to rummage in, no rat-hole too hidden to be ravaged; a gate represented something to be climbed over: an open door was an invitation, a locked one a challenge. They could dodge under the fences of the law and climb the barbed wire of morality with equal impunity, and the utmost rigor of punishment had little terror for those whose hardships could scarcely be artificially worsened. The stagger of despair, the stricken, helpless aspect of such people, their gaunt faces and blurred eyes might conceivably be their stock-in-trade, the keys wherewith they unlocked hearts and purses and area-doors. It must be so when the sun was shining and birds were singing across fields not immeasurably distant, and children in walled gardens romped among fruits and flowers. She would believe this, for it was the early morning when one must believe, but when the nighttime came again she would laugh to scorn such easy beliefs, she would see the lean ribs of humanity when she undressed herself.

VIII

After her mother had gone Mary Makebelieve occupied herself settling the room and performing the various offices which the keeping in order of even one small room involves. There were pieces of the wall-paper flapping loosely; these had to be gummed down with strips of stamp-paper. The bed had to be made, the floor scrubbed, and a miscellany of objects patted and tapped into order. Her few dresses also had to be gone over for loose buttons, and the darning of threadbare places was a duty exercising her constant attention. Her clothing was always made by her mother, whose needle had once been noted for expertness, and, therefore, fitted more accurately than is customary in young girls' dresses. The arranging and rearranging of her beads was a frequent and enjoyable labor. She had four different necklaces, representing four different pennyworths of beads purchased at a shop whose merchandise was sold for one penny per item. One pennyworth of these beads was colored green, another red, a third was colored like pearls, and the fourth was a miscellaneous packet of many colors. A judicious selection of these beads could always provide a new and magnificent necklace at the expense of little more than a half-hour's easy work.

Because the sun was shining she brought out her white dress, and for a time was busy on it. There had been five tucks in the dress, but one after one they had to be let out. This was the last tuck that remained, and it also had to go, but even with such extra lengthening the dress would still swing free of her ankles. Her mother had promised to add a false hem to it when she got time, and Mary determined to remind her of this promise as soon as she came in from work. She polished her shoes, put on the white dress, and then did up her hair in front of the cracked looking-glass. She always put up her hair very plainly. She first combed it down straight, then parted it in the center, and rolled it into a great ball at the back of her neck. She often wished to curl her hair, and, indeed, it would have curled with the lightest persuasion: but her mother being approached on the subject, said that curls were common and were seldom worn by respectable people, excepting very small children or actresses, both of whose slender mentalities were registered by these tiny daintinesses. Also, curls took up too much time in arranging, and the slightest moisture in the air was liable to draw them down into lank and unsightly plasters, and, therefore, saving for a dance or a picnic, curls should not be used.

Mary Makebelieve, having arranged her hair, hesitated for

some time in the choice of a necklace. There was the pearl-colored necklace—it was very pretty, but every one could tell at once that they were not genuine pearls. Real pearls of the big-ness of these would be very valuable. Also there was something childish about pearls which latterly she wished to avoid. She had quite grown up now. The letting down of the last tuck in her dress marked an epoch as distinct as did the first rolling up of her hair. She wished her dress would go right down to her heels so that she might have a valid reason for holding up her skirts with one hand. She felt a trifle of impatience because her mother had delayed making the false hem; she could have stitched it on herself if her mother had cut it out, but for this day the dress would have to do. She wished she owned a string of red coral; not that round beady sort, but the jagged crisscross coral—a string of these long enough to go twice round her neck, and yet hang down in front to her waist. If she owned a string as long as that she might be able to cut enough off to make a slender wristlet. She would have loved to see such a wristlet sagging down to her hand.

Red, it seemed, would have to be the color for this day, so she took the red beads out of a box and put them on. They looked very nice against her white dress, but still—she did not quite like them: they seemed too solid, so she put them back into the box again, and instead tied round her neck a narrow ribbon of black velvet, which satisfied her better. Next she put on her hat; it was of straw, and had been washed many times. There was a broad ribbon of black velvet around it. She wished earnestly that she had a sash of black velvet about three inches deep to go round her waist. There was such a piece about the hem of her mother's Sunday skirt, but, of course, that could not be touched; maybe, her mother would give it to her if she asked. The skirt would look quite as well without it, and when her mother knew how nice it looked round her waist she would certainly give it to her.

She gave a last look at herself in the glass and went out, turn-ing up to the quays in the direction of the Phœnix Park. The sun was shining gloriously, and the streets seemed wonderfully clean in the sunlight. The horses under the heavy drays pulled their loads as if they were not heavy. The big, red-faced drivers leaned back at ease, with their hard hats pushed back from their foreheads and their eyes puckered at the sunshine. The tram-cars whizzed by like great jewels. The outside cars went spanking down the broad road, and every jolly-faced jarvey winked at her as he jolted by. The people going up and down the street seemed contented and happy. It was one o'clock, and from all kinds of offices and shops young men and women were darting forth for their lunch; none of the young men were so hurried but they had a moment to glance admiringly at Mary Make-believe before diving into a cheap restaurant or cheaper public-house for their food. The gulls in the river were flying in long, lazy curves, dipping down to the water, skimming it an instant, and then wheeling up again with easy, slanting wings. Every few minutes a boat laden with barrels puffed swiftly from beneath a bridge. All these boats had pretty names—there was the *Shannon*, the *Suir*, the *Nore*, the *Lagan*, and many others. The men on board sat contentedly on the barrels and smoked and made slow remarks to one another; and overhead the sky was blue and wonderful, immeasurably distant, filled from horizon to horizon with sparkle and warmth. Mary Makebelieve went slowly on towards the Park. She felt very happy. Now and then a darker spot flitted through her mind, not at all obscuring, but toning the brightness of her thoughts to a realizable serenity. She wished her skirts were long enough to be held up languidly like the lady walking in front: the hand holding up the skirt had a golden curb-chain on the wrist which drooped down to the neatly gloved hand and between each link of the chain was set a blue turquoise, and upon this jewel the sun danced splendidly. Mary Makebelieve wished she had a slender red coral wristlet; it also would have hung down to her palm and been lovely in the sunlight, and it would, she thought, have been far nicer than the bangle.

IX

She walked along for some time in the Park. Through the railings flanking the great road many beds of flowers could be seen. These were laid out in a great variety of forms—of stars and squares and crosses and circles, and the flowers were arranged in exquisite patterns. There was a great star which flamed with red flowers at the deep points, and in its heart a heavier mass of yellow blossom glared suddenly. There were circles wherein each ring was a differently colored flower, and others where three rings alternated—three rings white, three purple, and three orange, and so on in slenderer circles to the tiniest diminishing. Mary Makebelieve wished she knew the names of all the flowers, but the only ones she recognized by sight were the geraniums, some species of roses, violets, and forget-me-nots and pansies. The more exotic sorts she did not know, and, while she admired them greatly, she had not the same degree of affection for them as for the commoner, friendly varieties.

Leaving the big road she wandered into wider fields. In a few moments the path was hidden, the outside cars, motor cars and bicycles had vanished as completely as though there were no such things in the world. Great numbers of children were playing about in distinct bands; each troop was accompanied by one and sometimes two older people, girls or women who lay stretched out on the warm grass or leaned against the tree-trunks reading novelettes, and around them the children whirled and screamed and laughed. It was a world of waving pinafores and thin black-stockinged legs and shrill, sweet voices. In the great spaces the children's voices had a strangely remote quality; the sweet, high tones were not such as one heard in the streets or in houses. In a house or a street these voices thudded upon the air and beat sonorously back again from the walls, the houses, or the pavements; but out here the slender sounds sang to a higher tenuity and disappeared out and up and away into the tree-tops and the clouds and the wide, windy reaches. The little figures partook also of this diminuendo effect; against the great grassy curves they seemed smaller than they really were; the trees stirred hugely above them, the grass waved vast beneath them, and the sky ringed them in from immensity. Their forms scarcely disturbed the big outline of nature, their laughter only whispered against the silence, as ineffectual to disturb that gigantic serenity as a gnat's wing fluttered against a precipice.

Mary Makebelieve wandered on; a few cows lifted solemnly curious faces as she passed and swung their heavy heads behind her. Once or twice half a dozen deer came trotting from beyond the trees, and were shocked to a halt on seeing her—a moment's gaze, and away like the wind, bounding in a delicious freedom. Now a butterfly came twisting on some eccentric journey—ten wing-beats to the left, twenty to the right, and then back to the left, or with a sudden twist, returning on the path which it had already traversed, jerking carelessly through the sunlight. Across the sky very far up a troop of birds sailed definitely—they knew where they were going; momently one would detach itself from the others in a burst of joyous energy and sweep a great circle and back again to its comrades, and then away, away, away to the skyline.—Ye swift ones! O, freedom and sweetness! A song falling from the heavens! A lilt through deep sunshine! Happy wanderers! How fast ye fly and how bravely—up and up, till the earth has fallen away and the immeasurable heavens and the deep loneliness of the sunlight and the silence of great spaces receive you!

Mary Makebelieve came to a tree around which a circular wooden seat had been placed. Here for a time she sat looking out on the wide fields. Far away in front the ground rolled down into valleys and up into little hills, and from the valleys the green heads of trees emerged, and on the farther hills, in slender, distinct silhouette, and in great masses, entire trees could be seen. Nearer were single trees, each with its separate shadow and a stream of sunlight flooding between; and everywhere the

greenery of leaves and of grass and the gold of myriad butter-
cups and multitudes of white daisies.

She had been sitting for some time when a shadow came from
behind her. She watched its lengthening and its queer bobbing
motion. When it grew to its greatest length it ceased to move.
She felt that some one had stopped. From the shape of the
shadow she knew it was a man, but being so close she did not
like to look. Then a voice spoke. It was a voice as deep as the
rolling of a sea.

"Hello," said the voice; "what are you doing here all alone,
young lady?"

Mary Makebelieve's heart suddenly spurted to full speed. It
seemed to want more space than her bosom could afford. She
looked up. Beside her stood a prodigious man: one lifted hand
curled his moustache, the other carelessly twirled a long cane. He
was dressed in ordinary clothing, but Mary Makebelieve knew
him at once for that great policeman who guided the traffic at
the Grafton Street crossing.

X

The policeman told her wonderful things. He informed her
why the Phœnix Park was called the Phœnix Park. He did not
believe there was a phœnix in the Zoölogical Gardens, although
they probably had every kind of bird in the world there. It had
never struck him, now he came to think of it, to look definitely for
that bird, but he would do so the next time he went into the
Gardens. Perhaps the young lady would allow him (it would be
a much-appreciated privilege) to escort her through the Gardens
some fine day, the following day for instance. . . . He rather inclined to the belief that the phœnix was extinct—that is, died out;
and then, again, when he called to mind the singular habits with
which this bird was credited, he conceived that it had never had
a real but only a mythical existence—that is, it was a makebelieve
bird, a kind of fairy tale.

He further informed Mary Makebelieve that this Park was the third largest in the world, but the most beautiful. His evidence for this statement was not only the local newspapers, whose opinion might be biased by patriotism—that is, led away from the exact truth—but in the more stable testimony of reputable English journals such as *Answers* and *Tit-Bits* and *Pearson's Weekly*, he found an authoritative and gratifying confirmation—that is, they agreed. He cited for Mary Makebelieve's incredulity the exact immensity of the Park in miles, in yards, and in acres, and the number of head of cattle which could be accommodated therein if it were to be utilized for grazing—that is, turned into grass lands; or, if transformed into tillage, the number of small farmers who would be the proprietors of economic holdings—that is, a recondite—that is, an abstruse and a difficult scientific and sociological term.

Mary Makebelieve scarcely dared lift her glance to his face. An uncontrollable shyness had taken possession of her. Her eyes could not lift without an effort: they fluttered vainly upwards, but before reaching any height they flinched aside and drooped again to her lap. The astounding thought that she was sitting beside a man warmed and affrighted her blood so that it rushed burningly to her cheeks and went shuddering back again coldly. Her downcast eyes were almost mesmerized by the huge tweed-clad knees which towered like monoliths beside her. They rose much higher than her knees did, and extended far out more than a foot and a half beyond her own modest stretch. Her knees slanted gently downwards as she sat, but his jagged straightly forward, like the immovable knees of a god which she had seen once in the Museum. On one of these great knees an equally great hand rested. Automatically she placed her own hand on her lap and, awe-stricken, tried to measure the difference. Her hand was very tiny and as white as snow; it seemed so light that the breathing of a wind might have fluttered it. The wrist was slender and delicate, and through its milky covering faint blue veins glimmered. A sudden and passionate wish came to her as she watched

her wrist. She wished she had a red coral bracelet on it, or a
chain of silver beaten into flat discs, or even two twists of little
green beads. The hand that rested on the neighboring knee was
bigger by three times than her own, the skin on it was tanned
to the color of ripe mahogany-wood, and the heat of the day had
caused great purple veins to grow in knots and ridges across the
back and running in big twists down to the wrists. The specific
gravity of that hand seemed tremendous; she could imagine it
holding down the strong neck of a bull. It moved continually
while he spoke to her, closing in a tense strong grip that changed
the mahogany color to a dull whiteness and opening again to a
ponderous, inert width.

She was ashamed that she could find nothing to say. Her
vocabulary had suddenly and miserably diminished to a "yes"
and "no," only tolerably varied by a timid "indeed" and "I did not
know that." Against the easy clamor of his speech she could find
nothing to oppose, and ordinarily her tongue tripped and eddied
and veered as easily and nonchalantly as a feather in a wind. But
he did not mind silence. He interpreted it rightly as the natural
homage of a girl to a policeman. He liked this homage because
it helped him to feel as big as he looked, and he had every belief
in his ability to conduct a polite and interesting conversation with
any lady for an indefinite time.

After a while Mary Makebelieve arose and was about bidding
him a timid good-by. She wished to go away to her own little
room where she could look at herself and ask herself questions.
She wanted to visualize herself sitting under a tree beside a man.
She knew that she could reconstruct him to the smallest detail,
but feared that she might not be able to reconstruct herself.
When she arose he also stood up and fell so naturally into step
beside her that there was nothing to do but to walk straight on.
He still withstood the burden of conversation easily and pleas-
antly and very learnedly. He discussed matters of high political
and social moment, explaining generously the more unusual and
learned words that bristled from his vocabulary. Soon they came

to a more populous part of the Park. The children ceased from
their play to gaze roundeyed at the little girl and the big man,
their attendants looked and giggled and envied. Under these eyes
Mary Makebelieve's walk became afflicted with a sideward bias
which jolted her against her companion. She was furious with
herself and ashamed. She set her teeth to walk easily and
straightly, but constantly the jog of his elbow on her shoulder or
the swing of his hand against her blouse sent her ambling
wretchedly arms-length from him. When this had occurred half a
dozen times she could have plumped down on the grass and
wept loudly and without restraint. At the Park gate she stopped
suddenly and with the courage of despair bade him good-by. He
begged courteously to be allowed to see her a little way to her
home, but she would not permit it, and so he lifted his hat to her.
(Through her distress she could still note in a subterranean and
half-conscious fashion the fact that this was the first time a man
had ever uncovered before her.) As she went away down the road
she felt that his eyes were following her and her tripping walk
hurried almost to a run. She wished frantically that her dress was
longer than it was—that false hem! If she could have gathered
a skirt in her hand the mere holding on to something would have
given her self-possession, but she feared he was looking critically
at her short skirt and immodest ankles.

He stood for a time gazing after her with a smile on his great
face. He knew that she knew he was watching, and as he stood
he drew his hand from his pocket and tapped and smoothed his
moustache. He had a red moustache; it grew very thickly, but
was cropped short and square, and its fiber was so strong that it
stood out above his lip like wire. One expected it to crackle
when he touched it, but it never did.

XI

When Mrs. Makebelieve came home that night she seemed
very tired, and complained that her work at Mrs. O'Connor's

house was arduous beyond any which she had yet engaged in. She enumerated the many rooms that were in the house: those that were covered with carpets, the margins whereof had to be bees-waxed: those others, only partially covered with rugs, which had to be entirely waxed: the upper rooms were uncarpeted and un-rugged, and had, therefore, to be scrubbed: the basement, con-sisting of two red-flagged kitchens and a scullery, had also to be scoured out. The lady was very particular about the scouring of wainscotings and doors. The upper part of the staircase was bare and had to be scrubbed down, and the part down to the hall had a thin strip of carpet on it secured by brazen rods; the margins on either side of this carpet had to be beeswaxed and the brass rods polished. There was a great deal of unnecessary and vexatious brass of one kind or another scattered about the house, and as there were four children in the family, besides Mrs. O'Connor and her two sisters, the amount of washing which had constantly to be done was enormous and terrifying.

During their tea Mrs. Makebelieve called to mind the different ornaments which stood on the parlor mantelpiece and on the top of the piano. There was a china shepherdess with a basket of flowers at one end of the mantelpiece and an exact duplicate on the other. In the center a big clock of speckled marble was surmounted by a little domed edifice with Corinthian pillars in front, and this again was topped by the figure of an archer with a bent bow—there was nothing on top of this figure because there was not any room. Between each of these articles there stood little framed photographs of members of Mrs. O'Connor's family, and behind all there was a carved looking-glass with beveled edges having many shelves. Each shelf had a cup or a saucer or a china bowl on it. On the left-hand side of the fire-place there was a plaque whereon a young lady dressed in a sky-blue robe crossed by means of well-defined stepping-stones a thin but furious stream; the middle distance was embellished by a cow, and the horizon sustained two white lambs, a brown dog, a fountain and a sundial. On the right-hand side a young

gentleman clad in a crimson coat and yellow knee-breeches
carried a three-cornered hat under his arm, and he also crossed
a stream which seemed the exact counterpart of the other one
and whose perspective was similarly complicated. There were
three pictures on each wall—nine in all; three of these were pictures of ships, three were pictures of battles: two portrayed
saintly but emaciated personages sitting in peculiarly disheart-
ening wildernesses (each wilderness contained one cactus plant
and a camel). One of these personages stared fixedly at a skull,
the other personage looked with intense firmness away from a
lady of scant charms in a white and all too insufficient robe:
above the robe a segment of the lady's bosom was hinted at
bashfully—it was probably this the personage looked firmly away
from. The remaining picture showed a little girl seated in a big
armchair and reading with profound culture the most massive
of bibles: she had her grandmother's mutch cap and spectacles
on, and looked very sweet and solemn; a doll sat bolt upright
beside her, and on the floor a kitten hunted a ball of wool with
great earnestness.

All these things Mrs. Makebelieve discussed to her daughter,
as also the carpet which might have been woven in Turkey or
elsewhere, the sideboard that possibly was not mahogany, and
the chairs and occasional tables whose legs had attained to
rickets through convulsions; the curtains of cream-colored lace
which were reinforced by rep hangings and guarded shutters
from Venice, also the deer's head which stood on a shelf over
the door and was probably shot by a member of the family in
a dream, and the splendid silver tankards which flanked this
trophy and were possibly made of tin.

Mrs. Makebelieve further spoke of the personal characteristics
of the householder with an asperity which was still restrained.
She had a hairy chin, said Mrs. Makebelieve: she had buck teeth
and a solid smile, and was given to telling people who knew their
business how things ought to be done. Beyond this she would
not say anything.—The amount of soap the lady allowed to wash

out five rooms and a lengthy staircase was not as generous as one was accustomed to, but, possibly, she was well-meaning enough when one came to know her better.

Mary Makebelieve, apropos of nothing, asked her mother did she ever know a girl who got married to a policeman, and did she think that policemen were good men?

Her mother replied that policemen were greatly sought after as husbands for several reasons—firstly, they were big men, and big men are always good to look upon; secondly, their social standing was very high and their respectability undoubted; thirdly, a policeman's pay was such as would bring comfort to any household which was not needlessly and criminally extravagant; and this was often supplemented in a variety of ways which rumor only hinted at: there was also the safe prospect of a pension and the possibility of a sergeantship, where the emoluments were very great: and fourthly, a policeman, being subjected for many years to a rigorous discipline, would likely make a nice and obedient husband. Personally Mrs. Makebelieve did not admire policemen—they thought too much of themselves, and their continual pursuit of and intercourse with criminals tended to deteriorate their moral tone; also, being much admired by a certain type of woman, their morals were subjected to so continuous an assault that the wife of such a one would be worn to a shadow in striving to preserve her husband from designing and persistent females.

Mary Makebelieve said she thought it would be nice to have other women dying for love of one's husband, but her mother opposed this with the reflection that such people did not die for love at all, they were merely anxious to gratify a foolish and excessive pride or to inflict pain on respectable married women. On the whole, a policeman was not an ideal person to marry. The hours at which he came home were liable to constant and vexatious changes, so that there was a continual feeling of insecurity, which was bad for housekeeping; and if one had not stability in one's home all discipline and all real home life was at an end. There was this to be said for them—that they all loved little children. But, all things considered, a clerk made a better husband: his hours were regular and, knowing where he was at any moment, one's mind was at ease.

Mary Makebelieve was burning to tell some one of her adventure during the day, but although she had never before kept a secret from her mother she was unable to tell her this one. Something—perhaps the mere difference of age, and also a kind of shyness—kept her silent. She wished she knew a nice girl of her own age, or even a little younger, to whose enraptured ear she might have confided her story. They would have hugged each other during the recital, and she would have been able to enlarge upon a hundred trivialities of moustache and hair and eyes the wonder of which older minds can seldom appreciate.

Her mother said she did not feel at all well. She did not know what was the matter with her, but she was more tired than she could remember being for a long time. There was a dull aching in all her bones, a coldness in her limbs, and when she pressed her hair backwards it hurt her head; so she went to bed much earlier than was usual. But long after her regular time for sleep had passed Mary Makebelieve crouched on the floor before the few warm coals. She was looking into the redness, seeing visions of rapture, strange things which could not possibly be true; but these visions warmed her blood and lifted her heart on light and tremulous wings; there was a singing in her ears to which she could never be tired listening.

XII

Mrs. Makebelieve felt much better the next morning after the extra sleep which she had. She still confessed to a slight pain in her scalp when she brushed her hair and was a little languid, but not so much as to call for complaint. She sat up in bed while her daughter prepared the breakfast and her tongue sped as rapidly as heretofore. She said she had a sort of feeling that her

brother Patrick must come back from America some time, and
she was sure that when he did return he would lose no time
finding out his relatives and sharing with them the wealth which
he had amassed in the rich country. She had memories of his
generosity even as a mere infant when he would always say "no"
if only half a potato remained in the dish or a solitary slice of
bread was on the platter. She delighted to talk of his good looks
and high spirits and of the amazingly funny things he had said
and done. There was always, of course, the chance that Patrick
had got married and settled down in America, and, if so, that
would account for so prolonged a silence. Wives always came
between a man and his friends, and this woman would do all
she could to prevent Patrick benefiting his own sister and her
child. Even in Ireland there were people like that, and the more
one heard of America the less one knew what to expect from the
strange people who were native to that place. She had often
thought she would like to go out there herself, and, indeed, if
she had a little money she would think nothing of packing up
her things tomorrow and setting out for the States. There were
fine livings to be made there, and women were greatly in request,
both as servants and wives. It was well known, too, that the
Americans loved Irish people, and so there would be no difficulty
at all in getting a start. The more she thought of Mrs. O'Connor
the more favorably she pondered on emigration. She would say
nothing against Mrs. O'Connor yet, but the fact remained that
she had a wen on her cheek and buck teeth. Either of these
afflictions taken separately were excusable but together she fancied they betoken a bad, sour nature; but maybe the woman was
to be pitied: she might be a nice person in herself, but, then,
there was the matter of the soap, and she was very fond of giving
unnecessary orders. However, time would show, and, clients
being as scarce as they were, one could not quarrel with one's
bread and butter.

The opening of a door and the stamping downstairs of heavy
feet shot Mrs. Makebelieve from her bed and into her clothing

with furious speed. Within five minutes she was dressed, and after kissing her daughter three times she fled down ·the stairs and away to her business.

Mary had obtained her mother's consent to do as she pleased with the piece of black velvet on the hem of her Sunday skirt, so she passed some time in ripping this off and cleaning it. It would not come as fresh as she desired, and there were some parts of it frayed and rubbed so that the velvet was nearly lost, but other portions were quite good, and by cutting out the worn parts and neatly joining the good pieces she at last evolved a quite passable sash. Having the sash ready she dressed herself to see how it looked, and was delighted. Then becoming dissatisfied with the severe method of doing her hair she manipulated it gently for a few minutes until a curl depended by both ears and two or three very tiny ones fluttered above her forehead. She put on her hat and stole out, walking very gently for fear any of the other people in the house would peep through their doors as she went by. Walk as gently as she could these bare, solid stairs rang loudly to each footfall, and so she ended in a rush and was out and away without daring to look if she was observed. She had a sort of guilty feeling as she walked, which she tried to allay by saying very definitely that she was not doing anything wrong. She said to herself with determined candor that she would walk up to the St. Stephen's Green Park and look at the ducks and the flower-beds and the eels, but when she reached the quays she blushed deeply, and turning towards the right went rapidly in the direction of the Phœnix Park. She told herself that she was not going in there, but would merely take a walk by the river, cross at Island Bridge, and go back on the opposite side of the Liffey to the Green. But when she saw the broad sunlit road gleaming through the big gates she thought she would go for a little way up there to look at the flowers behind the railings. As she went in a great figure came from behind the newspaper kiosk outside the gates and followed Mary up the road. When she paused to look at the flowers the

great figure halted also, and when she went on again it followed.
Mary walked past the Gough Statue and turned away into the
fields and the trees, and here the figure lengthened its stride. In
the middle of the field a big shadow bobbed past her shoulder,
and she walked on holding her breath and watching the shadow
growing by queer forward jerks. In a moment the dull beat of
the shadow, and then there came a cheerful voice in her ears,
and the big policeman was standing by her side. For a few
moments they were stationary, making salutation and excuse and
explanation, and then they walked slowly on through the sunshine. Wherever there was a bush there were flowers on it. Every
tree was thronged with birds that sang shrilly and sweetly in
sudden thrills and clear sustained melodies, but in the open
spaces the silence was more wonderful; there was no bird note
to come between Mary and that deep voice, no shadow of a
tree to swallow up their own two shadows; and the sunlight was
so mildly warm, the air was so sweet and pure, and the little
wind that hushed by from the mountains was a tender and a
peaceful wind.

XIII

After that day Mary Makebelieve met her new friend frequently.
Somehow, wherever she went, he was not far away; he seemed
to spring out of space—one moment she was alone watching the
people passing and the hurrying cars and the thronged and
splendid shop windows, and then a big voice was booming down
to her and a big form was pacing deliberately by her side. Twice
he took her into a restaurant and gave her lunch. She had never
been in a restaurant before, and it seemed to her like a place in
fairyland. The semidarkness of the retired rooms faintly colored
by tiny electric lights, the beautifully clean tables and the
strange foods, the neatly dressed waitresses with quick, deft
movements and gravely attentive faces—these things thrilled her.
She noticed that the girls in the restaurant, in spite of their

gravity and industry, observed both herself and the big man with the minutest inspection, and she felt that they all envied her the attentions of so superb a companion. In the street also she found that many people looked at them, but, listening to his constant and easy speech, she could not give these people the attention they deserved.

When they did not go to the Park they sought the most reserved streets or walked out to the confines of the town and up by the River Dodder. There are exquisitely beautiful places along the side of the Dodder: shy little harbors and backwaters, and now and then a miniature waterfall or a broad placid reach upon which the sun beats down like silver. Along the river bank the grass grows rank and wildly luxurious, and at this season, warmed by the sun, it was a splendid place to sit. She thought she could sit there forever watching the shining river and listening to the great voice by her side.

He told her many things about himself and about his comrades—those equally huge men. She could see them walking with slow vigor through their barrack-yard, falling in for exercise or gymnastics or for school. She wondered what they were taught, and who had sufficient impertinence to teach giants, and were they ever slapped for not knowing their lessons? He told her of his daily work, the hours when he was on and off duty, the hours when he rose in the morning and when he went to bed. He told her of night duty, and drew a picture of the blank deserted streets which thrilled and frightened her . . . the tense darkness, and how through the silence the sound of a footstep was magnified a thousandfold, ringing down the desolate pathways away and away to the smallest shrill distinctness, and she saw also the alleys and lane-ways hooded in blackness, and the one or two human fragments who drifted aimless and frantic along the lonely streets, striving to walk easily for fear of their own thundering footsteps, cowering in the vastness of the city, dwarfed and shivering beside the gaunt houses; the thousands upon thousands of black houses, each deadly silent, each seeming to wait and listen for the morning, and each teeming with men and women who slept in peace because he was walking up and down outside, flashing his lantern on shop windows and feeling doors to see if they were by any chance open. Now and again a step from a great distance would tap-tap-tap, a far-off delicacy of sound and either die away down echoing side streets or come clanking on to where he stood, growing louder and clearer and more resonant, ringing again and again in doubled and trebled echoes; while he, standing far back in a doorway, watched to see who was abroad at the dead of night—and then that person went away on his strange errand, his footsteps tramping down immense distances, till the last echo and the last faint tremble of his feet eddied into the stillness. Now and again a cat dodged gingerly along a railing or a strayed dog slunk fearfully down the pathway, nosing everywhere in and out of the lamplight, silent and hungry and desperately eager. He told her stories also, wonderful tales of great fights and cunning tricks, of men and women whose whole lives were tricks, of people who did not know how to live except by theft and violence; people who were born by stealth, who ate by subterfuge, drank by dodges, got married in antics and slid into death by strange, subterranean passages. He told her the story of the Two Hungry Men, and of The Sailor Who Had Been Robbed, and a funny tale about the Barber Who Had Two Mothers. He also told her the stories of The Eight Tinkers, and of the Old Women Who Steal Fish at Nighttime, and the story of The Men He Let Off, and he told her a terrible story of how he fought five men in a little room, and he showed her a great livid scar hidden by his cap, and the marks in his neck where he had been stabbed with a jagged bottle, and his wrist which an Italian madman had thrust through and through with a dagger.

But though he was always talking he was not always talking of himself. Through his conversation there ran a succession of queries—tiny slender questions which ran out of his stories and into her life. Questions so skillful and natural and spontaneous that only a girl could discover the curiosity which prompted them. He wanted her name, her address, her mother's name, her father's name; had she other relatives, did she go to work yet, what was her religion, was it a long time since she left school, and what was her mother's business? To all of these Mary Makebelieve answered with glad candor. She saw each question coming, and the personal curiosity lying behind it she divined and was glad of. She would have loved to ask him personal and intimate questions about his parents, his brothers and sisters, and what he said when he said his prayers, and had he walked with other girls, and, if so, what had he said to them, and what did he really and truly think of her? Her curiosity on all these points was abundant and eager, but she did not dare to even hint a question.

One of the queries often touched upon by him she eluded—she shrank from it with something like terror—it was, "What was her mother's business?" She could not bear to say that her mother was a charwoman. It did not seem fitting. She suddenly hated and was ashamed of this occupation. It took on an aspect of incredible baseness. It seemed to be the meanest employment wherein any one could be engaged; and so when the question, conveyed in a variety of ways, had to be answered it was answered with reservations—Mary Makebelieve told him a lie. She said her mother was a dressmaker.

XIV

One night when Mrs. Makebelieve came home she was very low-spirited indeed. She complained once more of a headache and of a languor which she could not account for. She said it gave her all the trouble in the world to lift a bucket. It was not exactly that she could not lift a bucket, but that she could scarcely close her mind down to the fact that a bucket had to be lifted. Some spring of willingness seemed to be temporarily absent. To close her two hands on a floor-cloth and twist it into a spiral in order to wring it thoroughly was a thing which she found herself imagining she could do if she liked, but had not the least wish to do. These duties, even when she was engaged in them, had a curious quality of remoteness. The bucket into which her hand had been plunged a moment before seemed somehow incredibly distant. To lift the soap lying beside the bucket one would require an arm of more than human reach, and having washed, or rather dabbed, at a square of flooring, it was a matter of grave concern how to reach the unwashed part just beyond without moving herself. This languor alarmed her. The pain in her head, while it was severe, did not really matter. Every one had pains and aches, sores and sprains, but this unknown weariness and disinclination for the very slightest exertion gave her a fright.

Mary tempted her to come out and watch the people going into the Gayety Theater. She said a certain actor was playing whom all the women of Dublin make pilgrimages, even from distant places, to look at; and by going at once they might be in time to see him arriving in a motor car at the stage door, when they could have a good look at him getting out of the car and going into the theater. At these tidings Mrs. Makebelieve roused for a moment from her strange apathy. Since tea-time she had sat (not as usual upright and gesticulating, but humped up and flaccid) staring at a blob of condensed milk on the outside of the tin. She said she thought she would go out and see the great actor, although what all the women saw in him to go mad about she did not know, but in another moment she settled back to her humped-up position and restored her gaze to the condensed milk tin. With a little trouble Mary got her to bed, where, after being hugged for one moment, she went swiftly and soundly to sleep.

Mary was troubled because of her mother's illness, but, as it is always difficult to believe in the serious illness of another person until it has demonstrated its gravity, she soon dismissed the matter from her mind. This was the more easily done because her mind was teeming with impressions and pictures and scraps of dialogue.

As her mother was sleeping peacefully, Mary put on her hat

and went out. She wanted, in her then state of mind to walk in the solitude which can only be found in the crowded places, and also she wanted some kind of distraction. Her days had lately been so filled with adventure that the placid immobility of the top back room was not only irksome, but maddening, and her mother's hasty and troubled breathing came between her and her thoughts. The poor furniture of the room was hideous to her eyes, the uncarpeted floor and bleak, stained walls dulled her.

She went out, and in a few moments was part of the crowd which passes and repasses nightly from the Rotunda up the broad pathways of Sackville Street, across O'Connell Bridge, up Westmoreland Street, past Trinity College, and on through the brilliant lights of Grafton Street to the Fusiliers' Arch at the entrance to St. Stephen's Green Park. Here from half-past seven o'clock in the evening youthful Dublin marches in joyous procession. Sometimes bevies of young girls dance by, each a giggle incarnate. A little distance behind these a troop of young men follow stealthily and critically. They will be acquainted and more or less happily paired before the Bridge is reached. But generally the movement is in couples. Appointments, dating from the previous night, have filled the streets with happy and careless boys and girls—they are not exactly courting, they are enjoying the excitement of fresh acquaintance; old conversation is here poured into new bottles, old jokes have the freshness of infancy, every one is animated, and polite to no one but his partner; the people they meet and pass and those who overtake and pass them are all subjects for their wit and scorn, while they, in turn, furnish a moment's amusement and conversation to each succeeding couple. Constantly there are stoppages when very high-bred introductions result in a redistribution of the youngsters. As they move apart the words "Tomorrow night," or "Thursday," or "Friday," are called laughingly back, showing that the late partner is not to be lost sight of utterly; and then the procession begins anew.

Among these folk Mary Makebelieve passed rapidly. She knew

that if she walked slowly some partially elaborate gentleman would ask suddenly what she had been doing with herself since last Thursday? and would introduce her as Kate Ellen to six precisely similar young gentlemen, who smiled blandly in a semi-circle six feet distant. This had happened to her once before, and as she fled the six young gentlemen had roared "bow, wow, wow" after her, while the seventh mewed earnestly and with noise.

She stood for a time watching the people thronging into the Gayety Theater. Some came in motor cars, others in carriages. Many hearse-like cabs deposited weighty and respectable solemnities under the glass-roofed vestibule. Swift outside cars buzzed on rubber tires with gentlemen clad in evening dress, and ladies whose silken wraps blew gently from their shoulders, and, in addition, a constant pedestrian stream surged along the pathway. From the shelter of an opposite doorway Mary watched these gayly animated people. She envied them all innocently enough, and wondered would the big policeman ever ask her to go to the theater with him, and if he did, would her mother let her go. She thought her mother would refuse, but was dimly certain that in some way she would manage to get out if such a delightful invitation were given her. She was dreaming of the alterations she would make in her best frock in anticipation of such a treat when, half-consciously, she saw a big figure appear round the corner of Grafton Street and walk towards the theater. It was he, and her heat jumped with delight. She prayed that he would not see her, and then she prayed that he would, and then, with a sudden, sickening coldness, she saw that he was not alone. A young, plump, rosy-cheeked girl was at his side. As they came nearer the girl put her arm into his and said something. He bent down to her and replied, and she flashed a laugh up at him. There was a swift interchange of sentences, and they both laughed together, then they disappeared into the half-crown door.

Mary shrank back into the shadow of the doorway. She had a

strange notion that everybody was trying to look at her, and that they were all laughing maliciously. After a few moments she stepped out on the path and walked homewards quickly. She did not hear the noises of the streets, nor see the promenading crowds. Her face was bent down as she walked, and beneath the big brim of her straw hat her eyes were blinded with the bitterest tears she had ever shed.

XV

Next morning her mother was no better. She made no attempt to get out of bed, and listened with absolute indifference when the morning feet of the next-door man pounded the stairs. Mary awakened her again and again, but each time, after saying "All right, dearie," she relapsed to a slumber which was more torpor than sleep. Her yellow, old-ivory face was faintly tinged with color; her thin lips were relaxed, and seemed a trifle fuller, so that Mary thought she looked better in sickness than in health; but the limp arm lying on the patchwork quilt seemed to be more skinny than thin, and the hand was more waxen and claw-like than heretofore.

Mary laid the breakfast on the bed as usual, and again awakened her mother, who, after staring into vacancy for a few moments, forced herself to her elbow, and then, with sudden determination, sat up in the bed and bent her mind inflexibly on her breakfast. She drank two cups of tea greedily, but the bread had no taste in her mouth, and after swallowing a morsel she laid it aside.

"I don't know what's up with me at all, at all," said she.

"Maybe it's a cold, mother," replied Mary.

"Do I look bad, now?"

Mary scrutinized her narrowly.

"No," she answered, "your face is redder than it does be, and your eyes are shiny. I think you look splendid and well. What way do you feel?"

"I don't feel at all, except that I'm sleepy. Give me the glass in my hand, dearie, till I see what I'm like."

Mary took the glass from the wall and handed it to her.

"I don't look bad at all. A bit of color always suited me. Look at my tongue, though, it's very, very dirty; it's a bad tongue altogether. My mother had a tongue like that, Mary, when she died."

"Have you any pain?" said her daughter.

"No, dearie; there is a buzz in the front of my head as if something was spinning round and round very quickly, and that makes my eyes tired, and there's a sort of feeling as if my head was twice as heavy as it should be. Hang up the glass again. I'll try and get a sleep, and maybe I'll be better when I waken up. Run you out and get a bit of steak, and we'll stew it down and make beef tea, and maybe that will do me good. Give me my purse out of the pocket of my skirt."

Mary found the purse and brought it to the bed. Her mother opened it and brought out a thimble, a bootlace, five buttons, one sixpenny piece and a penny. She gave Mary the sixpence.

"Get half a pound of leg beef," said she, "and then we'll have fourpence left for bread and tea; no, take the other penny, too, and get half a pound of pieces at the butcher's for twopence and a twopenny tin of condensed milk, that's fourpence, and a three ha'penny loaf and one penny for tea, that's sixpence ha'penny, and get onions with the odd ha'penny, and we'll put them in the beef tea. Don't forget, dearie, to pick lean bits of meat; them fellows do be always trying to stick bits of bone and gristle on a body. Tell him it's for beef tea for your mother, and that I'm not well at all, and ask how Mrs. Quinn is; she hasn't been down in the shop for a long time. I'll go to sleep now. I'll have to go to work in the morning whatever happens, because there isn't any money in the house at all. Come home as quick as you can, dearie."

Mary dressed herself and went out for the provisions, but she did not buy them at once. As she went down the street she turned suddenly, clasping her hands in a desperate movement, and walked very quickly in the opposite direction. She turned up the side streets to the quays, and along these to the Park Gates. Her hands were clasping and unclasping in an agony of impatience, and her eyes roved busily here and there, flying among the few pedestrians like lanterns. She went through the gates and up the broad central path, and here she walked more slowly; but she did not see the flowers behind the railings, or even the sunshine that bathed the world in glory. At the monument she sped a furtive glance down the road she had traveled—there was nobody behind her. She turned into the fields, walking under trees which she did not see, and up hills and down valleys without noticing the incline of either. At times, through the tatter of her mind there blazed a memory of her mother lying sick at home, waiting for her daughter to return with food, and at such memories she gripped her hands together frightfully and banished the thought.—A moment's reflection and she could have hated her mother.

It was nearly five o'clock before she left the Park. She walked in a fog of depression. For hours she had gone hither and thither in the well-remembered circle, every step becoming more wayward and aimless. The sun had disappeared, and a gray evening bowed down upon the fields; the little wind that whispered along the grass or swung the light branches of the trees had a bleak edge to it. As she left the big gates she was chilled through and through, but the memory of her mother now set her running homewards. For the time she forgot her quest among the trees and thought only, with shame and fear, of what her mother would say, and of the reproachful, amazed eyes which would be turned on her when she went in. What could she say? She could not imagine anything. How could she justify a neglect which must appear gratuitous, coldblooded, inexplicable?

When she had bought the food and climbed the resonant stairs she stood outside the door crying softly to herself. She hated to open the door. She could imagine her mother sitting up in the bed dazed and unbelieving, angry and frightened,

imagining accidents and terrors, and when she would go in . . .
she had an impulse to open the door gently, leave the food just
inside and run down the stairs out into the world anywhere and
never come back again. At last in desperation she turned the
handle and stepped inside. Her face flamed, the blood burned
her eyes physically so that she could not see through them. She
did not look at the bed, but went direct to the fireplace, and
with a dogged patience began mending the fire. After a few
stubborn moments she twisted violently to face whatever might
come, ready to break into angry reproaches and impertinences,
but her mother was lying very still. She was fast asleep, and a
weight, an absolutely real pressure, was lifted from Mary's heart.
Her fingers flew about the preparation of the beef tea. She forgot the man whom she had gone to meet. Her arms were tired
and hungry to close around her mother. She wanted to whisper
little childish words to her, to rock her to and fro on her breast,
and croon little songs and kiss her, and pat her face.

XVI

Her mother did not get better. Indeed, she got worse. In addition to the lassitude of which she had complained she suffered
also from great heat and great cold, and furthermore, sharp
pains darted so swiftly through her brows that at times she was
both dizzy and sightless. A twirling movement in her head prevented her from standing up. Her center of gravity seemed
destroyed, for when she did stand and attempted to walk she
had a strange bearing away on one side, so that on striving to
walk towards the door she veered irresistibly at least four feet
to the left-hand side of that point. Mary Makebelieve helped her
back to bed, where she lay for a time watching horizontal lines
spinning violently in front of her face and these lines after a
time crossed and recrossed each other in so mazy and intricate
a pattern that she became violently sick from the mere looking
at them.

All of these things she described to her daughter, tracing the

queer patterns which were spinning about her with such fidelity
that Mary was almost able to see them. She also theorized about
the cause and ultimate effect of these symptoms, and explained
the degrees of heat and cold which burned or chilled her, and
the growth of a pain to its exquisite startling apex, its subsequent
slow recession, and the thud of an india-rubber hammer which
ensued when the pain had ebbed to its easiest level. It did not
occur to either of them to send for a doctor. Doctors in such
cases are seldom sent for, seldom even thought of. One falls sick
according to some severely definite, implacable law with which
it is foolish to quarrel, and one gets well again for no other
reason than that it is impossible to be sick forever. As the night
struggles slowly into day so sickness climbs stealthily into health,
and nature has a system of medicining her ailments which might
only be thwarted by the ministrations of a mere doctor. Doctors
also expect payment for their services—an expectation so wildly
beyond the range of common sense as to be ludicrous. Those
who can scarcely fee a baker when they are in health can certainly not remunerate a physician when they are ill.

But, despite her sickness, Mrs. Makebelieve was worried with
the practical common politics of existence. The food purchased
with her last sevenpence was eaten beyond remembrance. The
vital requirements of the next day and the following day and of
all subsequent days thronged upon her, clamoring for instant
attention. The wraith of a landlord sat on her bed demanding
rent and threatening grisly alternatives. Goblins that were bakers
and butchers and grocers grinned and leered and jabbered from
the corners of the room.

Each day Mary Makebelieve went to the pawn office with
something. They lived for a time on the only capital they had—
the poor furniture of their room. Everything which had even the
narrowest margin of value was sold. Mary's dresses kept them
for six days. Her mother's Sunday skirt fed them for another day.
They held famine at bay with a patchwork quilt and a crazy
washstand. A water-jug and a strip of oilcloth tinkled momen-

tarily against the teeth of the wolf and disappeared. The maw of hunger was not incommoded by the window curtain.

At last the room was as bare as a desert and almost as uninhabitable. A room without furniture is a ghostly place. Sounds made therein are uncanny, even the voice puts off its humanity and rings back with a bleak and hollow note, an empty resonance tinged with the frost of winter. There is no other sound so deadly, so barren and dispiriting as the echoes of an empty room. The gaunt woman in the bed seemed less gaunt than her residence, and there was nothing more to be sent to the pawnbroker or the secondhand dealer.

A post-card came from Mrs. O'Connor requesting, in a peremptory language customary to such communications, that Mrs. Makebelieve would please call on her the following morning before eight o'clock. Mrs. Makebelieve groaned as she read it. It meant work and food and the repurchase of her household goods, and she knew that on the following morning she would not be able to get up. She lay a while thinking, and then called her daughter.

"Deary," said she, "you will have to go to this place in the morning and try what you can do. Tell Mrs. O'Connor that I am sick, and that you are my daughter and will do the work, and try and do the best you can for a while."

She caught her daughter's head down to her bosom and wept over her, for she saw in this work a beginning and an end, the end of the little daughter who could be petted and rocked and advised, the beginning of a womanhood which would grow up to and beyond her, which would collect and secrete emotions and aspirations and adventures not to be shared even by a mother, and she saw the failure which this work meant, the expanding of her daughter's life ripples to a bleak and miserable horizon where the clouds were soapsuds and floor cloths, and the beyond a blank resignation only made energetic by hunger.

"Oh, my dear," said she, "I hate to think of you having to do such work, but it will only be for a while, a week, and then I

will be well again. Only a little week, my love, my sweetheart,
my heart's darling."

XVII

Early on the following morning Mary Makebelieve awakened
with a start. She felt as if some one had called her, and lay for
a few moments to see had her mother spoken. But her mother
was still asleep. Her slumber was at all times almost as energetic
as her wakening hours. She twisted constantly and moved her
hands and spoke ramblingly. Odd interjections, such as "ah, well,
no matter, certainly not, and indeed aye," shot from her lips like
bullets, and at intervals a sarcastic sniff fretted or astonished
her bedfellow into wakefulness. But now as she lay none of these
strenuous ejaculations were audible. Sighs only, weighty and
deep drawn and very tired, broke on her lips and lapsed sadly
into the desolate room.

Mary Makebelieve lay for a time wondering idly what had
awakened her so completely, for her eyes were wide open and
every vestige of sleep was gone from her brain; and then she
remembered that on this morning, and for the first time in her
life, she had to go to work. That knowledge had gone to bed
with her and had awakened her with an imperious urgency. In an
instant she sprang out of bed, huddled on sufficient clothing for
warmth, and set about lighting the fire. She was far too early
awake, but could not compose herself to lie for another moment
in bed. She did not at all welcome the idea of going to work,
but the interest attaching to a new thing, the freshness which
vitalizes for a time even the dreariest undertaking, prevented
her from ruing with any bitterness her first day's work. To a
young person even work is an adventure, and anything which
changes the usual current of life is welcome. The fire also went
with her; in quite a short time the flames had gathered to a
blaze, and matured, and concentrated to the glowing redness of
perfect combustion, then, when the smoke had disappeared with

the flames, she put on the saucepan of water. Quickly the saucepan boiled, and she wet the tea. She cut the bread into slices, put a spoonful of condensed milk into each cup, and awakened her mother.

All through the breakfast her mother advised her on the doing of her work. She cautioned her daughter when scrubbing woodwork always to scrub against the grain, for this gave a greater purchase to the brush, and removed the dirt twice as quickly as the seemingly easy opposite movement. She told her never to save soap. Little soap meant much rubbing, and advised that she should scrub two minutes with one hand and then two minutes with the other hand, and she was urgent on the necessity of thoroughness in the wringing out of one's floor cloth, because a dry floor cloth takes up twice as much water as a wet one, and thus lightens labor; also she advised Mary to change her positions as frequently as possible to avoid cramp when scrubbing, and to kneel up or stand up when wringing her cloths, as this would give her a rest, and the change of movement would relieve her very greatly, and above all to take her time about the business, because haste seldom resulted in clean work and was never appreciated by one's employer.

Before going out Mary Makebelieve had to arrange for some one to look after her mother during the day. This is an arrangement which, among poor people, is never difficult of accomplishment. The first to whom she applied was the laboring man's wife in the next room; she was a vast woman with six children and a laugh like the rolling of a great wind, and when Mary Makebelieve advanced her request she shook six children off her like toys and came out on the landing.

"Run off to your work now, honey," said she, "and let you be easy in your mind about your mother, for I'll go up to her this minute, and when I'm not there myself I'll leave one of the children with her to call me if she wants anything, and don't you be fretting at all, God help you! for she'll be as safe and as comfortable with me as if she was in Jervis Street Hospital or the Rotunda itself. What's wrong with her now? Is it a pain in her head she has or a sick stomach, God help her?"

Mary explained briefly, and as she went down the stairs she saw the big woman going into her mother's room.

She had not been out in the streets so early before, and had never known the wonder and beauty of the sun in the early morning. The streets were almost deserted, and the sunlight—a most delicate and nearly colorless radiance—fell gently on the long silent paths. Missing the customary throng of people and traffic she seemed almost in a strange country, and had to look twice for turnings which she could easily have found with her eyes shut. The shutters were up in all the shops and the blinds were down in most of the windows. Now and again a milk cart came clattering and rattling down a street, and now and again a big red-painted baker's cart dashed along the road. Such few pedestrians as she met were poorly dressed men, who carried tommy cans and tools, and they were all walking at a great pace, as if they feared they were late for somewhere. Three or four boys passed her running; one of these had a great lump of bread in his hand, and as he ran he tore pieces off the bread with his teeth and ate them. The streets looked cleaner than she had thought they could look, and the houses seemed very quiet and beautiful. When she came near a policeman she looked at him keenly from a distance, hoping and fearing that it might be her friend, but she did not see him. She had a sinking feeling at the thought that maybe he would be in the Phœnix Park this day looking for her, and might, indeed, have been there for the past few days, and the thought that he might be seeking for her unavailingly stabbed through her mind like a pain. It did not seem right, it was not in proportion, that so big a man should seek for a mere woman and not find one instantly to hand. It was pitiful to think of the huge man looking on this side and on that, peering behind trees and through distances, and thinking that maybe he was forgotten or scorned. Mary Makebelieve almost wept at the idea that he should fancy she scorned him. She wondered how, under such circumstances, a small girl can comfort a big man. One may fondle his hand, but that is miserably inadequate. She wished she was twice as big as he was, so that she might lift him bodily to her breast and snuggle and hug him like a kitten. So comprehensive an embrace alone could atone for injury to a big man's feelings.

In about twenty minutes she reached Mrs. O'Connor's house and knocked. She had to knock half a dozen times before she was admitted, and on being admitted had a great deal of trouble explaining who she was, and why her mother had not come, and that she was quite competent to undertake the work. She knew the person who opened the door for her was not Mrs. O'Connor, because she had not a hairy wart on her chin, nor had she buck teeth. After a little delay she was brought to the scullery and given a great pile of children's clothing to wash, and after starting this work she was left to herself for a long time.

XVIII

It was a dark house. The windows were all withered away behind stiff curtains, and the light that labored between these was chastened to the last degree of respectability. The doors skulked behind heavy plush hangings. The floors hid themselves decently under thick red and black carpets, and the margins which were uncarpeted were disguised by beeswax, so that no one knew they were there at all. The narrow hall was steeped in shadow, for there two black velvet portieres, at distances of six feet apart, depended from rods in the ceiling. Similar palls flopped on each landing of the staircase, and no sound was heard in the house at all, except dim voices that droned from somewhere, muffled and sepulchral and bodyless.

At ten o'clock, having finished the washing, Mary was visited by Mrs. O'Connor, whom she knew at once by the signs she had been warned of. The lady subjected each article that had been washed to a particular scrutiny, and, with the shadowy gallop of a smile that dashed into and out of sight in an instant, said they would do. She then conducted Mary to the kitchen and, pointing to a cup of tea and two slices of bread, invited her to breakfast, and left her for six minutes, when she reappeared with the suddenness of a marionette and directed her to wash her cup and saucer, and then to wash the kitchen, and these things also Mary did.

She got weary very soon, but not dispirited, because there were many things to look at in the kitchen. There were pots of various sizes and metals, saucepans little and big, jugs of all shapes, and a regiment of tea things were ranged on the dresser; on the walls were hung great pot lids like the shields of barbarous warriors which she had seen in a story book. Under the kitchen table there was a row of boots all wrinkled by usage, and each wearing a human and almost intelligent aspect—a well-wrinkled boot has often an appearance of mad humanity which can chain and almost hypnotize the observer. As she lifted the boots out of her way she named each by its face. There was Grubtoes, Sloucher, Thump-thump, Hoppit, Twitter, Hide-away, and Fairybell.

While she was working a young girl came into the kitchen and took up the boots called Fairybell. Mary just tossed a look at her as she entered and bent again to her washing. Then with an extreme perturbation she stole another look. The girl was young and as trim as a sunny garden. Her face was packed with laughter and freedom, like a young morning when tender rosy clouds sail in the sky. She walked with a light spring of happiness; each step seemed the beginning of a dance, light and swift and certain. Mary knew her in a pang, and her bent face grew redder than the tiles she was scrubbing. Like lightning she knew her. Her brain swung in a clamor of "where, where?" and even in the question she had the answer, for this was the girl she had seen going into the Gayety Theater swinging on the arm of her big policeman. The girl said good morning to her in a kindly voice, and Mary with a swift, frightened glance, whispered back good morning, then the girl went upstairs again, and Mary continued to scrub the floor.

When the kitchen was finished and inspected and approved of, she was instructed to wash out the front hall, and set about the work at once. "Get it done as quickly as you can," said the mistress, "I am expecting my nephew here soon, and he dislikes washing."

So Mary bent quickly to her work. She was not tired now. Her hands moved swiftly up and down the floor without effort. Indeed, her actions were almost mechanical. The self that was thinking and probing seemed somehow apart from the body bending over the bucket, and the hands that scrubbed and dipped and wrung. She had finished about three quarters of the hall when a couple of sharp raps came to the door. Mrs. O'Connor flew noiselessly up from the kitchen.

"I knew," said she, bitterly, "that you would not be finished before he came. Dry that puddle at once, so that he can walk in, and take the soap out of the way."

She stood with her hand on the door while Mary followed these directions, then, when a couple of hasty movements had removed the surplus water, Mrs. O'Connor drew the bolt and her nephew entered. Mary knew him on the doorstep, and her blood froze in terror and boiled again in shame.

Mrs. O'Connor drew the big policeman inside and kissed him. "I can't get these people to do things in time," said she. "They are that slow. Hang up your hat and coat and come into the parlor."

The policeman, with his eyes fixed steadily on Mary, began to take off his coat. His eyes, his moustache, all his face and figure seemed to be looking at her. He was an enormous and terrifying interrogation. He tapped his tough moustache and stepped over the bucket; at the entrance to the parlor he stood again and hung his monstrous look on her. He seemed about to speak, but it was to Mrs. O'Connor his words went.

"How's everything?" said he, and then the door closed behind him.

Mary, with extraordinary slowness, knelt down again beside

the bucket and began to scrub. She worked very deliberately, sometimes cleaning the same place two or three times. Now and again she sighed, but without any consciousness of trouble. These were sighs which did not seem to belong to her. She knew she was sighing, but could not exactly see how the dull sounds came from her lips when she had no desire to sigh and did not make any conscious effort to do so. Her mind was an absolute blank, she could think of nothing but the bubbles which broke on the floor and in the bucket, and the way the water squeezed down from the cloth. There was something she could have thought about if she wanted to, but she did not want to.

Mrs. O'Connor came out in a few minutes, inspected the hall and said it would do. She paid Mary her wages and told her to come again the next day, and Mary went home. As she walked along she was very careful not to step on any of the lines on the pavement; she walked between these, and was distressed because these lines were not equally distant from each other, so that she had to make unequal paces as she went.

XIX

The name of the woman from next door was Mrs. Cafferty. She was big and round, and when she walked her dress whirled about her like a tempest. She seemed to be always turning round; when she was going straight forward in any direction, say towards a press, she would turn aside midway so sharply that her clothing spun gustily in her wake—This probably came from having many children. A mother is continually driving in oblique directions from her household employments to rescue her children from a multitude of perils. An infant and a fireplace act upon each other like magnets; a small boy is always trying to eat a kettle or a piece of coal or the backbone of a herring; a little girl and a slop bucket are in immediate contact; the baby has a knife in its mouth; the twin is on the point of swallowing a marble, or is trying to wash itself in the butter, or the cat is

about to take a nap on its face. Indeed, the woman who has six
children never knows in what direction her next step must be,
and the continual strain of preserving her progeny converts
many a one into regular cyclones of eyes and arms and legs.
It also induces in some a perpetual good-humored irritability
wherein one can slap and cuddle a child in the same instant, or
shout threateningly or lovingly, call warningly and murmur en-
couragingly in an astonishing sequence. The woman with six children must both physically and mentally travel at a tangent, and
when a husband has to be badgered or humored into the bargain, then the life of such a woman is more complex than is
readily understood.

When Mary came home Mrs. Cafferty was sitting on her
mother's bed, two small children and a cat were also on the
bed, two slightly bigger children were under the bed, and two
others were galloping furiously up and down the room. At one
moment these latter twain were runaway horses, at another
they were express trains. When they were horses they snorted
and neighed and kicked, when they were trains they backed and
shunted, blew whistles and blew off steam. The children under
the bed were tigers in a jungle, and they made the noises proper
to such beasts and such a place; they bit each other furiously,
and howled and growled precisely as tigers do. The pair of infants on the bed were playing the game of bump; they would
stand upright, then spring high into the air and come crashing
down on the bed, which then sprung them partly up again. Each
time they jumped they screamed loudly, each time they fell they
roared delighted congratulations to each other, and when they
fell together they fought with strong good humor. Sometimes
they fell on Mrs. Makebelieve; always they bumped her. At the
side of the bed their mother sat telling with a gigantic voice a
story wherein her husband's sister figured as the despicable person she was to the eye of discernment, and this story was punc-
tuated and shot through and dislocuted by objurgations, threats,
pleadings, admirations, alarms and despairs addressed to the

children separately and en masse, by name, nickname, and hastily created epithet.

Mary halted in amazement in the doorway. She could not grasp all the pandemonium at once, and while she stood Mrs. Cafferty saw her.

"Come on in, honey," said she. "Your ma's as right as a trivet. All she wanted was a bit of good company and some children to play with. Deed," she continued, "children are the best medicine for a woman that I know of. They don't give you time to be sick, the creatures! Patrick John, I'll give you a smack on the side of the head if you don't let your little sister alone, and don't you, Norah, be vexing him or you'll deserve all you get. Run inside, Julia Elizabeth, cut a slice of bread for the twins, and put a bit of sugar on it, honey. Yes, alanna, you can have a slice for yourself, too, you poor child you, well you deserve it."

Mrs. Makebelieve was sitting up in the bed with two pillows propping up her back. One of her long thin arms was stretched out to preserve the twins from being bruised against the wall in their play. Plainly they had become great friends with her, for every now and then they swarmed over her, and a hugging match of extreme complexity ensued. She looked almost her usual self, and all the animation that had been so marked a feature of her personality had returned to her.

"Are you better, mother?" said Mary.

Mrs. Makebelieve took her daughter's head in her hands and kissed her until the twins butted them apart clamoring for caresses.

"I am, honey," said she. "Those children done me good. I could have got up at one o'clock, I felt so well, but Mrs. Cafferty thought I'd better not."

"I did so," said Mrs. Cafferty. "Not a foot do you stir out of that bed 'till your daughter comes home, ma'am, said I. For do you see, child, many's the time you'd be thinking you were well and feeling as fit as a fiddle, and nothing would be doing you but to be up and gallivanting about, and then the next day you'd

have a relapse, and the next day you'd be twice as bad, and the
day after that they'd be measuring you for your coffin maybe.
I knew a woman was taken like that—up she got; I'm as well as
ever I was, said she, and she ate a feed of pig's cheek and cabbage and finished her washing, and they buried her in a week.
It's the quare thing, sickness. What I say is when you're sick
get into bed and stop there."

"It's easy saying that," said Mrs. Makebelieve.

"Sure, don't I know, you poor thing you," said Mrs. Cafferty,
"but you should stay in bed as long as you are able to anyhow."

"How did you get on with Mrs. O'Connor?" said Mrs. Makebelieve.

"That's the mistress, isn't it?" queried Mrs. Cafferty; "an ould
devil, I'll bet you."

Mrs. Makebelieve rapidly and lightly sketched Mrs. O'Connor's leading peculiarities.

"It's queer the people one has to work for, God knows it is,"
said Mrs. Cafferty.

At this point a grave controversy on work might have arisen,
but the children, caring little for conversation, broke into so
tumultuous play that talk could not be proceeded with. Mary
was enticed into a game composed in part of pussy-four-corners
and tip-an-tig, with a general flavor of leap-frog working through.
In five minutes her hair and her stockings were both down, and
the back of her skirt had crawled three-quarters round to the
front. The twins shouted and bumped on the bed, upon which
and on Mrs. Makebelieve they rubbed bread and butter and
sugar, while their mother roared an anecdote at Mrs. Makebelieve in tones that ruled the din as a fog horn rules the waves.

XX

Mary had lavished the entire of her first day's wages on delicate foods wherewith to tempt her mother's languid appetite,
and when the morning dawned she arose silently, lit the fire,

wet the tea and spread her purchases out on the side of the bed. There was a slice of brawn, two pork sausages, two eggs, three rashers of bacon, a bun, a pennyworth of sweets and a pig's foot. These, with bread, and butter, and tea, made a collection amid which an invalid might browse with some satisfaction. Mary then awakened her, and sat by in a dream of happiness watching her mother's eye roll slowly and unbelievingly from item to item. Mrs. Makebelieve tipped each article with her first finger and put its right name on it unerringly. Then she picked out an important looking sweet that had four colors and shone like the sun, and put it in her mouth.

"I never saw anything like it, you good child you," said she.

Mary rocked herself to and fro and laughed loudly for delight, and then they ate a bit of everything, and were very happy.

Mrs. Makebelieve said that she felt altogether better that morning. She had slept like a top all through the night, and, moreover, had a dream wherein she saw her brother Patrick standing on the remotest sea point of distant America, from whence he had shouted loudly across the ocean that he was coming back to Ireland soon, that he had succeeded very well indeed, and that he was not married. He had not changed in the slightest degree, said Mrs. Makebelieve, and he looked as young and as jolly as when he was at home with her father and herself in the County Meath twenty-two years before. This mollifying dream and the easy sleep which followed it had completely restored her health and spirits. Mrs. Makebelieve further intimated that she intended to go to work that day. It did not fit in with her ideas of propriety that her child should turn into a charwoman, the more particularly as there was a strong—an almost certain—possibility of an early betterment of her own and her daughter's fortunes.

Dreams, said Mrs. Makebelieve, did not come for nothing. There was more in dreams than was generally understood. Many and many were the dreams which she herself had been visited by, and they had come true so often that she could no longer disregard their promises, admonishments or threats. Of course many people had dreams which were of no consequence, and these could usually be traced to gluttony or a flighty inconstant imagination. Drunken people, for instance, often dreamed strange and terrible things, but, even while they were awake, these people were liable to imaginary enemies whom their clouded eyes and intellects magnified beyond any thoughtful proportions, and when they were asleep their dreams would also be subject to this haze and whirl of unreality and hallucination.

Mary said that sometimes she did not dream at all, and at other times she dreamed very vividly, but usually could not remember what the dream had been about when she awakened, and once she had dreamed that some one gave her a shilling which she placed carefully under her pillow, and this dream was so real that in the morning she put her hand under the pillow to see if the shilling was there, but it was not. The very next night she dreamed the same dream, and as she put the phantom money under her pillow she said out loudly to herself, "I am dreaming this, and I dreamt it last night also." Her mother said if she had dreamt it for the third time some one would have given her a shilling surely. To this Mary agreed, and admitted that she had tried very hard to dream it on the third night, but somehow could not do it.

"When my brother comes home from America," said Mrs. Makebelieve, "we'll go away from this part of the city at once. I suppose he'd want a rather big house on the south side—Rathfarnham or Terenure way, or, maybe, Donnybrook. Of course he'll ask me to mind the house for him and keep the servants in order, and provide a different dinner every day, and all that; while you could go out to the neighbors' places to play lawn tennis or cricket, and have lunch. It will be a very great responsibility."

"What kind of dinners would you have?" said Mary.

Mrs. Makebelieve's eyes glistened, and she leaned forward in the bed; but just as she was about to reply the laboring man in

the next room slammed his door, and went thundering down
the stairs. In an instant Mrs. Makebelieve bounded from her
bed; three wide twists put up her hair, eight strange billow-like
movements put on her clothes; as each article of clothing reached
a definite point on her person Mary stabbed it swiftly with a
pin—four ordinary pins in this place, two safety pins in that: then
Mrs. Makebelieve kissed her daughter sixteen times and fled
down the stairs and away to her work.

XXI

In a few minutes Mrs. Cafferty came into the room. She was,
as every woman is in the morning, primed with conversation
about husbands, for in the morning husbands are unwieldy,
morose creatures without joy, without lightness, lacking even the
common, elemental interest in their own children, and capable
of detestably misinterpreting the conversation of their wives. It
is only by mixing amongst other men that this malignant humor
may be dispelled. To them the company of men is like a great
bath into which a husband will plunge wildly, renouncing as
he dives wives and children, all anchors and securities of hearth
and roof, and from which he again emerges singularly refreshed
and capable of being interested by a wife, a family, and a home
until the next morning. To many women this is a grievance
amounting often to an affront, and although they endeavor, even
by cooking, to heal the singular breach, they are utterly unable
to do so, and perpetually seek the counsel of each other on the
subject. Mrs. Cafferty had merely asked her husband would he
hold the baby while she poured out his stirabout, and he had
incredibly threatened to pour the stirabout down the back of
her neck if she didn't leave him alone.

It was upon this morning madness she had desired to consult
her friend, and when she saw that Mrs. Makebelieve had gone
away her disappointment was quite evident. But this was only
for a moment. Almost all women are possessed of a fine social

sense in relation to other women. They are always on their best behavior towards one another. Indeed, it often seems as if they feared and must by all possible means placate each other by flattery, humor or a serious tactfulness. There is very little freedom between them, because there is no real freedom or acquaintance but between things polar. There is nothing but a superficial resemblance between like and like, but between like and unlike there is space wherein both curiosity and spirit may go adventuring. Extremes must meet, it is their urgent necessity; the reason for their distance, and the greater the distance between them, the swifter will be their return and the warmer their impact: they may shatter each other to fragments or they may fuse and become indissoluble and new and wonderful, but there is no other fertility. Between the sexes there is a really extraordinary freedom of intercourse. They meet each other something more than half way. A man and a woman may become quite intimate in a quarter of an hour. Almost certainly they will endeavor to explain themselves to each other before many minutes have elapsed; but a man and a man will not do this, and even less so will a woman and a woman, for these are the parallel lines which never meet. The acquaintanceship of the latter, in particular, often begins and ends in an armed and calculating neutrality. They preserve their distances and each other's suffrage by the exercise of a grave social tact which never deserts them, and which more than anything else has contributed to build the ceremonials which are nearly one-half of our civilization. It is a common belief amongst men that women cannot live together without quarreling, and that they are unable to get work done by other women with any of the good will which men display in the same occupations. If this is true, the reason should not be looked for in any intersexual complications, such as fear or an acrid rivalry, but only in the perpetually recurring physical disturbances to which, as a sex, they are subjected; and as the ability and willingness of a man to use his fists in response to an affront has imposed sobriety and good humor towards each other in almost all their relations, so women have placed barriers of politeness and ceremonial between their fellow-women and their own excoriated sensibilities.

Mrs. Cafferty, therefore, dissembled her disappointment, and with an increased cordiality addressed herself towards Mary. Sitting down on the bedside she discoursed on almost every subject upon which a woman may discourse. It is considered that the conversation of women, while incessant in its use, is rigorously bounded between the parlor and the kitchen, or, to be more precise, between the attic and the scullery, but these extremes are more inclusive than is imagined, for the attic has an outlook on the stars while the scullery usually opens on the kitchen garden or the dust heap—vistas equal to horizons. The mysteries of death and birth occupy women far more than is the case with men, to whom political and mercantile speculations are more congenial. With immediate buying and selling, and all the absolute forms of exchange and barter, women are deeply engaged, so that the realities of trade are often more intelligent to them than to many merchants. If men understood domestic economy half as well as women do, then their political economy and their entire consequent statecraft would not be the futile muddle which it is.

It was all very interesting to Mary, and, moreover, she had a great desire for companionship at the moment. If she had been left alone it might have become necessary to confront certain thoughts, memories, pictures, from which she had a dim idea it would be wise to keep her distance. Her work on the previous day, the girl she had met in the house, the policeman—from all or any of these recollections she swerved mentally. She steadily rejected all impressions that touched upon these. The policeman floated vaguely on her consciousness not as a desirable person, not even as a person but as a distance, as an hour of her childhood, as a half-forgotten quaintness, a memory which it would be better should never be revived. Indeed her faint thought shadowed him as a person who was dead, and would never again be visible to her anywhere. So, resolutely, she let him drop down

into her mind to some uncomfortable oubliette from whence he
threatened with feeble insistence to pop up at any moment like
a strange question or a sudden shame. She hid him in a rosy flush
which a breath could have made flame unbearably, and she hid
from him behind the light garrulity of Mrs. Cafferty, through
which now and again, as through a veil, she saw the spike of his
helmet, a wiry bristling moustache, a surge of great shoulders.
On these ghostly indications she heaped a tornado of words
which swamped the wraith, but she knew he was waiting to catch
her alone, and would certainly catch her, and the knowledge
made her hate him.

XXII

Mrs. Cafferty suggested that she and Mary should go out together to purchase that day's dinner, and by the time she had
draped her shoulders in a shawl, buried her head in a bonnet,
cautioned all her brood against going near the fireplace, the coal
box and the slop bucket, cut a slice of bread for each of them,
and placed each of them in charge of all the rest, Mary's more
elaborate dressing was within two stages of her hat.

"Wait until you have children, my dear," said Mrs. Cafferty,
"you won't be so pernickety then." She further told Mary that
when she was herself younger she had often spent an hour and
a half doing up her hair, and she had been so particular that the
putting on of a blouse or the pinning of a skirt to a belt had
tormented her happily for two hours. "But, bless you," she roared,
"you get out of all that when you get children. Wait till you have
six of them to be dressed every morning, and they with some of
their boots lost and the rest of them mixed up, and each of them
wriggling like an eel on a pan until you have to slap the devil
out of them before their stocking can be got on: the way they
screw their toes up in the wrong places! and the way they squeal
that you're pinching them! and the way that they say you've
rubbed soap in their eyes!"—Mrs. Cafferty lifted her eyes and her

hands to the ceiling in a dumb remonstrance with Providence, and dropped them again forlornly as one in whom Providence had never been really interested—"You'll have all the dressing you want and a bit over for luck," said she.

She complimented Mary on her hair, her complexion, the smallness of her feet, the largeness of her eyes, the slenderness of her waist, the width of her hat and of her shoe strings: so impartially and inclusively did she compliment her that by the time they went out Mary was rosy with appreciation and as self-confident as a young girl is entitled to be.

It was a beautiful gray day with a massy sky which seemed as if it never could move again or change, and, as often happens in Ireland in cloudy weather, the air was so very clear that one could see to a great distance. On such days everything stands out in sharp outline. A street is no longer a congery of houses huddling shamefully together and terrified lest any one should look at them and laugh. Each house then recaptures its individuality. The very roadways are aware of themselves and bear their horses, and cars, and trams in a competent spirit, adorned with modesty as with a garland. It has a beauty beyond sunshine, for sunshine is only youth and carelessness. The impress of a thousand memories, the historic visage becomes apparent: the quiet face which experience has ripened into knowledge and mellowed into the wisdom of charity is seen then: the great social beauty shines from the streets under this sky that broods like a thoughtful forehead.

While they walked Mrs. Cafferty planned, as a general might, her campaign of shopping. Her shopping differed greatly from Mrs. Makebelieve's, and the difference was probably caused by her necessity to feed and clothe eight people as against Mrs. Makebelieve's two. Mrs. Makebelieve went to the shop nearest her house, and there entered into a stanch personal friendship with the proprietor. When she was given anything of doubtful value or material she instantly returned and handed it back, and the prices which were first quoted to her and settled upon be-

came to Mrs. Makebelieve an unalterable standard from which
no departure would be tolerated. Eggs might go up in price for
the remainder of the world, but not for her. A change of price
threw Mrs. Makebelieve into so wide-eyed, so galvanic, so power-
fully-verbal and friendship-shattering an anger that her terms
were accepted and registered as Median exactitudes. Mrs. Cafferty, on the other hand, knew shopkeepers as personal enemies
and as foes to the human race, who were bent on despoiling the
poor, and against whom a remorseless warfare should be conducted by all decent people. Her knowledge of material, of
quality, of degrees of freshness, of local and distant prices was
profound. In Clanbrassil Street she would quote the prices of
Moore Street with shattering effect, and if the shopkeeper declined to revise his tariff her good-humored voice toned so huge
a disapproval that other intending purchasers left the shop impressed by the unmasking of a swindler. Her method was abrupt.
She seized an article, placed it on the counter and uttered these
words, "Sixpence and not a penny more; I can get it in Moore
Street for five pence half penny." She knew all the shops having
a cheap line in some special article, and, therefore, her shopping
was of a very extended description, not that she went from point
to point, for she continually departed from the line of battle
with the remark "Let's try what they have here," and when
inside the shop her large eye took in at a glance a thousand details
of stock and price which were never afterwards forgotten.

Mrs. Cafferty's daughter, Norah, was going to celebrate her
first Communion in a few days. This is a very important ceremony for a young girl and for her mother. A white muslin dress
and a blue sash, a white muslin hat with blue ribbons, tan shoes,
and stockings as germane to the color of tan as may be—these
all have to be provided. It is a time of grave concern for everybody intimately connected with the event. Every girl in the world
has performed this ceremony: they have all been clad in these
garments and shoes, and for a day or so all women, of whatever
age, are in love with the little girl making her first Communion.

Perhaps more than anything else it swings the passing stranger back to the time when she was not a woman but a child with present gayety and curiosity, and a future all expectation and adventure. Therefore, the suitable appareling of one's daughter is a public duty, and every mother endeavors to do the thing that is right, and live, if only for one day, up to the admiration of her fellow-creatures.

It was a trial, but an enjoyable one, to Mrs. Cafferty and Mary, this matching of tan stockings with tan shoes. The shoes were bought, and then an almost impossible quest began to find stockings which would exactly go with them. Thousands of boxes were opened, ransacked and waved aside without the absolute color being discovered. From shop to shop and from street to street they went, and the quest led them through Grafton Street en route to a shop where months before Mrs. Cafferty had seen stockings of a color so nearly approximating to tan that they almost might be suitable.

As they went past the College and entered the winding street Mary's heart began to beat. She did not see any of the traffic flowing up and down, or the jostling, busy foot passengers, nor did she hear the eager lectures of her companion. Her eyes were straining up the street towards the crossing. She dared not turn back or give any explanation to Mrs. Cafferty, and in a few seconds she saw him, gigantic, calm, adequate, the monarch of his world. His back was turned to her, and the great sweep of his shoulders, his solid legs, his red neck and close-cropped, wiry hair were visible to her strangely. She had a peculiar feeling of acquaintedness and of aloofness, intimate knowledge and a separation of sharp finality caused her to stare at him with so intent a curiosity that Mrs. Cafferty noticed it.

"That's a fine man," said she, "he won't have to go about looking for girls."

As she spoke they passed by the policeman, and Mary knew that when her eyes left him his gaze almost automatically fell upon her. She was glad that he could not see her face. She was glad that Mrs. Cafferty was beside her: had she been alone she would have been tempted to walk away very quickly, almost to run, but her companion gave her courage and self-possession, so that she walked gallantly. But her mind was a fever. She could feel his eyes raking her from head to foot, she could see his great hand going up to tap his crinkly moustache. These things she could see in her terrified mind, but she could not think, she could only give thanks to God because she had her best clothes on.

XXIII

Mrs. Makebelieve was planning to get back such of her furniture and effects as had been pawned during her illness. Some of these things she had carried away from her father's house many years before when she got married. They had been amongst the earliest objects on which her eyes had rested when she was born, and around them her whole life of memories revolved. A chair in which her father had sat and on the edge whereof her husband had timidly balanced himself when he came courting her, and into which her daughter had been tied when she was a baby. A strip of carpet and some knives and forks had formed portion of her wedding presents. She loved these things, and had determined that if work could retrieve them they should not be lost forever. Therefore, she had to suffer people like Mrs. O'Connor, not gladly, but with the resignation due to the hests of Providence which one must obey but may legitimately criticise. Mrs. Makebelieve said definitely that she detested the woman. She was a cold-eyed person whose only ability was to order about other people who were much better than she was. It distressed Mrs. Makebelieve to have to work for such a person, to be subject to her commands and liable to her reproofs or advice; these were things which seemed to her to be out of all due proportion. She did not wish the woman any harm, but some day or other she would undoubtedly have to put her in her proper place. It was a day to which she looked forward. Any one who had a sufficient income could have a house and could employ and pay for outside help without any particular reason for being proud, and many people, having such an income, would certainly have a better appointed house and would be more generous and civil to those who came to work for them. Everybody, of course, could not have a policeman for a nephew, and there were a great many people who would rather not have anything to do with a policeman at all. Overbearing rough creatures to whom everybody is a thief! If Mrs. Makebelieve had such a nephew she would certainly have wrecked his pride —the great beast! Here Mrs. Makebelieve grew very angry: her black eyes blazed, her great nose grew thin and white and her hands went leaping in fury. "You're not in Court now, you jack-anapes you,—said I, with his whiskers and his baton, and his feet that were bigger than anything in the world except his ignorant self-conceit. 'Have you a daughter, mam, said he, what's her age, mam, said he, is she a good girl, mam, said he?'—but she had settled him,—and that woman was prouder of him than a king would be of his crown! never mind," said Mrs. Makebelieve, and she darted fiercely up and down the room, tearing pieces off the atmosphere and throwing them behind her.

In a few minutes, however, she sat down on the floor and drew her daughter's head to her breast, and then, staring into the scrap of fire, she counseled Mary wisely on many affairs of life and the conduct of a girl under all kinds of circumstances—to be adequate in spirit if not in physique: that was her theme. Never be a servant in your heart, said she. To work is nothing; the king on his throne, the priest kneeling before the Holy Altar, all people in all places had to work, but no person at all need be a servant. One worked and was paid, and went away keeping the integrity of one's soul unspotted and serene. If an employer was wise or good or kind Mrs. Makebelieve was prepared to accord such a person instant and humble reverence. She would work for such a one until the nails dropped off her fingers and her feet crumpled up under her body; but a policeman or a rich person, or a person who ordered one about . . . ! until she died and was buried in the depths of the world, she would never give in to such a person or admit anything but their thievishness and ill-breeding. Bad manners to the like of them, said she, and might have sailed boisterously away upon an ocean of curses but that Mary turned her face closer to her breast and began to speak.

For suddenly there had come to Mary a vision of peace: like a green island in the sea it was, like a white cloud on a broiling day; the sheltered life where all mundane preoccupations were far away, where ambition and hope and struggle were incredibly distant foolishness. Lowly and peaceful and unjaded was that life: she could see the nuns pacing quietly in their enclosed gardens, fingering their beads as they went to and fro and praying noiselessly for the sins of the world, or walking with solemn happiness to the Chapel to praise God in their own small companies, or going with hidden feet through the great City to nurse the sick and to comfort those who had no other comforter than God—to pray in a quiet place, and not to be afraid any more or doubtful or despised . . . ! These things she saw and her heart leaped to them, and of these things she spoke to her mother, who listened with a tender smile and stroked her hair and hands. But her mother did not approve of these things. She spoke of nuns with reverence and affection. Many a gentle, sweet woman had she known of that sisterhood, many a one before whom she could have abased herself with tears and love, but such a life of shelter and restraint could never have been hers, nor did she believe it could be Mary's. For her a woman's business was life, the turmoil and strife of it was good to be in, it was a cleansing and a bracing. God did not need any assistance, but man did, bitterly he wanted it, and the giving of such assistance was the proper business of a woman. Everywhere there was a man to be helped, and the quest of a woman was to find the man who most needed her aid, and having found him to cleave to him forever. In most of the trouble of life she divined men and women not knowing or not doing their duty, which was to love one another and to be neighborly and obliging to their fellows. A partner, a home and children—through the loyal co-operation of these she saw happiness and, dimly, a design of so vast an architecture as scarcely to be discussed. The bad and good of humanity moved her to an equal ecstasy of displeasure and approbation, but her God was Freedom and her religion Love. Freedom! even the last rags of it that remain to a regimented world! That was a passion with her. She must order her personal life without any ghostly or bodily supervision. She would oppose an encroachment on that with her nails and her teeth; and this last fringe of freedom was what nuns had sacrificed and all servants and other people had bartered away. One must work, but one must never be a slave—these laws seemed to her equally imperative; the structure of the world swung upon them, and whoever violated these laws was a traitor to both God and man.

But Mary did not say anything. Her mother's arms were around her, and suddenly she commenced to cry upon a bosom that was not strange. There was surely healing in that breast of love, a rampart of tenderness against the world, a door which would never be closed against her or opened to her enemies.

XXIV

In a little city like Dublin one meets every person whom one knows within a few days. Around each bend in the road there is a friend, an enemy, or a bore striding towards you, so that, with a piety which is almost religious, one says "touch wood" before turning any corner. It was not long, therefore, until Mary again met the big policeman. He came up behind her and walked by her side, chatting with a pleasant ease, in which, however, her curious mind could discover some obscure distinctions. On looking backwards it seemed to Mary that he had always come from behind her, and the retrospect dulled his glory to the diminishing point. For indeed his approach was too consistently policeman-like, it was too crafty; his advent hinted at a gross espionage, at a mind which was no longer a man's but a detective's who tracked everybody by instinct, and arrested his friends instead of saluting them.

As they walked along Mary was in a fever of discomfort. She wished dumbly that the man would go away, but for the wealth of the world she could not have brought herself to hurt the feelings of so big a man. To endanger the very natural dignity of a big man was a thing which no woman could do without a pang; the shame of it made her feel hot: he might have blushed or stammered, and the memory of that would sting her miserably for weeks as though she had insulted an elephant or a baby.

She could not get away from him. She had neither the courage nor the experience which enables a woman to dismiss a man without wounding him, and so, perforce, she continued walking by his side while he treated her to an intelligent dissertation on current political events and the topography of the city of Dublin.

But, undoubtedly, there was a change in the policeman, and it was not difficult to account for. He was more easy and familiar in his speech: while formerly he had bowed as from the peaks of manly intellect to the pleasant valleys of girlish incompetence he now condescended from the loftiness of a policeman and a person of quality to the quaint gutters of social inferiority. To many people mental inferiority in a companion has a charm, for it induces in one's proper person a feeling of philosophic detachment, a fine effect of personal individuality and superiority which is both bracing and uplifting—there is not any particular harm in this: progress can be, and is, accelerated by the hypocrisies and snobbishness, all the minor, unpleasant adjuncts of mediocrity. Snobbishness is a puling infant, but it may grow to a deeply whiskered ambition, and most virtues are, on examination, the amalgam of many vices. But while intellectual poverty may be forgiven and loved, social inequality can only be utilized. Our fellows, however addled, are our friends, our inferiors are our prey, and since the policeman had discovered Mary publicly

washing out an alien hall his respect for her had withered and
dropped to death almost in an instant; whence it appears that
there is really only one grave and debasing vice in the world,
and that is poverty.

In many little ways the distinction and the difference was
apparent to Mary. The dignity of a gentleman and a man of the
world was partly shorn away: the gentleman portion, which com-
prised kindness and reticence, had vanished, the man of the
world remained, typified by a familiarity which assumed that
this and that, understood but not to be mentioned, shall be taken
for granted: a spurious equalization perched jauntily but insecurely on a non-committal, and that base flattery which is the
only coin wherewith a thief can balance his depredations. For
as they went pacing down a lonely road towards the Dodder the
policeman diversified his entertaining lore by a succession of
compliments which ravaged the heavens and the earth and the
deep sea for a fitting symbology. Mary's eyes and the gay heavens were placed in juxtaposition and the heavens were censured,
the vegetable, animal and mineral worlds were discomfited, the
deep sea sustained a reproof and the by-products of nature and
of art drooped into a nothingness too vast even for laughter.
Mary had not the slightest objection to hearing that all the other
women in the world seemed cripples and gargoyles when viewed
against her own transcendent splendor, and she was prepared to
love the person who said this innocently and happily. She would
have agreed to be an angel or a queen to a man demanding
potentates and powers in his sweetheart, and would joyfully
have equalized matters by discovering the buried god in her
lover and believing in it as sincerely as he permitted.—But this
man was not saying the truth. She could see him making the
things up as he talked. There was eagerness in him, but no
spontaneity. It was not even eagerness, it was greediness: he
wanted to eat her up and go away with her bones sticking out
of his mouth as the horns of a deer protrude from the jaws of an
anaconda, veritable evidence to it and his fellows of a victory

and an orgy to command respect and envy. But he was familiar,
he was complacent and—amazedly she discovered it—he was big.
Her vocabulary could not furnish her with the qualifying word,
or, rather, epithet for his bigness. Horrible was suggested and
retained, but her instinct clamored that there was a fat, oozy
word somewhere which would have brought comfort to her
brains and her hands and feet. He did not keep his arms quiet,
but tapped his remarks into her blouse and her shoulder. Each
time his hands touched her they remained a trifle longer. They
seemed to be great red spiders, they would grip her all round
and squeeze her clammily while his face spiked her to death
with its moustache. . . . And he smiled also, he giggled and cut
capers; his language now was a perpetual witticism at which
he laughed in jerks, and at which she laughed tightly like an
obedient, quick echo: and then, suddenly, without a word, in a
dazing flash, his arms were about her. There was nobody in sight
at all, and he was holding her like a great spider, and his bristly
moustache darted forward to spike her to death, and then, somehow, she was free, away from him, scudding down the road
lightly and fearfully and very swiftly. "Wait, wait," he called,
"wait," but she did not wait.

XXV

Mrs. Cafferty came in that evening for a chat with Mrs. Makebelieve. There were traces of worry on the lady's face, and she
hushed the children who trooped in her wake with less of good
humor than they were accustomed to. Instead of threatening to
smack them on the head as was usual she did smack them, and
she walked surrounded by lamentations as by a sea.

Things were not going at all well with her. There was a slack-
ness in her husband's trade so that for days together he was idle,
and although the big woman amended her expenditure in every
direction she could not by any means adjust eight robust appetites to a shrunken income. She explained her position to Mrs.

Makebelieve:—Children would not, they could not, consent to go on shorter rations than they had been accustomed to, and it seemed to her that daily, almost hourly, their appetites grew larger and more terrible. She showed her right hand whereon the mere usage of a bread-knife had scored a ridge which was now a permanent disfigurement.

"God bless me," she shouted angrily, "what right have I to ask the creatures to go hungry? Am I to beat them when they cry? It's not their fault that they want food, and it's not my poor man's fault that they haven't any. He's ready to work at his trade if anybody wants him to do so, and if he can't get work and if the children are hungry whose fault is it?"

Mrs. Cafferty held that there was something wrong somewhere, but whether the blame was to be allocated to the weather, the employer, the government or the Deity, she did not know, nor did Mrs. Makebelieve know; but they were agreed that there was an error somewhere, a lack of adjustment with which they had nothing to do, but the effects whereof were grievously visible in their privations. Meantime it had become necessary that Mrs. Cafferty should adjust herself to a changing environment. A rise or fall in wages is automatically followed by a similar enlargement or shrinkage of one's necessities, and the consequent difference is registered at all points of one's life-contact. The physical and mental activities of a well-to-do person can reach out to a horizon, while those of very poor people are limited to their immediate, stagnant atmosphere, and so the lives of a vast portion of society are liable to a ceaseless change, a flux swinging from good to bad forever, an expansion and constriction against which they have no safeguards and not even any warning. In free nature this problem is paralleled by the shrinking and expansion of the seasons; the summer with its wealth of food, the winter following after with its famine, but many wild creatures are able to make a thrifty provision against the bad time which they know comes as certainly and periodically as the good time. Bees and squirrels and many others fill their barns with the plentiful overplus of the summer fields, birds can migrate and find sunshine and sustenance elsewhere, and others again can store during their good season a life energy by means whereof they may sleep healthily through their hard times. These organizations can be adjusted to their environments because the changes of the latter are known and can be more or less accurately predicted from any point. But the human worker has no such regularity. His food period does not ebb and recur with the seasons. There is no periodicity in their changes and, therefore, no possibility for defensive or protective action. His physical structure uses and excretes energy so rapidly that he cannot store it up and go to sleep on his savings, and his harvests are usually so lean and disconnected that the exercise of thrift is equally an impossibility and a mockery. The life, therefore, of such a person is composed of a constant series of adjustments and readjustments, and the stern ability wherewith these changes are met and combated are more admirably ingenious than the much-praised virtues of ants and bees to which they are constantly directed as to exemplars.

Mrs. Cafferty had now less money than she had been used to, but she had still the same rent to pay, the same number of children to feed, and the same personal dignity to support as in her better days, and her problem was to make up, by some means to which she was a stranger, the money which had drifted beyond the reach of her husband. The methods by which she could do this were very much restricted. Children require an attention which occupies the entire of a mother's time, and, consequently, she was prevented from seeking abroad any mitigation of her hardships. The occupations which might be engaged in at home were closed to her by mere overwhelming competition. The number of women who are prepared to make ten million shirts for a penny are already far in excess of the demand, and so, except by a severe undercutting such as a contract to make twenty million shirts for a halfpenny, work of this description is very difficult to obtain.

Under these circumstances nothing remained for Mrs. Cafferty but to take in a lodger. This is a form of co-operation much practiced among the poorer people. The margin of direct profit accruing from such a venture is very small, but this is compensated for by the extra spending power achieved. A number of people pooling their money in this way can buy to greater advantage and in a cheaper market than is possible to the solitary purchaser, and a moderate toll for wear and tear and usage, or, as it is usually put, for rent and attendance, gives the small personal profit at which such services are reckoned.

Through the good offices of a neighboring shopkeeper Mrs. Cafferty had secured a lodger, and, with the courage which is never separate from despair, she had rented a small room beside her own. This room, by an amazing economy of construction, contained a fireplace and a window: it was about one square inch in diameter, and was undoubtedly a fine room. The lodger was to enter into possession on the following day, and Mrs. Cafferty said he was a very nice young man indeed and did not drink.

XXVI

Mrs. Cafferty's lodger duly arrived. He was young and as thin as a lath, and he moved with fury. He was seldom in the place at all: he fled into the house for his food, and, having eaten it, he fled away from the house again, and did not reappear until it was time to go to bed. What he did with himself in the interval Mrs. Cafferty did not know, but she was prepared to wager her soul, the value of which she believed was high, on the fact that he was a good young man who never gave the slightest trouble, saving that his bedclothes were always lying on the floor in the morning, that there was candle grease on one corner of his pillow, and that he cleaned his boots on a chair. But these were things which one expected a young man to do, and the omission of them might have caused one to look curiously at the creature and to doubt his masculinity.

Mrs. Makebelieve replied that habits of order and neatness were rarely to be found in young people of either sex; more especially were these absent in boys who are released in early youth by their mothers from all purely domestic employments. A great many people believed, and she believed herself, that it was not desirable a man or boy should conform too rigidly to household rules. She had observed that the comfort of a home was lost to many men if they were expected to take their boots off when they came into the house or to hang their hats up in a special place. The women of a household, being so constantly indoors, find it easy and businesslike to obey the small rules which comprise household legislation, but as the entire policy of a house was to make it habitable and comfortable for its men folk all domestic ordinances might be strained to the uttermost until the compromise was found to mollify even exceptional idiosyncrasies. A man, she held, bowed to quite sufficient discipline during his working hours, and his home should be a place free from every vexatious restraint and wherein he might enjoy as wide a liberty as was good for him.

These ideas were applauded by Mrs. Cafferty, and she supplemented them by a recital of how she managed her own husband, and of the ridiculous ease whereby any man may be governed; for she had observed that men were very susceptible to control if only the control was not too apparent. If a man did a thing twice the doing of that thing became a habit and a passion, any interference with which provoked him to an unreasoning bull-like wrath wherein both wives and crockery were equally shattered; and, therefore, a woman had only to observe the personal habits of her beloved and fashion her restrictions according to that standard. This meant that men made the laws and women administered them—a wise allocation of prerogatives, for she conceived that the executive female function was every whit as important as the creative faculty which brought these laws into being. She was quite prepared to leave the creative powers in male hands if they would equally abstain from interference with the subsequent working details, for she was of opinion that in the pursuit of comfort (not entirely to their credit was it said) men were far more anxiously concerned than were women, and they flew to their bourne with an instinct for short cuts wherewith women were totally unacquainted.

But in the young man who had come to lodge with her Mrs. Cafferty discerned a being in whom virtue had concentrated to a degree that almost amounted to a congestion. He had instantly played with the children on their being presented to him: this was the sign of a good nature. Before he was acquainted with her ten minutes he had made four jokes: this was the sign of a pleasant nature; and he sang loudly and unceasingly when he awoke in the morning, which was the unfailing index to a happy nature. Moreover, he ate the meals provided for him without any of that particular, tedious examination which is so insulting, and had complimented Mrs. Cafferty on an ability to put a taste on food which she was pleased to obtain recognition of.

Both Mary and her mother remarked on these details with an admiration which was as much as either politeness or friendship could expect. Mrs. Makebelieve's solitary method of life had removed her so distantly from youth that information about a young man was almost tonic to her. She had never wished for a second husband, but had often fancied that a son would have been a wonderful joy to her. She considered that a house which had no young man growing up in it was not a house at all, and she believed that a boy would love his mother, if not more than a daughter could, at least with a difference which would be strangely sweet—a rash, impulsive, unquiet love: a love which would continually prove her love to the breaking point; a love that demanded, and demanded with careless assurance, that accepted her goodness as unquestioningly as she accepted the fertility of the earth, and used her knowing blindly and flatteringly how inexhaustively rich her depths were. . . . She could have wept for this: it was priceless beyond kingdoms: the smile on a boy's face lifted her to an exaltation. Her girl was inexpressibly sweet, surely an island in her wide heart, but a little boy . . . her breasts could have filled with milk for him, him she could have nourished in the rocks and in desert places: he would have been life to her and adventure, a barrier against old age, an incantation against sorrow, a fragrance and a grief and a defiance. . . .

It was quite plain that Mrs. Cafferty was satisfied with this addition to her household, but the profit which she had expected to accrue from his presence was not the liberal one she had in mind when making the preliminary arrangements. For it appeared that the young man had an appetite of which Mrs. Cafferty spoke with the respect proper to something colossal and awesome. A half-loaf did not more than break the back of a hunger which could wriggle disastrously over another half-loaf: so that, instead of being relieved by his advent, she was confronted by a more immediate and desolating bankruptcy than that from which she had attempted to escape. Exactly how to deal with this situation she did not know, and it was really in order to discuss her peculiar case that she had visited Mrs. Make-believe. She could, of course, have approached the young man and demanded from him an increase of money that would still be equitable to both parties, but she confessed a repugnance to this course. She did not like to upbraid or trouble any one on account of an appetite which was so noteworthy. She disliked, in any event, to raise a question about food: her instinct for hospitality was outraged at the thought, and as she was herself the victim, or the owner, of an appetite which had often placed a strain on her revenues, a fellow-feeling operated still further in mitigation of his disqualification.

Mrs. Makebelieve's advice was that she should stifle the first fierce and indiscriminate cravings of the young man's hunger by a liberal allowance of stirabout, which was a cheap, wholesome and very satisfying food, and in that way his destruction of more costly victuals would be kept within reasonable limits. Appetite, she held, was largely a matter of youth, and as a boy who was scarcely done growing had no way of modifying his passion for nourishment, it would be a lapse from decency to insult him on so legitimate a failing.

Mrs. Cafferty thought that this might be done, and thanked her friend for the counsel; but Mary, listening to these political matters, conceived Mrs. Cafferty as a person who had no longer any claim to honor, and she pitied the young man whose appetite was thus publicly canvassed, and who might at any moment be turned out of house and home on account of a hunger against which he had no safeguard and no remedy.

XXVII

It was not long until Mary and Mrs. Cafferty's lodger met. As he came in by the hall door one day Mary was carrying upstairs a large water bucket, the portage of which two or three times a day is so heavy a strain on the dweller in tenements. The youth instantly seized the bucket and, despite her protestations and appeals, he carried it upstairs. He walked a few steps in advance of Mary, whistling cheerfully as he went, so she was able to get a good view of him. He was so thin that he nearly made her laugh, but he carried the bucket, the weight of which she had often bowed under, with an ease astonishing in so slight a man, and there was a spring in his walk which was pleasant to see. He laid the bucket down outside her room, and requested her urgently to knock at his door whenever she required more water fetched, because he would be only too delighted to do it for her, and it was not the slightest trouble in the world. While he spoke he was stealing glances at her face and Mary was stealing glances at his face, and when they caught one another doing this at the same moment they both looked hurriedly away, and the young man departed to his own place.

But Mary was very angry with this young man. She had gone downstairs in her house attire, which was not resplendent, and she objected to being discovered by any youth in raiment not suitable to such an occasion. She could not visualize herself speaking to a man unless she was adorned as for a festivity. The gentlemen and ladies of whom her mother sometimes spoke, and of whom she had often dreamt, were never mean in their habiliments. The gentlemen frequently had green silken jackets with a foam of lace at the wrists and a cascade of the same rich material brawling upon their breasts, and the ladies were attired in a magnificent scarcity of clothing, the fundamental principle whereof, although she was quite assured of its righteousness, she did not yet understand.

Indeed, at this period Mary's interest in dress far transcended any interest she had ever known before. She knew intimately the window contents of every costumier's shop in Grafton and Wicklow and Dawson streets, and could follow with intelligent amazement the apparently trifling, but exceedingly important, differences of line or seam or flounce which ranked one garment as a creation and its neighbor as a dress. She and her mother often discussed the gowns wherein the native dignity of their souls might be adequately caparisoned. Mrs. Makebelieve, with a humility which had still a trace of anger, admitted that the period when she could have been expressed in color had expired, and she decided that a black silk dress, with a heavy gold chain falling along the bosom, was as much as her soul was now entitled to. She had an impatience, amounting to contempt, for those florid flamboyant souls whose outer physical integument so grievously misrepresented them. She thought that after a certain time one should dress the body and not the soul, and, discovering an inseparability between the two, she held that the mean shrine must hold a very trifling deity and that an ill-made or time-worn body should never dress gloriously under pain of an accusation of hypocrisy or foolishness.

But for Mary she planned garments with a freedom and bravery which astonished while it delighted her daughter. She combined twenty styles into one style of terrifying originality. She conceived dresses of a complexity beyond the labor of any but a divinely inspired needle, and others again whose simplicity was

almost too tenuous for human speech. She discussed robes whose
trailing and voluminous richness could with difficulty be sup-
ported by ten strong attendants, and she had heard of a dress
the fabric whereof was of such gossamer and ethereal insub-
stancy that it might be packed into a walnut more conveniently
than an ordinary dress could be impressed into a portmanteau.
Mary's exclamations of delight and longing ranged from every
possible dress to every impossible one, and then Mrs. Makebelieve reviewed all the dresses she had worn from the age of three
years to the present day, including wedding and mourning
dresses, those which were worn at picnics and dances and for
traveling, with an occasional divergence which comprehended
the clothing of her friends and her enemies during the like period.
She explained the basic principles of dress to her daughter,
showing that in this art, as in all else, order cannot be dispensed
with. There were things a tall person might wear, but which a
short person might not, and the draperies which adorned a portly
lady were but pitiable weeds when trailed by her attenuated sister. The effect of long thin lines in a fabric will make a short
women appear tall, while round, thick lines can reduce the al-
titude of people whose height is a trouble to be combated. She
illustrated the usage of large and small checks and plaids and
all the mazy interweaving of other cloths, and she elucidated
the mystery of color, tone, half-tone, light and shade so inter-
estingly that Mary could scarcely hear enough of her lore. She
was acquainted with the colors which a dark person may wear
and those which are suitable to a fair person, and the shades
proper to be used by the wide class ranging between these extremes she knew also, with a special provision for red-haired
and sandy folk and those who have no complexion at all. Certain
laws which she formulated were cherished by her daughter as
oracular utterances—that one should match one's eyes in the
house and one's hair in the street, was one; that one's hat and
gloves and shoes were of vastly more importance than all the
rest of one's clothing, was another; that one's hair and stockings

should tone as nearly as possible, was a third. Following these rules, she assured her daughter, a woman could never be other than well dressed, and all of these things Mary learned by heart and asked her mother to tell her more, which her mother was quite able and willing to do.

XXVIII

When the sexual instinct is aroused men and dogs and frogs and beetles, and such other creatures as are inside or outside of this catalogue, are very tenacious in the pursuit of their ambition. We can seldom get away from that which attracts or repels us. Love and hate are equally magnetic and compelling, and each, being supernormal, drags us willingly or woefully in their wake, until at last our blind persistency is either routed or appeased and we advance our lauds or gnash our teeth as the occasion bids us. There is no tragedy more woeful than the victory of hate, nor any attainment so hopelessly barren as the sterility of that achievement; for hate is finality, and finality is the greatest evil which can happen in a world of movement. Love is an inaugurator displaying his banners on captured peaks and pressing forever to a new and more gracious enterprise, but the victories of hate are gained in a ditch from which there is no horizon visible and whence there does not go even one limping courier.

After Mary fled from the embrace of the great policeman he came to think more closely of her than he had been used; but her image was throned now in anger: she came to him like a dull brightness wherefrom desolate thunder might roll at an instant. Indeed, she began to obsess him so that not even the ministrations of his aunt nor the obeisances of that pleasant girl, the name of whose boots was Fairybell, could give him any comfort or wean him from a contemplation which sprawled gloomily between him and his duties to the traffic. If he had not discovered the lowliness of her quality his course might have been

simple and straightforward: the issue, in such an event, would
have narrowed to every man's poser—whether he should marry
this girl or that girl? but the arithmetic whereby such matters
are elucidated would at the last have eased his perplexity, and
the path indicated could have been followed with the fullest
freedom on his part and without any disaster to his self-love. If,
whichever way his inclination wavered, there was any pang of
regret (and there was bound to be) such a feeling would be
ultimately waived by his reason or retained as a memorial which
had a gratifying savor. But the knowledge of Mary's social inferiority complicated matters, for, although this automatically
put her out of the question as his wife, her subsequent ill-treatment of himself had injected a virus to his blood which was one-
half a passion for her body and one-half a frenzy for vengeance.
He could have let her go easily enough if she had not first let
him go; for he read dismissal in her action and resented it as a
trespass on his own just prerogative.—He had but to stretch out
his hand and she would have dropped to it as tamely as a kitten,
whereas now she eluded his hand, would, indeed, have nothing
to do with it; and this could not be forgiven. He would gladly
have beaten her into submission, for what right has a slip of a
girl to withstand the advances of a man and a policeman? That
is a crooked spirit demanding to be straightened with a trun-
cheon: but as we cannot decently, or even peaceably, beat a
girl until she is married to us he had to relinquish that dear idea.
He would have dismissed her from his mind with the contempt
she deserved, but, alas! he could not: she clung there like a burr
not to be dislodged saving by possession or a beating—two shuddering alternatives—for she had become detestably dear to him.
His senses and his self-esteem conspired to heave her to a pedes-
tal where his eye strained upwards in bewilderment—that she
who was below him could be above him! This was astounding:
she must be pulled from her eminence and stamped back to her
native depths by his own indignant hoofs; thence she might be
gloriously lifted again with a calm, benignant, masculine hand

shedding pardons and favors, and perhaps a mollifying unguent
for her bruises. Bruises! a knee, an elbow—they were nothing;
little damages which to kiss was to make well again. Will not
women cherish a bruise that it may be medicined by male kisses?
Nature and precedent have both sworn to it. . . . But she was
out of reach; his hand, high-flung as it might be, could not get
to her. He went furiously to the Phœnix Park, to St. Stephen's
Green, to outlying leafy spots and sheltered lanes, but she was
in none of these places. He even prowled about the neighborhood of her home and could not meet her. Once he had seen
Mary as she came along the road, and he drew back into a doorway. A young man was marching by her side, a young man who
gabbled without ceasing and to whom Mary chattered again
with an equal volubility. As they passed by Mary caught sight
of him, and her face went flaming. She caught her companion's
arm, and they hurried down the road at a great pace. . . . She
had never chattered to him. Always he had done the talking, and
she had been an obedient grateful listener. Nor did he quarrel
with her silence, but her reserve shocked him—it was a pretense,
worse, a lie, a masked and hooded falsehood. She had surrendered to him willingly, and yet drew about her a protective
armor of reserve wherein she skulked immune to the arms which
were lawfully victorious. Is there, then, no loot for a conqueror?
We demand the keys of the City Walls and unrestricted entry,
or our torches shall blaze again. This chattering Mary was a girl
whom he had never caught sight of at all. She had been hiding
from him even in his presence. In every aspect she was an anger.
But she could talk to the fellow with her . . . a skinny whipper-
snapper, whom the breath of a man could shred into remote,
eyeless vacuity. Was this man another insult? Did she not even
wait to bury her dead? Pah! she was not value for his thought.
A girl so lightly facile might be blown from here to there and
she would scarcely notice the difference. Here and there were
the same places to her, and him and him were the same person.
A girl of that type comes to a bad end: he had seen it often, the

type and the end, and never separate. Can one not prophesy from facts? He saw a slut in a slum, a drab hovering by a dark entry, and the vision cheered him mightily for one glowing minute and left him unoccupied for the next, into which she thronged with the flutter of wings and the sound of a great mocking.

His aunt tracked his brows back to the responsible duties of his employment and commiserated with him, and made a lamentation about matters with which he never had been occupied, so that the last tag of his good manners departed from him, and he damned her unswervingly into consternation. That other pleasant girl, whose sweetness he had not so much tasted as sampled, had taken to brooding in his presence: she sometimes drooped an eye upon him like a question. . . . Let her look out or maybe he'd blaze into her teeth: howl menace down her throat until she swooned. Some one should yield to him a visible and tangible agony to balance his. Does law probe no deeper than the pillage of a watch? Can one filch our self-respect and escape free? Shall not our soul also sue for damages against its aggressor? Some person rich enough must pay for his lacerations or there was less justice in heaven than in the Police Courts; and it might be that girl's lot to expiate the sins of Mary. It would be a pleasure, if a sour one, to make somebody wriggle as he had, and somebody should wriggle; of that he was blackly determined.

XXIX

Indeed, Mrs. Cafferty's lodger and Mary had become quite intimate, and it was not through the machinations of either that this had happened. Ever since Mrs. Makebelieve had heard of that young man's appetite and the miseries through which he had to follow it she had been deeply concerned on his behalf. She declined to believe that the boy ever got sufficient to eat, and she enlarged to her daughter on the seriousness of this privation to a young man. Disabilities, such as a young girl could not comprehend, followed in the train of insufficient nourishment. Mrs. Cafferty was her friend, and was, moreover, a good decent woman against whom the tongue of rumor might wag in vain; but Mrs. Cafferty was the mother of six children and her natural kindliness dared not expand to their detriment. Furthermore, the fact of her husband being out of work tended to still further circumscribe the limits of her generosity. She divined a lean pot in the Cafferty household, and she saw the young man getting only as much food as Mrs. Cafferty dared to give him, so that the pangs of his hunger almost gnawed at her own vitals. Under these circumstances she had sought for an opportunity to become better acquainted with him, and had very easily succeeded; so when Mary found him seated on their bed and eating violently of their half-loaf if she was astonished at first she was also very glad. Her mother watched the demolition of their food with a calm happiness, for, although the amount she could contribute was small, every little helped, and not alone were his wants assisted, but her friend, Mrs. Cafferty, and her children were also aided by this dulling of an appetite which might have endangered their household peace.

The young man repaid their hospitality by an easy generosity of speech covering affairs which neither Mrs. Makebelieve nor her daughter had many opportunities for studying. He spoke of those very interesting matters with which a young man is concerned, and his speculations on various subjects, while often quite ignorant, were sufficiently vivid to be interesting and were wrong in a boyish fashion which was not unpleasant. He was very argumentative, but was still open to reason; therefore, Mrs. Makebelieve had opportunities for discussion which were seldom granted to her. Insensibly she adopted the position of guide, philosopher and friend to him, and Mary also found new interests in speech, for, although the young man thought very differently from her, he did think upon her own plane, and the things which secretly engrossed him were also the things wherewith she was deeply preoccupied. A community of ignorances may be as

binding as a community of interests. We have a dull suspicion
of that him or her who knows more than we do, but the person
who is prepared to go out adventuring with us with surmise
only for a chart and enjoyment for a guide may use our hand as
his own and our pockets as his treasury.

As the young man had no more shyness than a cat it soon fell
out that he and Mary took their evening walks together. He was
a clerk in a large retail establishment, and had many things to
tell Mary which were of great interest to both of them. For in
his place of business he had both friends and enemies of whom
he was able to speak with the fluency which was their due. Mary
knew, for instance, that the chief was bald but decent (she
could not believe that the connection was natural), and that the
second in command had neither virtues nor whiskers. (She saw
him as a codfish with a malignant eye.) He epitomized the vices
which belonged in detail to the world, but were peculiar to
himself in bulk. (He must be hairy in that event.) Language,
even the young man's, could not describe him adequately. (He
ate boys for breakfast and girls for tea.) With this person the
young man was in eternal conflict (a bear with little ears and
big teeth); not open conflict, for that would have meant instant
dismissal (not hairy at all—a long slimy eel with a lot of sense),
but a veiled unremitting warfare which occupied all their spare
attention. The young man knew for an actual fact that some
day he would be compelled to hit that chap, and it would be a
sorry day for the fellow, because his ability to hit was startling.
He told Mary of the evil results which had followed some of his
blows, and Mary's incredulity was only heightened by a display
of the young man's muscles. She extolled these because she
thought it was her duty to do so, but preserved some doubts of
their unique destructiveness. Once she asked him could he fight
a policeman, and he assured her that policemen are not able to
fight at all singly, but only in squads, when their warfare is
callous and ugly and conducted mainly with their boots; so that
decent people have no respect for their fighting qualities or their

private characters. He assured her that not only could he fight a policeman, but he could also tyrannize over the seed, breed and generation of such a one, and, moreover, he could accomplish this without real exertion. Against all policemen and soldiers the young man professed an eager hostility, and with these bad people he included landlords and many employers of labor. His denunciation of these folk might be traced back to the belief that none of them treated one fairly. A policeman, he averred, would arrest a man for next door to nothing, and any resistance offered to their spleen rendered the unfortunate prisoner liable to be man-handled in his cell until their outraged dignity was appeased. The three capital crimes upon which a man is liable to arrest are for being drunk, or disorderly, or for refusing to fight, and to these perils a young man is peculiarly susceptible and is, to that extent, interested in the Force, and critical of their behavior. The sight of a soldier annoyed him, for he saw a conqueror, trampling vaingloriously through the capital of his country, and the inability of his land to eject the braggart astonished and mortified him. Landlords had no bowels of compassion. There was no kindliness of heart among them, nor any wish to assist those whose whole existence was engaged on their behalf. He saw them as lazy unproductive gluttons who cried forever "Give, give," and who gave nothing in return but an increased insolent tyranny. Many employers came into the same black category. They were people who had disowned all duty to humanity, and who saw in themselves the beginning and the end of all things. They gratified their acquisitiveness not in order that they might become benefactors of their kind (the only righteous freedom of which we know) but merely to indulge a petty exercise of power and to attain that approval which is granted to wealth and the giving of which is the great foolishness of mankind. These people used their helpers and threw them away, they exploited and bought and sold their fellow-men while their arrogant self-assurance and the monstrous power which they had gathered for their security shocked him like a thing unbelievable in spite of its reality. That such things could be fretted him into clamor. He wanted to point them out to all people. He saw his neighbors' ears clogged, and he was prepared to die howling if only he could pierce those encrusted auditories. That what was so simple to him should not be understood by everybody! He could see plainly and others could not, although their eyes looked straightly forward and veritably rolled with intent and consciousness! Did their eyes and ears and brains not differently to his, or was he a singular monster cursed from his birth with madness? At times he was prepared to let humanity and Ireland go to the devil their own way, he being well assured that without him they were bound quickly for deep perdition. Of Ireland he sometimes spoke with a fervor of passion which would be outrageous if addressed to a woman. Surely he saw her as a woman, queenly and distressed and very proud. He was physically anguished for her, and the man who loved her was the very brother of his bones. There were some words the effect of which were almost hypnotic on him—The Isle of the Blest; The Little Dark Rose, The Poor Old Woman and Caitlin the Daughter of Holohan. The mere repetition of these phrases lifted him to an ecstasy; they had hidden, magical meanings which pricked deeply to his heartstrings and thrilled him to a tempest of pity and love. He yearned to do deeds of valor, violent, grandiose feats which would redound to her credit and make the name of Irishmen synonymous with either greatness or singularity: for, as yet, the distinction between these words was no more clear to him than it is to any other young man who reads violence as heroism and eccentricity as genius. Of England he spoke with something like stupefaction—as a child cowering in a dark wood tells of the ogre who has slain his father and carried his mother away to a drear captivity in his castle built of bones—so he spoke of England. He saw an Englishman stalking hideously forward with a princess tucked under each arm, while their brothers and their knights were netted in enchantment and slept heedless of the wrongs done to their ladies and of the defacement of their shields. . . . "Alas, alas and alas, for the once-proud people of Banba!"

XXX

Mrs. Makebelieve was astonished when the policeman knocked at her door. A knock at her door was a rare sound, for many years had gone by since any one had come to visit her. Of late Mrs. Cafferty often came to talk to her, but she never knocked: she usually shouted, "Can I come in?" and then she came in. But this was a ceremonious knock which startled her, and the spectacle of the great man bending through the doorway almost stopped her breath. Mary also was so shocked into terror that she stood still, forgetful of all good manners, and stared at the visitor open-eyed. She knew and did not know what he had come for; but that, in some way, his appearance related to her she was instantly assured, although she could not even dimly guess at a closer explanation of his visit. His eyes stayed on her for an instant and then passed to her mother, and, following her rather tremulous invitation, he came into the room. There was no chair to sit on, so Mrs. Makebelieve requested him to sit down on the bed, which he did. She fancied he had come on some errand from Mrs. O'Connor, and was inclined to be angry at a visit which she construed as an intrusion, so, when he was seated, she waited to hear what he might have to say.

Even to her it was evident that the big man was perplexed and abashed; his hat was in his way and so were his hands, and when he spoke his voice was so husky as to be distressful. On Mary, who had withdrawn to the very end of the room, this discomfort of speech had a peculiar effect: the unsteady voice touched her breast to a kindred fluttering, and her throat grew parched and so irritated that a violent fit of coughing could not be restrained, and this, with the nervousness and alarm which his appearance had thronged upon her, drove her to a very fever of distress. But she could not take her eyes away from him, and she wondered and was afraid of what he might say. She knew there were a great many things he might discuss which she would be loath to hear in her mother's presence, and which her mother would not be gratified to hear either.

He spoke for a few moments about the weather, and Mrs. Makebelieve hearkened to his remarks with a perplexity which she made no effort to conceal. She was quite certain he had not called to speak about the weather, and she was prepared to tell him so if a suitable opportunity should occur. She was also satisfied that he had not come on a formal, friendly visit—the memory of her last interview with him forbade such a conjecture, for on that occasion politeness had been deposed from her throne and acrimony had reigned in her stead. If his aunt had desired him to undertake an embassy to her he would surely have delivered his message without preamble, and would not have been thrown by so trifling a duty into the state of agitation in which he was. It was obvious, therefore, that he had not come with a message relating to her work. Something of fear touched Mrs. Makebelieve as she looked at him, and her voice had an uneasy note when she requested to know what she could do for him.

The policeman suddenly, with the gesture of one throwing away anchors, plunged into the heart of his matter, and as he spoke the look on Mrs. Makebelieve's face changed quickly from bewilderment to curiosity and dulled again to a blank amazement. After the first few sentences she half turned to Mary, but an obscure shame prevented her from searching out her daughter's eyes. It was borne quickly and painfully to her that Mary had not treated her fairly: there was a secret here with which a mother ought to have been trusted, and one which she could not believe Mary would have withheld from her; and so, gauging her child's feelings by her own, she steadfastly refused to look at her lest the shocked surprise in her eyes might lacerate the girl she loved, and who she knew must at the instant be in a sufficient agony—Undoubtedly the man was suggesting that he

wanted to marry her daughter, and the unexpectedness of such
a proposal left her mentally gaping; but that there must have
been some preliminaries of meeting and courtship became obvious to her. Mary also listened to his remarks in a stupor. Was
there no possibility at all of getting away from the man? A
tenacity such as this seemed to her malignant. She had the
feeling of one being pursued by some relentless and unscrupu-
lous hunter. She heard him speaking through a cloud, and the
only things really clear to her were the thoughts which she knew
her mother must be thinking. She was frightened and ashamed,
and the sullenness which is the refuge of most young people
descended upon her like a darkness. Her face grew heavy and
vacant, and she stared in front of her in the attitude of one who
had nothing to do with what was passing. She did not believe
altogether that he was in earnest: her immediate discomfort
showed him as one who was merely seeking to get her into
trouble with her mother in order to gratify an impotent rage.
Twice or three times she flamed suddenly, went tiptoe to run
from the room. A flash, and she would be gone from the place,
down the stairs, into the streets and away anywhere, and she
tingled with the very speed of her vision; but she knew that one
word from her mother would halt her like a barrier, and she
hated the thought that he should be a witness to her obedience.

While he was speaking he did not look at Mary. He told Mrs.
Makebelieve that he loved her daughter very much, and he
begged her permission and favor for his suit. He gave her to
understand that he and Mary had many opportunities of becoming acquainted, and were at one in this desire for matrimony—
To Mrs. Makebelieve's mind there recurred a conversation which
she had once held with her daughter, when Mary was curious
to know if a policeman was a desirable person for a girl to
marry? She saw this question now, not as being prompted by a
laudable, an almost scientific curiosity, but as the interested, sly
speculation of a schemer hideously accomplished in deceit. Mary
could see that memory flitting back through her mother's brain,

and it tormented her. Nor was her mother at ease—there was no chair to sit upon, she had to stand and listen to all this while he spoke, more or less at his ease, from the bed. If she also had been sitting down she might have been mistress of her thoughts and able to deal naturally with the situation; but an easy pose is difficult when standing: her hands would fold in front of her and the schoolgirl attitude annoyed and restrained her. Also, the man appeared to be in earnest in what he said. His words at the least and the intention which drove them seemed honorable. She could not give rein to her feelings without lapsing to a barbarity which she might not justify to herself even in anger and might, indeed, blush to remember. Perhaps his chief disqualification consisted in a relationship to Mrs. O'Connor for which he could not justly be held to blame, and for which she sincerely pitied him. But this certainly was a disqualification never to be redeemed. He might leave his work, or his religion, or his country, but he could never quit his aunt, because he carried her with him under his skin; he was her with additions, and at times Mrs. Makebelieve could see Mrs. O'Connor looking cautiously at her through the policeman's eyes; a turn of his forehead and she was there like a thin wraith that vanished and appeared again. The man was spoiled for her. He did not altogether lack sense, and the fact that he wished to marry her daughter showed that he was not so utterly beyond the reach of redemption as she had fancied.

Meanwhile, he had finished his statement as regarded the affection which he bore to her daughter and the suitability of their temperaments, and had hurled himself into an explanation of his worldly affairs, comprising his salary as a policeman, the possibility of promotion and the increased emoluments which would follow it, and the certain pension which would sustain his age. There were, furthermore, his parents, from whose decease he would reap certain monetary increments, and the deaths of other relatives from which an additional enlargement of his revenues might reasonably be expected. Indeed, he had not desired to speak of these matters at all, but the stony demeanor of Mrs. Makebelieve and the sullen aloofness of her daughter forced him, however reluctantly, to draw even ignoble weapons from his armory. He had not conceived they would be so obdurate: he had, in fact, imagined that the elder woman must be flattered by his offer to marry her daughter, and when no evidence to support this was forthcoming he was driven to appeal to the cupidity which he believed occupies the heart of every middle-aged, hard-worked woman. But these statements also were received with a dreadful composure. He could have smashed Mrs. Makebelieve where she stood. Now and again his body strained to a wild, physical outburst, a passionate, red fury that would have terrified these women to their knees, while he roared their screams into thin whimpers as a man should. He did not even dare to stop speaking, and his efforts at an easy, good-humored, half-careless presentation of his case was bitterly painful to him as it was to his auditors. The fact that they were both standing up unnerved him also—the pleasant equality which should have formed the atmosphere of such an interview was destroyed from the first moment, and, having once sat down, he did not like to stand up again. He felt glued to the bed on which he sat, and he felt also that if he stood up the tension in the room would so relax that Mrs. Makebelieve would at once break out into speech sarcastic and final, or her daughter might scream reproaches and disclaimers of an equal finality. At her he did not dare to look, but the corner of his eye could see her shape stiffened against the fireplace, an attitude so different from the pliable contours to which he was accustomed in her as almost to be repellant. He would have thanked God to find himself outside the room, but how to get out of it he did not know: his self-esteem forbade anything like a retreat without honor, his nervousness did not permit him to move at all, the anger which prickled the surface of his body and mind was held in check only by an instinct of fear as to what he might do if he moved, and so, with dreadful jocularity, he commenced to speak of himself, his personal character, his sobriety and steadiness—of all those safe negations on which many women place reliance he spoke, and also of certain small vices which he magnified merely for the sake of talking, such as smoking, an odd glass of porter and the shilling which, now and again, he had ventured upon a race horse.

Mary listened to him for a while with angry intentness. The fact that she was the subject of his extraordinary discourse quickened at the first all her apprehensions. Had the matter been less important she would have been glad to look at herself in this strange position, and to savor, with as much detachment as was possible, the whole spirit of the adventure. But when she heard him, as she put it, "telling on her," laying bare to her mother all the walks they had taken together, visits to restaurants and rambles through the streets and the parks, what he had said to her on this occasion and on that, and her remarks on such and such a matter, she could not visualize him save as a malignant and uncultivated person; and when he tacitly suggested that she was as eager for matrimony as he was, and so put upon her the horrible onus of rejecting him before a second person, she closed her mind and her ears against him. She refused to listen, although her perceptions admitted the trend of his speech. His words droned heavily and monotonously to her as through dull banks of fog. She made up her mind that if she were asked any questions by either of them she would not reply, and that she would not look at either of them, and then she thought that she would snap and stamp her feet and say that she hated him, that he had looked down on her because she worked for his aunt, that he had meanly been ashamed of and cut her because she was poor, that he had been going with another girl all the time he was going with her and that he only pursued her in order to annoy her, that she didn't love him, that she didn't even like him, that, in fact, she disliked him heartily. She wished to say all these things in one whirling outcry, but feared that before she had rightly begun she might become abashed, or, worse, might burst into tears and lose all the dignity which she meant to preserve in his presence for the purpose of showing to him in the best light exactly what he was losing.

But the big man had come to the end of his speech. He made a few attempts to begin anew on the desirability of such a union for both of them, and the happiness it would give him if Mrs. Makebelieve would come to live with them when they were married. He refused to let it appear that there was any doubt as to Mary's attitude in the matter, for up to the moment he came to their door he had not doubted her willingness himself. Her late avoidance of him he had put down to mere feminine tactics which leads on by holding off. The unwilling person he had been assured was himself—he stooped to her, and it was only after a severe battle that he had been able to do it. The astonishment and disapproval of his relatives and friends at such a step were very evident to him, for to a man of his position and figure girls were cheap creatures, the best of them to be had for the mere asking. Therefore, the fact that this girl could be seriously rejecting his offer of marriage came upon him like red astonishment. He had no more to say, however, and he blundered and fumbled into silence.

For a moment or two the little room was so still that the quietness seemed to hum and buzz like an eternity. Then, with a sigh, Mrs. Makebelieve spoke.

"I don't know at all," said she, "why you should speak to me about this, for neither my daughter nor yourself have ever even hinted to me before that you were courting one another. Why Mary should keep such a secret from her own mother I don't know. Maybe I've been cruel and frightened her, although I don't remember doing anything that she could have against me of that sort: or, maybe, she didn't think I was wise enough to advise her about a particular thing like her marriage, for, God knows, old women are foolish enough in their notions, or else they wouldn't be slaving and grinding for the sake of their children the way they do be doing year in and year out, every day in the week, and every hour of the day. It isn't any wonder at all that a child would be a liar and a sleeveen and a trampler of the roads with the first man that nods to her when her mother is a foolish person that she can't trust. Of course, I wouldn't be looking for a gentleman like yourself to mention the matter to me when I might be scrubbing out your aunt's kitchen or her hall door maybe, and you sitting in the parlor with the company. Sure, I'm only an old charwoman, and what does it matter at all what I'd be thinking, or whether I'd be agreeing or not to anything? Don't I get my wages for my work, and what more does anybody want in the world? As for me going to live with you when you are married—it was kind of you to ask me that; but it's not the sort of thing I'm likely to do, for if I didn't care for you as a stranger I'm not going to like you any better as my daughter's husband. You'll excuse me saying one thing, Sir, but while we are talking we may as well be talking out, and it's this, that I never did like you, and I never will like you, and I'd sooner see my daughter married to any one at all than to yourself. But, sure, I needn't be talking about it; isn't it Mary's business altogether, and she'll be settling it with you nicely I don't doubt. She's a practiced hand now at arranging things, like you are yourself, and it will do me good to be learning something from her."

Mrs. Makebelieve took a cloth in her hand and walked over to the fireplace, which she commenced to polish.

The big man looked at Mary. It was incumbent on him to say something. Twice he attempted to speak, and each time, on finding himself about to say something regarding the weather, he stopped. Mary did not look at him; her eyes were fixed stubbornly on a part of the wall well away from his neighborhood, and it seemed to him that she had made a vow to herself never to look at him again. But the utter silence of the room was unbearable. He knew that he ought to get up and go out, but he could not bring himself to do so. His self-love, his very physical strength, rebelled against so tame a surrender. One thought he gathered in from swaying vacuity—that the timid little creature whom he had patronized would not find the harsh courage to refuse him point-blank if he charged her straightly with the question, and so he again assayed speech.

"Your mother is angry with us, Mary," said he, "and I suppose she has good right to be angry; but the reason I did not speak to her before, as I admit I should have if I had done the right thing, was that I had very few chances of meeting her, and never did meet her without some other person being there at the same time. I suppose the reason you did not say anything was that you wanted to be quite sure of yourself and of me too before you mentioned it. We have both done the wrong thing in not being open, but maybe your mother will forgive us when she knows we had no intention of hurting her, or of doing anything behind her back. Your mother seems to hate me: I don't know why, because she hardly knows me at all, and I've never done her any harm or said a word against her. Perhaps when she knows me as well as you do she'll change her mind: but you know I love you better than any one else, and that I'd do anything I could to please you and be a good husband to you. What I want to ask you before your mother is,—will you marry me?"

Mary made no reply. She did not look or give the slightest sign that she had heard. But now it was that she did not dare to look at him. The spectacle of this big man badgered by her and by her mother, pleading to her, and pleading, as he and she well knew, hopelessly, would have broken her heart if she looked at him. She had to admire the good masculine fight he made of it. Even his tricks of word and tactic, which she instantly divined, moved her almost to tears; but she feared terribly that if she met his gaze she might not be able to resist his huge helplessness, and that she might be compelled to do whatever he begged of her even in despite of her own wishes.

The interval which followed his question weighed heavily upon them all. It was only broken by Mrs. Makebelieve, who began to hum a song as she polished the fire grate. She meant to show her careless detachment from the whole matter, but in the face of Mary's silence she could not keep it up. After a few moments she moved around and said:—

"Why don't you answer the gentleman, Mary?"

Mary turned and looked at her, and the tears which she had resisted so long swam in her eyes: although she could keep her features composed she had no further command over her tears.

"I'll answer whatever you ask me, mother," she whispered.

"Then, tell the gentleman whether you will marry him or not."

"I don't want to marry any one at all," said Mary.

"You are not asked to marry any one, darling," said Mrs. Make-believe, "but some one—this gentleman here whose name I don't happen to know. Do you know his name?"

"No," said Mary.

"My name . . ." began the policeman.

"It doesn't matter, Sir," said Mrs. Makebelieve. "Do you want to marry this gentleman, Mary?"

"No," whispered Mary.

"Are you in love with him?"

Mary turned completely away from him.

"No," she whispered again.

"Do you think you ever will be in love with him?"

She felt as a rat might when hunted to a corner. But the end must be very near; this could not last forever because nothing can. Her lips were parched, her eyes were burning. She wanted to lie down and go asleep and waken again laughing to say— "it was a dream."

Her reply was almost inaudible. "No," she said.

"You are quite sure? It is always better to be quite sure."

She did not answer any more, but the faint droop of her head gave the reply her mother needed.

"You see, Sir," said Mrs. Makebelieve, "that you were mistaken in your opinion. My daughter is not old enough yet to be thinking of marriage and such like. Children do be thoughtless. I am sorry for all the trouble she has given you, and"—a sudden compunction stirred her, for the man was standing up now, and there was no trace of Mrs. O'Connor visible in him: his face was as massive and harsh as a piece of wall. "Don't you be thinking too badly of us now," said Mrs. Makebelieve with some agitation; "the child is too young altogether to be asking her to marry. Maybe in a year or two—I said things I know, but I was vexed, and . . ."

The big man nodded his head and marched out.

Mary ran to her mother moaning like a sick person, but Mrs. Makebelieve did not look at her. She lay down on the bed and turned her face to the wall, and she did not speak to Mary for a long time.

XXXI

When the young man who lodged with Mrs. Cafferty came in on the following day he presented a deplorable appearance. His clothes were torn and his face had several large strips of sticking-plaster on it, but he seemed to be in a mood of extraordinary happiness notwithstanding, and proclaimed that he had participated in the one really great fight of his lifetime, that he wasn't injured at all, and that he wouldn't have missed it for a pension.

Mrs. Cafferty was wild with indignation, and marched him into Mrs. Makebelieve's room, where he had to again tell his story and have his injuries inspected and commiserated. Even Mr. Cafferty came into the room on this occasion. He was a large, slow man dressed very comfortably in a red beard—his beard was so red and so persistent that it quite overshadowed the rest of his wrappings and did, indeed, seem to clothe him. As he stood the six children walked in and out of his legs, and stood on his feet in their proper turns without causing him any apparent discomfort. During the young man's recital Mr. Cafferty every now and then solemnly and powerfully smote his left hand with his right fist, and requested that the aggressor should be produced to him.

The young man said that as he was coming home the biggest man in the world walked up to him. He had never set eyes on the man before in his life, and thought at first he wanted to borrow a match or ask the way to somewhere, or something like that, and, accordingly, he halted; but the big man gripped him by the shoulder and said "You damned young whelp," and then he laughed and hit him a tremendous blow with his other hand. He twisted himself free at that, and said "What's that for?" and then the big man made another desperate clout at him. A fellow wasn't going to stand that kind of thing, so he let out at him with his left and then jumped in with two short-arm jabs that must have tickled the chap; that fellow didn't have it all his own way anyhow. . . . The young man exhibited his knuckles, which were skinned and bleeding, as evidence of some exchange; but, he averred, you might as well be punching a sack of coal as that man's face. In another minute they both slipped and rolled over and over in the road, hitting and kicking as they sprawled: then a crowd of people ran forward and pulled them asunder. When they were separated he saw the big man lift his fist, and the person who was holding him ducked suddenly and ran for his life: the other folk got out of the way too, and the big man walked over to where he stood and stared into his face. His jaw was stuck out like the seat of a chair and his moustache was like a bristle of barbed wire. The young man said to him, "What the hell's wrong with you to go bashing a man for nothing at all?" and all of a sudden the big fellow turned and walked away. It was a grand fight altogether, said the youth, but the other man was a mile and a half too big for him.

As this story proceeded Mrs. Makebelieve looked once or twice at her daughter. Mary's face had gone very pale, and she nodded back a confirmation of her mother's conjecture; but it did not seem necessary or wise to either of them that they should explain their thoughts. The young man did not require either condolences or revenge. He was well pleased at an opportunity to measure his hardihood against a worthy opponent. He had found that his courage exceeded his strength, as it always should, for how could we face the gods and demons of existence if our puny arms were not backed up by our invincible eyes? and he displayed his contentment at the issue as one does a banner emblazoned with merits. Mrs. Makebelieve understood also that the big man's action was merely his energetic surrender, as of one who, instead of tendering his sword courteously to the victor, hurls it at him with a malediction; and that in assaulting their friend he was bidding them farewell as heartily and impressively as he was able. So they fed the young man and extolled him, applauding to the shrill winding of his trumpet until he glowed again in the full satisfaction of heroism.

He and Mary did not discontinue their evening walks. Of these Mrs. Makebelieve was fully cognizant, and, although she did not remark on the fact, she had been observing the growth of their intimacy with a care which was one part approval and one part pain; for it was very evident to her that her daughter was no longer a child to be controlled and directed by authority. Her little girl was a big girl; she had grown up and was eager to undertake the business of life on her own behalf. But the period of Mrs. Makebelieve's motherhood had drawn to a close, and her arms were empty. She was too used now to being a mother to relinquish easily the prerogatives of that status, and her discontent had this justification and assistance that it could be put into definite words, fronted and approved or rejected as reason urged. By knowledge and thought we will look through a stone wall if we look long enough, for we see less through eyes than through Time. Time is the clarifying perspective whereby myopia of any kind is adjusted, and a thought emerges in its field as visibly as a tree does in nature's. Mrs. Makebelieve saw seventeen years' apprenticeship to maternity canceled automatically without an explanation or a courtesy, and for a little time her world was in ruins, the ashes of existence powdered her hair and her forehead. Then she discovered that the debris was valuable in known currency; the dust was golden: her love remained to her undisturbed and unlikely to be disturbed by whatever event. And she discovered further that parentage is neither a game nor a privilege but a duty; it is, astounding thought, the care of the young until the young can take care of itself. It was for this freedom only that her elaborate care had been necessary; her bud had blossomed and she could add no more to its bloom or fragrance. Nothing had happened that was not natural, and whoso opposes his brow against that imperious urgency is thereby renouncing his kind and claiming a kinship with the wild boar and the goat, which they, too, may repudiate with leaden foreheads. There remained also the common human equality, not alone of blood, but of sex also, which might be fostered and grow to an intimacy more dear and enduring, more lovely and loving than the necessarily one-sided devotions of parentage. Her duties in that relationship having been per-formed, it was her daughter's turn to take up hers and prove her rearing by repaying to her mother the conscious love which intelligence and a good heart dictate. This given, Mrs. Make-believe could smile happily again, for her arms would be empty only for a little time. The continuity of nature does not fail saving for extraordinary instances. She sees to it that a breast and an arm shall not very long be unoccupied, and, conse-quently, as Mrs. Makebelieve sat contemplating that futurity which is nothing more than a prolongation of experience she could smile contentedly, for all was very well.

XXXII

If the unexpected did not often happen life would be a logical, scientific progression which might become dispirited and repudi-ate its goal for very boredom, but nature has cunningly diversi-fied the methods whereby she coaxes or coerces us to prosecute, not our own, but her own adventure. Beyond every corner there may be a tavern or a church wherein both the saint and the sinner may be entrapped and remolded. Beyond the skyline you may find a dynamite cartridge, a drunken tinker, a mad dog, or a shilling which some person has dropped; and any one of these unexpectednesses may be potent to urge the traveler down a side street and put a crook in the straight line which had been his life, and to which he had become miserably reconciled. The element of surprise being, accordingly, one of the commonest things in the world we ought not to be hypercritical in our review of singularities, or say—"These things do not happen,"— because it is indisputable that they do happen. That combination which comprises a dark night, a highwayman armed and hatted to the teeth, and myself, may be a purely fortuitous one, but will such a criticism bring any comfort to the highwayman? And the concourse of three benevolent millionaires with the person to whom poverty can do no more is so pleasant and possible that I marvel it does not occur more frequently. I am prepared to believe on the very lightest assurance that these things do happen; but are hushed up for reasons which would be cogent enough if they were available.

Mrs. Makebelieve opened the letter which the evening's post had brought to her. She had pondered well before opening it, and had discussed with her daughter all the possible people who could have written it. The envelope was long and narrow, it was addressed in a swift emphatic hand, the tail of the letter M enjoying a career distinguished beyond any of its fellows by length and beauty. The envelope, moreover, was sealed by a brilliant red lion with jagged whiskers and a simper, who threatened the person daring to open a missive not addressed to him with the vengeance of a battle-axe which was balanced lightly but truculently on his right claw.

This envelope contained several documents purporting to be copies of extraordinary originals, and amongst them a letter which was read by Mrs. Makebelieve more than ten thousand times or ever she went to bed that night. It related that more than two years previously one Patrick Joseph Brady had departed this life, and that his will, dated from a multitudinous address in New York, devised and bequeathed to his dearly beloved sister Mary Eileen Makebelieve, otherwise Brady, the following shares and securities for shares, to wit:—and the thereinafter mentioned houses and messuages, lands, tenements, hereditaments and premises, that was to say:—and all household furniture, books, pictures, prints, plate, linen, glass and objects of vertu, carriages, wines, liquors and all consumable stores and effects whatsoever then in the house so and so, and all money then in the Bank and thereafter to accrue due upon the thereinbefore mentioned stocks, funds, shares and securities. . . . Mrs. Makebelieve wept and besought God not to make a fool of a woman who was not only poor but old. The letter requested her to call on the following day, or at her earliest convenience, to "the above address," and desired that she should bring with her such letters or other documents as would establish her relationship to the deceased and assist in extracting the necessary Grant of Probate to the said Will, and it was subscribed by Messrs. Platitude & Glambe, Solicitors, Commissioners for Oaths and Protectors of the Poor.

To the Chambers of these gentlemen Mrs. Makebelieve and Mary repaired on the following day, and, having produced the letters and other documents for inspection, the philanthropists, Platitude and Glambe, professed themselves to be entirely satisfied as to their bona fides, and exhibited an eagerness to be of immediate service to the ladies in whatever capacity might be conceived. Mrs. Makebelieve instantly invoked the Pragmatic Sanction; she put the entire matter to the touchstone of absolute verity by demanding an advance of fifty pounds. Her mind reeled as she said the astounding amount, but her voice did not. A check was signed and a clerk dispatched, who returned with eight five-pound notes and ten sovereigns of massy gold. Mrs. Makebelieve secreted these, and went home marveling to find that she was yet alive. No trams ran over her. The motor cars pursued her, and were evaded. She put her hope in God, and explained so breathlessly to the furious street. One cyclist who took corners on trust she cursed by the Ineffable Name, but instantly withdrew the malediction for luck, and addressed his dwindling back with an eye of misery and a voice of benediction. For a little time neither she nor her daughter spoke of the change in their fortunes saving in terms of allusion; they feared that, notwithstanding their trust, God might hear and shatter them with His rolling laughter. They went out again that day furtively and feverishly and bought. . . .

But on the following morning Mrs. Makebelieve returned again to her labor. She intended finishing her week's work with Mrs. O'Connor (it might not last for a week). She wished to observe that lady with the exact particularity, the singleness of eye, the true, candid, critical scrutiny which had hitherto been impossible to her. It was, she said to Mary, just possible that Mrs. O'Connor might make some remarks about soap. It was possible that the lady might advance theories as to how this or that particular kind of labor ought to be conducted. . . . Mrs. Makebelieve's black eye shone upon her child with a calm peace, a benevolent happiness rare indeed to human regard.

In the evening of that day Mary and the young man who lodged with their neighbor went out for the walk which had become customary with them. The young man had been fed with an amplitude which he had never known before, so that not even the remotest slim thread, shred, hint, echo or memory of hunger remained with him: he tried but could not make a dint in himself anywhere, and, consequently, he was as sad as only a well-fed person can be. Now that his hunger was gone he deemed that all else was gone also. His hunger, his sweetheart, his hopes, his good looks (for his injuries had matured to the ripe purple of the perfect bruise) all were gone, gone, gone. He told it to Mary, but she did not listen to him; to the rolling sky he announced it and it paid no heed. He walked beside Mary at last in silence, listening to her plans and caprices, the things she would do and buy, the people to whom gifts should be made and the species of gift uniquely suitable to this person

and to that person, the people to whom money might be given
and the amounts, and the methods whereby such largesse could
be distributed. Hats were mentioned and dresses, and the new
house somewhere—a space-embracing-somewhere, beyond surmise, beyond geography. They walked onwards for a long time,
so long that at last a familiar feeling stole upon the youth. The
word "food" seemed suddenly a topic worthy of the most spirited
conversation. His spirits arose. He was no longer solid, space
belonged to him also, it was in him and of him, and so there was
a song in his heart. He was hungry and the friend of man again.
Now everything was possible. The girl? Was she not by his side?
The regeneration of Ireland and of Man? That could be done
also; a little leisure and everything that can be thought can be
done: even his good looks might be returned to him: he felt the
sting and tightness of his bruises and was reassured, exultant.
He was a man predestined to bruises; they would be his meat
and drink and happiness, his refuge and sanctuary forever. Let
us leave him, then, pacing volubly by the side of Mary, and
exploring with a delicate finger his half-closed eye, which, until
it was closed entirely, would always be half-closed by the decent
buffet of misfortune. His ally and stay was hunger, and there is
no better ally for any man: that satisfied and the game is up;
for hunger is life, ambition, good-will and understanding, while
fullness is all those negatives which culminate in greediness,
stupidity and decay; so his bruises troubled him no further than
as they affected the eyes of a lady wherein he prayed to be
comely.

Bruises, unless they are desperate indeed, will heal at the last
for no other reason than that they must. The inexorable compulsion of all things is towards health or destruction, life or death,
and we hasten our joys or our woes to the logical extreme. It is
urgent, therefore, that we be joyous if we wish to live. Our heads
may be as solid as is possible, but our hearts and our heels shall
be light or we are ruined. As to the golden mean—let us have
nothing to do with that thing at all; it may only be gilded, it is

very likely made of tin of a dull color and a lamentable sound, unworthy even of being stolen; and unless our treasures may be stolen they are of no use to us. It is contrary to the laws of life to possess that which other people do not want; therefore, your beer shall foam, your wife shall be pretty, and your little truth shall have a plum in it—for this is so; that your beer can only taste of your company, you can only know your wife when some one else does, and your little truth shall be savored or perish. Do you demand a big truth? Then, Oh Ambitious! you must turn aside from all your companions and sit very quietly, and if you sit long enough and quiet enough it may come to you; but this thing alone of all things you cannot steal, nor can it be given to you by the County Council. It cannot be communicated, and yet you may get it. It is unspeakable but not unthinkable, and it is born certainly and unaccountably as you were yourself, and is of just as little immediate consequence. Long, long ago in the dim beginnings of the world there was a careless and gay young man who said—"Let truth go to hell"—and it went there. It was his misfortune that he had to follow it; it is ours that we are his descendants. An evil will either kill you or be killed by you, and (the reflection is comforting) the odds are with us in every fight waged against humanity by the dark or elemental beings. But humanity is timid and lazy, a believer in golden means and subterfuges and compromises, loath to address itself to any combat until its frontiers are virtually overrun and its cities and granaries and places of refuge are in jeopardy from those gloomy marauders. In that wide struggle which we call Progress, evil is always the aggressor and the vanquished, and it is right that this should be so, for without its onslaughts and depredations humanity might fall to a fat slumber upon its corn sacks and die snoring: or, alternatively, lacking these valorous alarms and excursions it might become self-satisfied and formu- larized, and be crushed to death by the mere dull density of virtue. Next to good the most valuable factor in life is evil. By the interaction of these all things are possible, and, therefore

(or for any other reason that pleases you) let us wave a friendly
hand in the direction of that bold, bad policeman whose thoughts
were not governed by the Book of Regulations which is issued
to all recruits, and who, in despite of the fact that he was
enrolled among the very legions of order, had that chaos in his
soul which may "give birth to a Dancing Star."

As to Mary—even ordinary, workaday politeness frowns on too
abrupt a departure from a lady, particularly one whom we have
companioned thus distantly from the careless simplicity of girl-
hood to the equally careless but complex businesses of adoles-
cence. The world is all before her, and her chronicler may not
be her guide. She will have adventures, for everybody has. She
will win through with them, for everybody does. She may even
meet bolder and badder men than the policeman—Shall we then
detain her? I, for one, having urgent calls elsewhere, will salute
her fingers and raise my hat and stand aside, and you will do
likewise, because it is my pleasure that you should. She will go
forward, then, to do that which is pleasing to the gods, for less
than that she cannot do, and more is not to be expected of any
one.

THUS FAR THE STORY OF

MARY MAKEBELIEVE

from Here Are Ladies

A GLASS OF BEER

It was now his custom to sit there. The world has its habits, why should a man not have his? The earth rolls out of light and into darkness as punctually as a business man goes to and from his office; the seasons come with the regularity of automata, and go as if they were pushed by an ejector; so, night after night, he strolled from the Place de l'Observatoire to the Pont St. Michel, and, on the return journey, sat down at the same Café, at the same table, if he could manage it, and ordered the same drink.

So regular had his attendance become that the waiter would suggest the order before it was spoken. He did not drink beer because he liked it, but only because it was not a difficult thing to ask for. Always he had been easily discouraged, and he distrusted his French almost as much as other people had reason to. The only time he had varied the order was to request "un vin blanc gommée," but on that occasion he had been served with a postage stamp for twenty-five centimes, and he still wondered when he remembered it.

He liked to think of his first French conversation. He wanted something to read in English, but was timid of asking for it. He walked past all the newspaper kiosks on the Boulevard, anxiously scanning the vendors inside—they were usually very stalwart,

113

very competent females, who looked as though they had out-grown their sins but remembered them with pleasure. They had the dully-polished, slightly-battered look of a modern antique. The words "M'sieu, Madame" rang from them as from bells. They were very alert, sitting as it were, on tiptoe, and their eyes hit one as one approached. They were like spiders squatting in their little houses waiting for their daily flies.

He found one who looked jolly and harmless, sympathetic indeed, and to her, with a flourished hat, he approached. Said he, "Donnez-moi, Madame, s'il vous plaît, le *Daily Mail*." At the second repetition the good lady smiled at him, a smile compounded of benevolence and comprehension, and instantly, with a "V'là M'sieu," she handed him *The New York Herald*. They had saluted each other, and he marched down the road in delight, with his first purchase under his arm and his first foreign conversation accomplished.

At that time everything had delighted him—the wide, well-lighted Boulevard, the concierges knitting in their immense door-ways, each looking like a replica of the other, each seeming sister to a kiosk-keeper or a cat. The exactly-courteous speech of the people and their not quite so rigorously courteous manners pleased him. He listened to voluble men who went by, speaking in a haste so breathless that he marvelled how the prepositions and conjunctions stuck to their duty in so swirling an ocean of chatter. There was a big black dog with a mottled head who lay nightly on the pavement opposite the Square de l'Observatoire. At intervals he raised his lean skull from the ground and composed a low lament to an absent friend. His grief was respected. The folk who passed stepped sidewards for him, and he took no heed of their passage—a lonely, introspective dog to whom a caress or a bone were equally childish things: Let me alone, he seemed to say, I have my grief, and it is company enough. There was the very superior cat who sat on every window-ledge, winking at life. He (for in France all cats are masculine by order of philology), he did not care a rap

for man or dog, but he liked women and permitted them to
observe him. There was the man who insinuated himself between the tables at the Café, holding out postcard-representa-
tions of the Pantheon, the Louvre, Notre Dame, and other
places. From beneath these cards his dexterous little finger
would suddenly flip others. One saw a hurried leg, an arm that
shone and vanished, a bosom that fled shyly again, an audacious
swan, a Leda who was thoroughly enjoying herself and had
never heard of virtue. His look suggested that he thought better
of one than to suppose that one was not interested in the nude.
"M'sieu," he seemed to say, with his fixed, brown-eyed regard,
"this is indeed a leg, an authentic leg, not disguised by even the
littlest of stockings; it is arranged precisely as M'sieu would
desire it." His sorrow as he went away was dignified with regret
for an inartistic gentleman. One was *en garçon,* and yet one
would not look at one's postcards! One had better then cease to
be an artist and take to peddling onions and asparagus as the
vulgar do.

It was all a long time ago, and now, somehow, the savour had
departed from these things. Perhaps he had seen them too often.
Perhaps a kind of public surreptitiousness, a quite open furtive-
ness, had troubled him. Maybe he was not well. He sat at his
Café, three quarters down the Boulevard, and before him a
multitude of grotesque beings were pacing as he sipped his
bock.

Good manners decreed that he should not stare too steadfastly, and he was one who obeyed these delicate dictations. Alas!
he was one who obeyed all dictates. For him authority wore a
halo, and many sins which his heyday ought to have committed
had been left undone only because they were not sanctioned by
immediate social usage. He was often saddened when he thought
of the things he had not done. It was the only sadness to which he
had access, because the evil deeds which he had committed were
of so tepid and hygienic a character that they could not be
mourned for without hypocrisy, and now that he was released

from all privileged restraints and overlookings and could do whatever he wished he had no wish to do anything.

His wife had been dead for over a year. He had hungered, he had prayed for her death. He had hated that woman (and for how many years!) with a kind of masked ferocity. How often he had been tempted to kill her or to kill himself! How often he had dreamed that she had run away from him or that he had run away from her! He had invented Russian Princes, and Music Hall Stars, and American Billionaires with whom she could adequately elope, and he had both loved and loathed the prospect. What unending, slow quarrels they had together! How her voice had droned pitilessly on his ears! She in one room, he in another, and through the open door there rolled that unending recitation of woes and reproaches, an interminable catalogue of nothings, while he sat dumb as a fish, with a mind that smouldered or blazed. He had stood unseen with a hammer, a poker, a razor, in his hand, on tiptoe to do it. A movement, a rush, one silent rush and it was done! He had revelled in her murder. He had caressed it, rehearsed it, relished it, had jerked her head back and hacked, and listened to her entreaties bubbling through blood!

And then she died! When he stood by her bed he had wished to taunt her, but he could not do it. He read in her eyes—I am dying, and in a little time I shall have vanished like dust on the wind, but you will still be here, and you will never see me again —He wished to ratify that, to assure her that it was actually so, to say that he would come home on the morrow night, and she would not be there, and that he would return home every night, and she would never be there. But he could not say it. Somehow the words, although he desired them, would not come. His arm went to her neck and settled there. His hand caressed her hair, her cheek. He kissed her eyes, her lips, her languid hands; and the words that came were only an infantile babble of regrets and apologies, assurances that he loved her, that he had never loved any one before, and never would love any one again. . . . .

Every one who passed looked into the Café where he sat. Every one who passed looked at him. There were men with sallow faces and wide black hats. Some had hair that flapped about them in the wind, and from their locks one gathered, with some distaste, the spices of Araby. Some had cravats that fluttered and fell and rose again like banners in a storm. There were men with severe, spade-shaped, most responsible-looking beards, and quizzical little eyes which gave the lie to their hairy sedateness— eyes which had spent long years in looking sidewards as a woman passed. There were men of every stage of foppishness— men who had spent so much time on their moustaches that they had only a little left for their fingernails, but their moustaches exonerated them; others who were coated to happiness, trousered to grotesqueness, and booted to misery. He thought—In this city the men wear their own coats, but they all wear some one else's trousers, and their boots are syndicated.

He saw no person who was self-intent. They were all deeply conscious, not of themselves, but of each other. They were all looking at each other. They were all looking at him; and he returned the severe, or humorous, or appraising gaze of each with a look nicely proportioned to the passer, giving back exactly what was given to him, and no more. He did not stare, for nobody stared. He just looked away, and was as mannerly as was required.

A negro went by arm in arm with a girl who was so sallow that she was only white by courtesy. He was a bulky man, and as he bent greedily over his companion it was evident that to him she was whiter than the snow of a single night.

Women went past in multitudes, and he knew the appearance of them all. How many times he had watched them or their duplicates striding and mincing and bounding by, each moving like an animated note of interrogation! They were long, and medium, and short. There were women of a thinness beyond comparison, sheathed in skirts as featly as a rapier in a scabbard. There were women of a monumental, a mighty fatness, who billowed and rolled in multitudinous, stormy garments. There were slow eyes that drooped on one heavily as a hand, and quick ones that stabbed and withdrew, and glanced again appealingly, and slid away cursing. There were some who lounged with a false sedateness, and some who fluttered in an equally false timidity. Some wore velvet shoes without heels. Some had shoes, the heels whereof were of such inordinate length that the wearers looked as though they were perched on stilts and would topple to perdition if their skill failed for an instant. They passed and they looked at him; and from each, after the due regard, he looked away to the next in interminable procession.

There were faces also to be looked at: round chubby faces wherefrom the eyes of oxen stared in slow, involved rumination. Long faces that were keener than hatchets and as cruel. Faces that pretended to be scornful and were only piteous. Faces contrived to ape a temperament other than their own. Raddled faces with heavy eyes and rouged lips. Ragged lips that had been chewed by every mad dog in the world. What lips there were everywhere! Bright scarlet splashes in dead-white faces. Thin red gashes that suggested rat-traps instead of kisses. Bulbous, flabby lips that would wobble and shiver if attention failed them. Lips of a horrid fascination that one looked at and hated and ran to. . . . Looking at him slyly or boldly, they passed along, and turned after a while and repassed him, and turned again in promenade.

He had a sickness of them all. There had been a time when these were among the things he mourned for not having done, but that time was long past. He guessed at their pleasures, and knew them to be without salt. Life, said he, is as unpleasant as a plate of cold porridge. Somehow the world was growing empty for him. He wondered was he outgrowing his illusions, or his appetites, or both? The things in which other men took such interest were drifting beyond him, and (for it seemed that the law of compensation can fail) nothing was drifting towards him in recompense. He foresaw himself as a box with nothing inside it, and he thought—It is not through love or fear or distress that men commit suicide: it is because they have become empty: both the gods and the devils have deserted them and they can no longer support that solemn stagnation. He marvelled to see with what activity men and women played the most savourless of games! With what zest of pursuit they tracked what petty interests. He saw them as ants scurrying with scraps of straw, or apes that pick up and drop and pick again, and he marvelled from what fount they renewed themselves, or with what charms they exorcised the demons of satiety.

On this night life did not seem worth while. The taste had gone from his mouth; his bock was water vilely coloured; his cigarette was a hot stench. And yet a full moon was peeping in the trees along the path, and not far away, where the country-side bowed in silver quietude, the rivers ran through undistinguishable fields chanting their lonely songs. The seas leaped and withdrew, and called again to the stars, and gathered in ecstasy and roared skywards, and the trees did not rob each other more than was absolutely necessary. The men and women were all hidden away, sleeping in their cells, where the moon could not see them, nor the clean wind, nor the stars. They were sundered for a little while from their eternal arithmetic. The grasping hands were lying as quietly as the paws of a sleeping dog. Those eyes held no further speculation than the eyes of an ox who lies down. The tongues that had lied all day, and been treacherous and obscene and respectful by easy turn, said nothing more; and he thought it was very good that they were all hidden, and that for a little time the world might swing darkly with the moon in its own wide circle and its silence.

He paid for his bock, gave the waiter a tip, touched his hat to a lady by sex and a gentleman by clothing, and strolled back to his room that was little, his candle that was three-quarters consumed, and his picture which might be admired when he was dead but which he would never be praised for painting; and, after sticking his foot through the canvas, he tugged himself to bed, agreeing to commence the following morning just as he had the previous one, and the one before that, and the one before that again.

THE THREEPENNY-PIECE

When Brien O'Brien died, people said that it did not matter very much, because he would have died young in any case. He would have been hanged, or his head would have been split in two halves with a hatchet, or he would have tumbled down the cliff when he was drunk and been smashed into jelly. Something like that was due to him, and everybody likes to see a man get what he deserves to get.

But, as ethical writs cease to run when a man is dead, the neighbours did not stay away from his wake. They came, and they said many mitigating things across the body with the bandaged jaws and the sly grin, and they reminded each other of this and that queer thing which he had done, for his memory was crusted over with stories of wild, laughable things, and other things which were wild but not laughable.

Meanwhile, he was dead, and one was at liberty to be a trifle sorry for him. Further, he belonged to the O'Brien nation, a stock to whom reverence was due. A stock not easily forgotten. The historic memory could reconstruct forgotten glories of station and battle, of terrible villainy and terrible saintliness, the pitiful, valorous, slow descent to the degradation which was not yet wholly victorious. A great stock! The O'Neills remembered it. The O'Tools and the MacSweeneys had stories by the hundred of love and hate. The Burkes and the Geraldines and the new strangers had memories also.

His family was left in the poorest way, but they were used to that, for he had kept them as poor as he left them, or found them, for that matter. They had shaken hands with Charity so often that they no longer disliked the sallow-faced lady, and, so, certain small gifts made by the neighbours were accepted, not very thankfully, but very readily. These gifts were almost always in kind. A few eggs. A bag of potatoes. A handful of meal. A couple of twists of tea—such like.

One of the visitors, however, moved by an extraordinary dejection, slipped a silver threepenny-piece into the hand of Brien's little daughter, Sheila, aged four years, and later on she did not like to ask for it back again.

Little Sheila had been well trained by her father. She knew exactly what should be done with money, and so, when nobody was looking, she tip-toed to the coffin and slipped the threepenny-piece into Brien's hand. That hand had never refused money when it was alive, it did not reject it either when it was dead.

They buried him the next day.

He was called up for judgment the day after, and made his appearance with a miscellaneous crowd of wretches, and there he again received what was due to him. He was removed protesting and struggling to the place decreed.

"Down," said Rhadamanthus, pointing with his great hand, and down he went.

In the struggle he dropped the threepenny-piece, but he was so bustled and heated that he did not observe his loss. He went down, far down, out of sight, out of remembrance, to a howling, black gulf with others of his unseen kind.

A young seraph, named Cuchulain, chancing to pass that way shortly afterwards, saw the threepenny-piece peeping brightly from the rocks, and he picked it up.

He looked at it in astonishment. He turned it over and over, this way and that way. Examined it at the stretch of his arm, and peered minutely at it from two inches distance—

"I have never in my life seen anything so beautifully wrought," said he, and, having stowed it in his pouch along with some other trinkets, he strolled homewards again through the massy gates.

It was not long until Brien discovered his loss, and, suddenly, through the black region, his voice went mounting and brawling.

"I have been robbed," he yelled. "I have been robbed in heaven!"

Having begun to yell he did not stop. Sometimes he was simply angry and made a noise. Sometimes he became sarcastic and would send his query swirling upwards—

"Who stole the threepenny-bit?" he roared. He addressed the surrounding black space—

"Who stole the last threepenny-bit of a poor man?"

Again and again his voice pealed upwards. The pains of his habitation lost all their sting for him. His mind had nourishment and the heat within him vanquished the fumes without. He had a grievance, a righteous cause, he was buoyed and strengthened, nothing could silence him. They tried ingenious devices, all kinds of complicated things, but he paid no heed, and the tormentors were in despair.

"I hate these sinners from the kingdom of Kerry," said the Chief Tormentor, and he sat moodily down on his own circular saw; and that worried him also, for he was clad only in a loin cloth.

"I hate the entire Clan of the Gael," said he; "why cannot they send them somewhere else?" and then he started practising again on Brien.

It was no use. Brien's query still blared upwards like the sound of the great trump itself. It wakened and rung the rocky caverns, screamed through fissure and funnel, and was battered and slung from pinnacle to crag and up again. Worse! his companions in doom became interested and took up the cry, until at last the uproar became so appalling that the Master himself could not stand it.

"I have not had a wink of sleep for three nights," said that harassed one, and he sent a special embassy to the powers.

Rhadamanthus was astonished when they arrived. His elbow was leaning on his vast knee, and his heavy head rested on a hand that was acres long, acres wide.

"What is all this about?" said he.

"The Master cannot go to sleep," said the spokesman of the embassy, and he grinned as he said it, for it sounded queer even to himself.

"It is not necessary that he should sleep," said Rhadamanthus. "I have never slept since time began, and I will never sleep until time is over. But the complaint is curious. What has troubled your master?"

"Hell is turned upside down and inside out," said the fiend. "The tormentors are weeping like little children. The principalities are squatting on their hunkers doing nothing. The orders are running here and there fighting each other. The styles are leaning against walls shrugging their shoulders, and the damned are shouting and laughing and have become callous to torment."

"It is not my business," said the judge.

"The sinners demand justice," said the spokesman.

"They've got it," said Rhadamanthus, "let them stew in it."

"They refuse to stew," replied the spokesman, wringing his hands.

Rhadamanthus sat up.

"It is an axiom in law," said he, "that however complicated an event may be, there can never be more than one person at the extreme bottom of it. Who is the person?"

"It is one Brien of the O'Brien nation, late of the kingdom of Kerry. A bad one! He got the maximum punishment a week ago."

For the first time in his life Rhadamanthus was disturbed. He scratched his head, and it was the first time he had ever done that either.

"You say he got the maximum," said Rhadamanthus, "then it's a fix! I have damned him for ever, and better or worse than that cannot be done. It is none of my business," said he angrily, and he had the deputation removed by force.

But that did not ease the trouble. The contagion spread until ten million billions of voices were chanting in unison, and uncountable multitudes were listening between their pangs.

"Who stole the threepenny-bit? Who stole the threepenny-bit?"

That was still their cry. Heaven rang with it as well as hell. Space was filled with that rhythmic tumult. Chaos and empty Nox had a new discord added to their elemental throes. Another memorial was drafted below, showing that unless the missing coin was restored to its owner hell would have to close its doors. There was a veiled menace in the memorial also, for Clause 6 hinted that if hell was allowed to go by the board heaven might find itself in some jeopardy thereafter.

The document was dispatched and considered. In consequence a proclamation was sent through all the wards of Paradise, calling on whatever person, archangel, seraph, cherub, or acolyte had found a threepenny-piece since midday of the tenth of August then instant, that the same person, archangel, seraph, cherub, or acolyte, should deliver the said threepenny-piece to Rhadamanthus at his Court, and should receive in return a free pardon and a receipt.

The coin was not delivered.

That young seraph, Cuchulain, walked about like a person who was strange to himself. He was not tormented: he was angry. He frowned, he cogitated and fumed. He drew one golden curl through his fingers until it was lank and drooping; save the end only, that was still a ripple of gold. He put the end in his mouth and strode moodily chewing it. And every day his feet turned in the same direction—down the long entrance boulevard, through the mighty gates, along the strip of carved slabs, to that piled wilderness where Rhadamanthus sat monumentally.

Here delicately he went, sometimes with a hand outstretched to help his foothold, standing for a space to think ere he jumped to a further rock, balancing himself for a moment ere he leaped again. So he would come to stand and stare gloomily upon the judge.

He would salute gravely, as was meet, and say, "God bless the work"; but Rhadamanthus never replied, save by a nod, for he was very busy.

Yet the judge did observe him, and would sometimes heave

ponderous lids to where he stood, and so, for a few seconds, they regarded each other in an interval of that unceasing business.

Sometimes for a minute or two the young seraph Cuchulain would look from the judge to the judged as they crouched back or strained forward, the good and the bad all in the same tremble of fear, all unknowing which way their doom might lead. They did not look at each other. They looked at the judge high on his ebon throne, and they could not look away from him. There were those who knew, guessed clearly their doom; abashed and flaccid they sat, quaking. There were some who were uncertain—rabbit-eyed these, not less quaking than the others, biting at their knuckles as they peeped upwards. There were those hopeful, yet searching fearfully backwards in the wilderness of memory, chasing and weighing their sins; and these last, even when their bliss was sealed and their steps set in an easy path, went faltering, not daring to look around again, their ears strained to catch a—"Halt, miscreant! this other is your way!"

So, day by day, he went to stand near the judge; and one day Rhadamanthus, looking on him more intently, lifted his great hand and pointed—

"Go you among those to be judged," said he.

For Rhadamanthus knew. It was his business to look deep into the heart and the mind, to fish for secrets in the pools of being.

And the young seraph Cuchulain, still rolling his golden curl between his lips, went obediently forward and set down his nodding plumes between two who whimpered and stared and quaked.

When his turn came, Rhadamanthus eyed him intently for a long time—

"Well!" said Rhadamanthus.

The young Cuchulain blew the curl of gold away from his mouth—

"Findings are keepings," said he loudly, and he closed his mouth and stared very impertinently at the judge.

"It is to be given up," said the judge.

"Let them come and take it from me," said the seraph Cuchulain. And suddenly (for these things are at the will of spirits) around his head the lightnings span, and his hands were on the necks of thunders.

For the second time in his life Rhadamanthus was disturbed, again he scratched his head—

"It's a fix," said he moodily. But in a moment he called to those whose duty it was—

"Take him to this side," he roared.

And they advanced. But the seraph Cuchulain swung to meet them, and his golden hair blazed and shrieked; and the thunders rolled at his feet, and about him a bright network that hissed and stung—and those who advanced turned haltingly backwards and ran screaming.

"It's a fix," said Rhadamanthus; and for a little time he stared menacingly at the seraph Cuchulain.

But only for a little time. Suddenly he put his hands on the rests of his throne and heaved upwards his terrific bulk. Never before had Rhadamanthus stood from his ordained chair. He strode mightily forward and in an instant had quelled that rebel. The thunders and lightnings were but moonbeams and dew on that stony carcass. He seized the seraph Cuchulain, lifted him to his breast as one lifts a sparrow, and tramped back with him—

"Fetch me that other," said he, sternly, and he sat down.

Those whose duty it was sped swiftly downwards to find Brien of the O'Brien nation; and while they were gone, all in vain the seraph Cuchulain crushed flamy barbs against that bosom of doom. Now, indeed, his golden locks were drooping and his plumes were broken and tossed; but his fierce eye still glared courageously against the nipple of Rhadamanthus.

Soon they brought Brien. He was a sight of woe—howling, naked as a tree in winter, black as a tarred wall, carved and gashed, tattered in all but his throat, wherewith, until one's ears rebelled, he bawled his one demand.

But the sudden light struck him to wondering silence, and the

sight of the judge holding the seraph Cuchulain like a limp
flower to his breast held him gaping—

"Bring him here," said Rhadamanthus.

And they brought him to the steps of the throne—

"You have lost a medal!" said Rhadamanthus. "This one has it."

Brien looked straitly at the seraph Cuchulain.

Rhadamanthus stood again, whirled his arm in an enormous
arc, jerked, and let go, and the seraph Cuchulain went swirling
through space like a slung stone—

"Go after him, Kerryman," said Rhadamanthus, stooping; and
he seized Brien by the leg, whirled him wide and out and far;
dizzy, dizzy as a swooping comet and down, and down, and
down.

Rhadamanthus seated himself. He motioned with his hand—

"Next," said he, coldly.

Down went the seraph Cuchulain, swirling in wide tumbles,
scarcely visible for quickness. Sometimes, with outstretched
hands, he was a cross that dropped plumb. Anon, head urgently
downwards, he dived steeply. Again, like a living hoop, head and
heels together, he spun giddily. Blind, deaf, dumb, breathless,
mindless; and behind him Brien of the O'Brien nation came
pelting and whizzing.

What of that journey! Who could give it words? Of the suns
that appeared and disappeared like winking eyes. Comets that
shone for an instant, went black and vanished. Moons that came,
and stood, and were gone. And around all, including all, boundless space, boundless silence; the black unmoving void—the deep,
unending quietude, through which they fell with Saturn and
Orion, and mildly-smiling Venus, and the fair, stark naked moon
and the decent earth wreathed in pearl and blue. From afar she
appeared, the quiet one, all lonely in the void. As sudden as a
fair face in a crowded street. Beautiful as the sound of falling
waters. Beautiful as the sound of music in a silence. Like a white
sail on a windy sea. Like a green tree in a solitary place. Chaste

and wonderful she was. Flying afar. Flying aloft like a joyous bird when the morning breaks on the darkness and he shrills sweet tidings. She soared and sang. Gently she sang to timid pipes and flutes of tender straw and murmuring, distant strings. A song that grew and swelled, gathering to a multitudinous, deep-thundered harmony, until the over-burdened ear failed before the appalling uproar of her ecstasy, and denounced her. No longer a star! No longer a bird! A plumed and horned fury! Gigantic, gigantic, leaping and shrieking tempestuously, spouting whirlwinds of lightning, tearing gluttonously along her path, avid, rampant, howling with rage and terror she leaped, dreadfully she leaped and flew. . . .

Enough! They hit the earth—they were not smashed, there was that virtue in them. They hit the ground just outside the village of Donnybrook where the back road runs to the hills; and scarcely had they bumped twice when Brien of the O'Brien nation had the seraph Cuchulain by the throat—

"My threepenny-bit," he roared, with one fist up—

But the seraph Cuchulain only laughed—

"That!" said he. "Look at me, man. Your little medal dropped far beyond the rings of Saturn."

And Brien stood back looking at him—He was as naked as Brien was. He was as naked as a stone, or an eel, or a pot or a new-born babe. He was very naked.

So Brien of the O'Brien nation strode across the path and sat down by the side of a hedge—

"The first man that passes this way," said he, "will give me his clothes, or I'll strangle him."

The seraph Cuchulain walked over to him—

"I will take the clothes of the second man that passes," said he, and he sat down.

THREE LOVERS WHO LOST

Young Mr. O'Grady was in love. It was the first time he had been in love, and it was all sufficiently startling. He seemed to

have leaped from boyhood to manhood at a stroke, and the things
which had pretended to be of moment yesterday were to-day
discovered to have only the very meanest importance. Different
affairs now occupied him. A little while ago his cogitations had
included, where he would walk to on the next Sunday, whether
his aunt in Meath Street would lend him the price of a ticket
for the coming Bank Holiday excursion, whether his brother
would be using his bicycle on Saturday afternoon, and whether
the packet of cigarettes which he was momently smoking contained as many cigarettes as could be got elsewhere for two
pence.

These things were no longer noteworthy. Clothing had assumed an importance he could scarcely have believed in. Boots,
neckties, the conduct of one's hat and of one's head, the progress
of one's moustache, one's bearing towards people in the street
and in the house, this and that social observance—all these things
took on a new and important dignity. He bought a walking-stick,
a cardcase, a purse, a pipe with a glass bottom wherein one could
observe one's own nicotine inexorably accumulating.—He bought
a book on etiquette and a pot of paste for making moustaches
grow in spite of providence, and one day he insisted on himself
drinking a half glass of whisky—it tasted sadly, but he drank it
without a grimace. Etiquette and whisky! these things have to
be done, and one might as well do them with an air. He was in
love, he was grown up, he was a man, and he lived fearlessly up
to his razor and his lady.

From the book on etiquette he exhumed a miscellany of useful
and peculiar wisdom. Following information about the portage
of knives and forks at incredible dinners he discovered that a
well-bred person always speaks to the young lady's parents before he speaks to the young lady. He straightened his shoulders.—
It would be almost as bad, he thought, as having to drink whisky,
but if it had to be done why he would not shrink from this any
more than he had from that. He set forth on the tingling errand.

Mr. O'Reilly was a scrivener, a husband and a father. He made copies of all kinds of documents for a living. He also copied maps. It has been said that scriveners have to get drunk at least twice a week in order to preserve their sanity; but the person whose miserable employment is to draw copies of maps is more desperately environed than an ordinary scrivener. It was Mr. O'Reilly's misfortune that he was unable to get drunk. He disliked liquor, and, moreover, it disagreed with him. He had, to paraphrase Lamb, toiled after liquor as other people toil after virtue, but the nearer he got the less did he like it. As a consequence of this enforced decency the ill-temper, which is the normal state of scriveners, had surged and buzzed around him so long that he had quite forgotten what a good temper was like.— It might be said that he hated every one, not excepting his wife and daughter. He could avoid other people, but these he could never escape from. They wanted to talk to him when he wanted to be let alone. They worried him with this and that domestic question or uproar. He would gladly have sold them both as slaves to the Barbadoes or presented them to the seraglio of any eastern potentate. There they were! and he often gnashed his teeth and grinned at them in amazement because they were there.

On the evening when young Mr. O'Grady sallied forth to ask him for the hand of his daughter in marriage he was sitting at supper with his consort—

Mr. O'Reilly took the last slice of bread from under his wife's hand. It was loot, so he ate it with an extra relish and his good lady waddled away to get more bread from the cupboard—

"Everything's a trouble," said she, as she cut the loaf. "Doesn't it make you think of the hymn 'I'm but a stranger here, heaven is my home'?"

"No, ma'm," said her husband, "it does not. Where is Julia Elizabeth?" and he daringly and skilfully abstracted the next slice of bread while his wife was laying down the butter knife.

"I wish," said she, as she reached for the knife again, "I wish you would give me a chance, O'Reilly: you eat much quicker than I do, God help me!"

"I wish," rapped her husband fiercely, "that you would give a plain answer to a plain question. Now then, ma'm, in two words, where is that girl? My whole life seems to be occupied in asking that question, and yours seems to be spent in dodging the answer to it."

"I don't know!" replied his wife severely, "and that's three words."

"You don't know!" he looked around in helpless appeal and condemnation. "What sort of an answer is that for a mother to give about her daughter?" and under cover of his wrath he stole the next slice of bread.

His wife also became angry—she put her plate in her lap and sat up at him—

"Don't barge me, man," said she. "A nice daughter to have to give such an answer about. Leave me alone now for I'm not well, I say, on the head of her. I never know where she does be. One night it's (she endeavoured to reproduce her daughter's soprano) 'I am going to a dance, mother, at the Durkins'—'"

"Ha'penny hops!" said her husband fiercely. "Can't you cut me a bit of bread!"

"And another night, 'she wants to go out to see Mary Durkin.'"

"I know her well, a big hat and no morals, a bankrupt's baggage."

"And the night after she 'wants to go to the theatre, ma.'"

"Dens of infamy," said he. "If I had my way I'd shut them all up and put the actors in gaol, with their hamleting and gamy-acting and ha-ha'ing out of them."

"I can't keep her in," said his wife, wringing her hands, "and I won't try to any longer. I get a headache when I talk to her, so I do. Last night when I mentioned about her going out with that Rorke man she turned round as cool as you please and told me 'to shut up.' Her own mother!" and she surveyed Providence with a condemnatory eye—

At this point her husband swung his long arm and arrested the slice of bread in his wife's lap—

"If she spoke to me that way," he grinned, "I'll bet I'd astonish her."

His wife looked in amazement from her lap to his plate, but she had ability for only one quarrel at a time—

"And doesn't she talk to you like that? You never say a word to her but she has a look in her eye that's next door to calling you a fool.—I don't know where she is at all to-day."

"What time did she go out?"

"After breakfast this morning."

"And now it's supper-time—ha! that's good! Can't you give me a bit of bread, or do you want to eat the whole loaf yourself? Try to remember that I do pay for my food."

With an angry shake of the head his wife began to cut the loaf, and continued speaking—

" 'Where are you going to, Julia Elizabeth?' said I. 'Out,' said she, and not another word could I get from her. Her own mother, mind you, and her best clothes—"

Mr. O'Reilly ate the last slice of bread and arose from the table.

"I suppose," said he, "she is loafing about the streets with some young puppy who has nothing of his own but a cigarette and a walking-stick, and they both borrowed. I'll have a talk with her when she comes in, and we'll see if she tells me to shut up."

The door banged, the room shook, and Mrs. O'Reilly settled to her frustrated tea, but her thoughts still ran on her daughter.

It was at this point that, directed by love and etiquette, Mr. O'Grady knocked at the door. Mrs. O'Reilly was again cutting the loaf in an exasperation which was partly hunger and partly maternal, and, as she cut, she communed with herself—

"As if," said she, "I haven't enough trouble trying to keep a cranky man like her pa in good humour, without being plagued by Julia Elizabeth"—she paused, for there was a knock at the door.—"If," said she to the door, "you are a woman with ferns in a pot I don't want you, and I don't want Dublin Bay herrings, or boot-laces either, so you can go away.—The crankiness of that man is more than tongue can tell. As Miss Carty says, I shouldn't

stand it for an hour—Come in, can't you—and well she may say
it, and she a spinster without a worry under heaven but her
suspicious nature and her hair falling out. And then to be treated
the way I am by that girl! It'd make a saint waxy so it would.—
Good heaven! can't you come in, or are you deaf or lame or
what?" and in some exasperation she arose and went to the door.
She looked in perplexity for one moment from her food to her
visitor, but as good manners and a lady are never separate she
welcomed and drew the young man inside—

"Come in, Mr. O'Grady," said she. "How are you now at all?
Why it's nearly a week since you were here. Your mother's well
I hope (sit down there now and rest yourself). Some people are
always well, but I'm not—it's (sit there beside the window, like
a good boy) it's hard to have poor health and a crotchety husband, but we all have our trials. Is your father well too? but what's
the use of asking, every one's well but me. Did your aunt get
the pot of jam I sent her last Tuesday? Raspberry is supposed
to be good for the throat, but her throat's all right. Maybe she
threw it out: I'm not blaming her if she did. God knows she can
buy jam if she wants it without being beholden to any one for
presents and her husband in the Post Office.—Well, well, well,
I'm real glad to see you—and now, tell me all the news?"

The young man was a little embarrassed by this flood of
language and its multiplicity of direction, but the interval gave
him time to collect himself and get into the atmosphere.—He
replied—

"I don't think there is any news to tell, ma'am. Father and
mother are quite well, thank you, and Aunt Jane got the jam all
right, but she didn't eat it, because—"

"I knew she didn't," said Mrs. O'Reilly with pained humility,
"we all have our troubles and jam doesn't matter. Give her my
love all the same, but maybe she doesn't want it either."

"You see," said the young man, "the children got at the jam
before she could, and they cleaned the pot. Aunt Jane was very
angry about it."

"Was she now?" said the instantly interested lady. "It's real bad for a stout person to be angry. Apoplexy or something might ensue and death would be instantaneous and cemeteries the price they are in Glasnevin and all: but the children shouldn't have eaten all the jam at once, it's bad for the stomach that way: still, God is good and maybe they'll recover."

"They don't seem much the worse for it," said he, laughing; "they said it was fine jam."

"Well they might," replied his hostess, with suppressed indignation, "and raspberries eightpence the pound in Grafton Street, and the best preserving sugar twopence-three-farthings, and coal the way it is.—Ah, no matter, God is good, and we can't live for ever."

The four seconds of silence which followed was broken by the lover—

"Is Julia Elizabeth in, ma'm?" said he timidly.

"She's not, then," was the reply. "We all have our trials, Mr. O'Grady, and she's mine. I don't complain, but I don't deserve it, for a harder working woman never lived, but there you are."

"I'm rather glad she's out," said the youth hastily, "for I wanted to speak to yourself and your husband before I said anything to her."

Mrs. O'Reilly wheeled slowly to face him—

"Did you now?" said she, "and is it about Julia Elizabeth you came over? Well, well, well, just to think of it! But I guessed it long ago, when you bought the yellow boots. She's a real good girl, Mr. O'Grady. There's many and many's the young man, and they in good positions, mind you—but maybe you don't mean that at all. Is it a message from your Aunt Jane or your mother? Your Aunt Jane does send messages, God help her!"

"It's not, Mrs. O'Reilly: it's, if I may presume to say so, about myself."

"I knew it," was the rapid and enthusiastic reply. "She's a fine cook, Mr. O'Grady, and a head of hair that reaches down to her waist, and won prizes at school for composition. I'll call himself—he'll be delighted. He's in the next room making faces at a map.

Maps are a terrible occupation, Mr. O'Grady, they spoil his eyesight and make him curse—"

She ambled to the door and called urgently—

"O'Reilly, here's young Mr. O'Grady wants to see you."

Her husband entered with a pen in his mouth and looked very severely at his visitor—

"What brought you round, young man?" said he.

The youth became very nervous. He stood up stammering—

"It's a delicate subject, sir," said he, "and I thought it would only be right to come to you first."

Here the lady broke in rapturously—

"Isn't it splendid, O'Reilly! You and me sitting here growing old and contented, and this young gentleman talking to us the way he is. Doesn't it make you think of the song 'John Anderson, my Jo, John'?"

Her husband turned a bewildered but savage eye on his spouse—

"It does not, ma'm," said he. "Well," he barked at Mr. O'Grady, "what do you want?"

"I want to speak to you about your daughter, sir."

"She's not a delicate subject."

"No indeed," said his wife. "Never a day's illness in her life except the measles, and they're wholesome when you're young, and an appetite worth cooking for, two eggs every morning and more if she got it."

Her husband turned on her with hands of frenzy—

"Oh—!" said he, and then to their visitor, "What have you to say about my daughter?"

"The fact is, sir," he stammered, "I'm in love with her."

"I see, you are the delicate subject, and what then?"

"And I want to marry her, sir."

"That's not delicacy, that's disease, young man. Have you spoken to Julia Elizabeth about this?"

"No, sir, I wanted first to obtain your and Mrs. O'Reilly's permission to approach her."

"And quite right, too," said the lady warmly. "Isn't it delightful," she continued, "to see a young, bashful youth telling of his love for our dear child? Doesn't it make you think of Moore's beautiful song, 'Love's Young Dream,' O'Reilly?"

"It does not," her husband snapped, "I never heard of the song I tell you, and I never want to."

He turned again to the youth—

"If you are in earnest about this, you have my permission to court Julia Elizabeth as much as she'll let you. But don't blame me if she marries you. People who take risks must expect accidents. Don't go about lamenting that I hooked you in, or led you on, or anything like that.—I tell you, here and now, that she has a rotten temper—"

His wife was aghast—

"For shame, O'Reilly," said she.

Her husband continued, looking steadily at her—

"A rotten temper," said he, "she gives back answers."

"Never," was Mrs. O'Reilly's wild exclamation.

"She scratches like a cat," said her husband.

"It's a falsehood," cried the lady, almost in tears.

"She is obstinate, sulky, stubborn and cantankerous."

"A tissue," said his wife. "An absolute tissue," she repeated with the firmness which masks hysteria.

Her husband continued inexorably—

"She's a gad-about, a pavement-hopper, and when she has the toothache she curses like a carman. Now, young man, marry her if you like."

These extraordinary accusations were powerless against love and etiquette—the young man stood up: his voice rang—

"I will, sir," said he steadily, "and I'll be proud to be her husband."

In a very frenzy of enthusiasm, Mrs. O'Reilly arose—

"Good boy," said she. "Tell your Aunt Jane I'll send her another pot of jam." She turned to her husband, "Isn't it delightful, O'Reilly, doesn't it make you think of the song, 'True, True Till Death'?"

Mr. O'Reilly replied grimly—

"It does not, ma'm.—I'm going back to my work."

"Be a gentleman, O'Reilly," said his wife pleadingly. "Won't you offer Mr. O'Grady a bottle of stout or a drop of spirits?"

The youth intervened hastily, for it is well to hide one's vices from one's family—

"Oh no, ma'm not at all," said he, "I never drink intoxicating liquors."

"Splendid," said the beaming lady. "You're better without it. If you knew the happy homes it has ruined, and the things the clergy say about it you'd be astonished. I only take it myself for the rheumatism, but I never did like it, did I, O'Reilly?"

"Never, ma'm," was his reply. "I only take it myself because my hearing is bad. Now, listen to me, young man. You want to marry Julia Elizabeth, and I'll be glad to see her married to a sensible, sober, industrious husband.—When I spoke about her a minute ago I was only joking."

"I knew it all the time," said his wife. "Do you remember, Mr. O'Grady, I winked at you?"

"The girl is a good girl," said her husband, "and well brought up."

"Yes," said his wife, "her hair reaches down to her waist, and she won a prize for composition—*Jessica's First Prayer*, all about a girl with—"

Mr. O'Reilly continued—

"She brings me up a cup of tea every morning before I get up."

"She never wore spectacles in her life," said Mrs. O'Reilly, "and she got a prize for freehand drawing."

"She did so," said Mr. O'Reilly.

His wife continued—

"*The Schoolboy Baronet* it was; all about a young man that broke his leg down a coal mine and it never got well again until he met the girl of his heart."

"Tell me," said Mr. O'Reilly, "how are you young people going to live, and where?"

His wife interpolated—

"Your Aunt Jane told me that you had seventeen shillings and

sixpence a week.—Take my advice and live on the south side—
two rooms easily and most salubrious."

The young man coughed guardedly, he had received a rise of
wages since that information passed, but candour belongs to
childhood, and one must live these frailties down—

"Seventeen and six isn't very much, of course," said he, "but I
am young and strong—"

"It's more than I had," said his host, "when I was your age.
Hello, there's the post!"

Mrs. O'Reilly went to the door and returned instantly with a
letter in her hand. She presented it to her husband—

"It's addressed to you, O'Reilly," said she plaintively. "Maybe
it's a bill, but God's good and maybe it's a cheque."

Her husband nodded at the company and tore his letter open.
He read it, and, at once as it appeared, he went mad, he raved,
he stuttered, now slapping the letter with his forefinger, anon,
shaking his fist at his wife—

"Here's your daughter, ma'm," he stammered. "Here's your
daughter, I say."

"Where?" cried the amazed lady. "What is it, O'Reilly?" She
arose hastily and rolled towards him.

Mr. O'Reilly repelled her fiercely—

"A good riddance," he shouted.

"Tell me, O'Reilly, I command you," cried his wife.

"A minx, a jade," snarled the man.

"I insist," said she. "I must be told. I'm not well, I tell you. My
head's going round. Give me the letter."

Mr. O'Reilly drew about him a sudden and terrible calmness—

"Listen, woman," said he, "and you too, young man, and be
thankful for your escape.

"DEAR PA," he read, "this is to tell you that I got married to-day to
Christie Rorke. We are going to open a little fried-fish shop near
Amiens Street. Hoping this finds you as it leaves me at present, your
loving daughter,

"JULIA ELIZABETH.

"P.S.—Give Christie's love to Ma."

Mrs. O'Reilly sank again to her chair. Her mouth was partly open. She breathed with difficulty. Her eyes were fixed on space, and she seemed to be communing with the guardians of Chaos—

"Married!" said she in a musing whisper. "Christie!" said she. She turned to her husband—"What an amazing thing. Doesn't it make you think, O'Reilly, of the poem, 'The World Recedes, it Disappears'?"

"It does not, ma'm," said her husband savagely.

"And what is this young gentleman going to do?" she continued, gazing tearfully at the suitor.

"He's going to go home," replied her husband fiercely. "He ought to be in bed long ago."

"A broken heart," said his wife, "is a sad companion to go home with. Doesn't it make you think of the song—?"

"It does not, ma'm," roared her husband. "I'm going back to my work," and once again the door banged and the room shook.

Young Mr. O'Grady arose timidly. The world was swimming about him. Love had deserted him, and etiquette was now his sole anchor; he shook hands with Mrs. O'Reilly—

"I think I had better be going now," said he. "Good-bye, Mrs. O'Reilly."

"Must you really go?" said that lady with the smile of a maniac.

"I'm afraid so," and he moved towards the door.

"Well," said she, "give my love to your mother and your Aunt Jane."

"I will," was his reply, "and," with firm politeness, "thank you for a very pleasant evening."

"Don't mention it, Mr. O'Grady. Good-bye."

Mrs. O'Reilly closed the door and walked back toward the table smiling madly. She sank into a chair. Her eye fell on the butter-knife—

"I haven't had a bit to eat this day," said she in a loud and threatening voice, and once again she pulled the loaf towards her.

from The Demi-Gods

BOOK I: PATSY MAC CANN

CHAPTER I

"Will you leave that donkey alone," said Patsy Mac Cann to his daughter. "I never heard the like of it," he continued testily. "I tell you the way you do be going on with the ass is enough to make a Christian man swear, so it is."

"You let me be," she replied. "If I was doing hurt or harm to you I wouldn't mind, and if I am fond of the ass itself what does it matter to anybody?"

"It's this way, that I don't like to see a woman kissing an ass on the snout, it's not natural nor proper."

"A lot you know about natural and proper. Let you leave me alone now; and, besides that, doesn't the ass like it?"

"That's not a reason; sure it doesn't matter in the world what an ass likes or dislikes, and anyhow, an ass doesn't like anything except carrots and turnips."

"This one does," said she stoutly.

"And a body might be kissing an ass until the black day of doom and he wouldn't mind it."

"This one minds."

"Kissing an old ass!"

"One has to be kissing something."

"Let you kiss me then and get done with it," said he.

She regarded him in amazement.

"What would I kiss you for? Sure you're my father, and aren't you as old as the hills?"

"Well, well, you're full of fun, and that's what I say. Take the winkers off that donkey's face, and let him get a bit to eat; there's grass enough, God knows, and it's good grass."

Mary busied herself with the winkers and the bit while her father continued:

"What I wish is this, that Christian people were able to eat grass like the beasts, and then there wouldn't be any more trouble in the world. Are you listening to me, Mary, or are you listening to the donkey?"

"It's you I'm listening to."

"I say this, that if every person had enough to eat there'd be no more trouble in the world and we could fight our fill. What have you got in the basket?"

"I've the loaf that I bought in the shop at Knockbeg, and the half loaf that you took out of the woman's window—it's fresher than the other one."

"I was guided," said her father. "We'll eat that one first the way no person can claim it. What else have you got?"

"I've the white turnip that I found in a field."

"There's great nourishment in turnips; the cattle do get fat on them in winter."

"And I've the two handfuls of potatoes that you gathered at the bend of the road."

"Roast themselves in the embers, for that's the only road to cook a potato. What way are we going to eat to-night?"

"We'll eat the turnip first, and then we'll eat the bread, and after that we'll eat the potatoes."

"And fine they'll taste. I'll cut the turnip for you with the sailorman's jack-knife."

The day had drawn to its close. The stars had not yet come, nor the moon. Far to the west a red cloud poised on the horizon like a great whale and, moment by moment, it paled and faded until it was no more than a pink flush. On high, clouds of pearl and snow piled and fell and sailed away on easy voyages. It was the twilight—a twilight of such quietude that one could hear the soft voice of the world as it whispered through leaf and twig. There was no breeze to swing the branches of the trees or to creep among the rank grasses and set them dancing, and yet everywhere there was unceasing movement and a sound that never ceased. About them, for mile upon mile, there was no habitation of man; there was no movement anywhere except when a bird dipped and soared in a hasty flight homewards, or when a beetle went slugging by like a tired bullet.

Mary had unharnessed the ass and bade him, with an affectionate kiss, to eat his full. The donkey stood for a moment with his ears and his tail hanging down, then he lifted both his ears and his tail, slung up his ragged head, bared his solid teeth, and brayed furiously for two minutes. That accomplished he trotted briskly a few paces, bent to the grass, and began to eat so eagerly that one would think eating was more of a novelty to him than it could be to an ass of his years.

"The sound of that beast's voice does get on my nerves," said Patsy.

"He has a powerful voice, sure enough, God bless him! Sit down there by the hedge and light the fire while I'm getting the things ready; the night will be on us in a few minutes and it will be a cold night."

While she moved busily from the cart to the hedge her father employed himself lighting a fire of turf in a wrinkled bucket. When this was under way he pulled out a pipe, black as a coal, and off which half the shank was broken, and this he put into his mouth. At the moment he seemed to be sunken in thought, his eyes to the grass and his feet planted, and it was in a musing voice that he spoke:

"Do you know what I'd do, Mary, if I had a bottle of porter beside me in this field?"

"I do well," she replied; "you'd drink it."

"I would so, but before I'd drink it I'd put the end of this pipe into it, for it's newly cracked, and it sticks to my lips in a way that would anger a man wanting a smoke, and if I could stick it into the porter it would be cured. I don't suppose, now, that you have a sup of porter in the cart!"

"I have not."

"Because if you had a small sup I'd be able to get a smoke this night, as well as a drink."

"You're full of fun," said she sourly.

"I saw a bottle in your hand a while back," he continued musingly, "and it looked like a weighty bottle."

"It's full to the neck with spring water."

"Ah!" said her father, and he regarded that distant horizon whereon the pink cloud was now scarcely visible as a pinkness and was no longer the shape of a great whale.

After a moment he continued in a careless voice:

"You might hand me the bottle of spring water, alanna, till I wet my lips with it. It's a great thing for the thirst, I'm told, and it's healthy beside that."

"I'm keeping that sup of water to make the tea when we'd be wanting it."

"Well, I'll only take a drop out of it, and I won't lose the cork."

"You can get it yourself, then," said Mary, "for I've plenty to do and you haven't."

Her father, rolling his tough chin with his fingers, went to the cart. He found the bottle, lifted the cork, smelt it, tasted:

"It is spring water indeed," said he, and he thumped the cork back again with some irritation and replaced the bottle in the cart.

"I thought you wanted a drink," said his daughter mildly.

"So I do," he replied, "but I can't stand the little creatures that do be wriggling about in spring water. I wouldn't like to be swallowing them unknown. Ah! them things don't be in barrels that you buy in a shop, and that's a fact."

She was preparing the potatoes when a remark from her father caused her to pause.

"What is it?" said she.

"It's a bird. I saw it for a second against a white piece of a cloud and I give you my word that it's as big as a haystack. There it is again," he continued excitedly, "there's three of them."

For a few minutes they followed the flight of these amazing birds, but the twilight had almost entirely departed and darkness was brooding over the land. They did not see them any more.

Chapter II

And yet it was but a short distance from where they camped that the angels first put foot to earth.

It is useless to question what turmoil of wind or vagary of wing brought them to this desert hill instead of to a place more worthy of their grandeur, for, indeed, they were gorgeously apparelled in silken robes of scarlet and gold and purple; upon their heads were crowns high in form and of curious, intricate workmanship, and their wings, stretching ten feet on either side, were of many and shining colours.

Enough that here they did land, and in silence and darkness they stood for a few moments looking about them.

Then one spoke:

"Art," said he, "we were too busy coming down to look about us carefully; spring up again a little way, and see if there is any house in sight."

At the word one of the three stepped forward a pace, and leaped twenty feet into the air; his great wings swung out as he leaped, they beat twice, and he went circling the hill in steady, noiseless flight.

He returned in a minute:

"There are no houses here, but a little way below I saw a fire and two people sitting beside it."

"We will talk to them," said the other. "Show the way, Art."

"Up then," said Art.

"No," said the Angel who had not yet spoken. "I am tired of flying. We will walk to this place you speak of."

"Very well," replied Art, "let us walk."

And they went forward.

Around the little bucket of fire where Mac Cann and his daughter were sitting there was an intense darkness. At the distance of six feet they could still see, but delicately, indistinctly, and beyond that the night hung like a velvet curtain. They did not mind the night, they did not fear it, they did not look at it: it was around them full of strangeness, full of mystery and terror, but they looked only at the glowing brazier, and in the red cheer of that they were content.

They had eaten the bread and the turnip, and were waiting for the potatoes to be cooked, and as they waited an odd phrase, an exclamation, a sigh would pass from one to the other; and then suddenly, the dark curtain of night moved noiselessly, and the three angels stepped nobly in the firelight.

For an instant neither Mac Cann nor his daughter made a movement; they did not make a sound. Here was terror, and astonishment the sister of terror: they gaped: their whole being was in their eyes as they stared. From Mac Cann's throat came a noise; it had no grammatical significance, but it was weighted with all the sense that is in a dog's growl or a wolf's cry. Then the youngest of the strangers came forward:

"May we sit by your fire for a little time?" said he. "The night is cold, and in this darkness one does not know where to go."

At the sound of words Patsy seized hold of his sliding civilization.

"To be sure," he stammered. "Why wouldn't your honour sit down? There isn't a seat, but you're welcome to the grass and the light of the fire."

"Mary," he continued, looking hastily around—

But Mary was not there. The same instant those tall forms

strode from the darkness in front Mary had slipped, swift and noiseless as the shadow of a cat, into the darkness behind her.

"Mary," said her father again, "these are decent people, I'm thinking. Let you come from wherever you are, for I'm sure they wouldn't hurt yourself or myself."

As swiftly as she had disappeared she reappeared.

"I was looking if the ass was all right," said she sullenly.

She sat again by the brazier, and began to turn the potatoes with a stick. She did not appear to be taking any heed of the strangers, but it is likely that she was able to see them without looking, because, as is well known, women and birds are able to see without turning their heads, and that is indeed a necessary provision, for they are both surrounded by enemies.

Chapter III

The remarkable thing about astonishment is that it can only last for an instant. No person can be surprised for more than that time. You will come to terms with a ghost within two minutes of its appearance, and it had scarcely taken that time for Mac Cann and his daughter to become one with the visitors.

If the surprisor and the surprisee are mutually astonished, then, indeed, there is a tangle out of which anything may emerge, for two explanations are necessary at the one moment, and two explanations can no more hold the same position in time than two bodies can occupy the same lodgment in space.

It needed alone that the angels should proclaim their quality for the situation to arrange itself naturally.

Man is a scientific creature; he labels his ignorance and shelves it: mystery affrights him, it bores him, but when he has given a name to any appearance then mystery flies away, and reality alone remains for his cogitation. Later, perhaps, reality will enrage and mystify him more profoundly than any unexpectedness can do.

The Mac Canns, so far as they professed a religion, were

Catholics. Deeper than that they were Irish folk. From their cradles, if ever they had cradles other than a mother's breast and shoulder, they had supped on wonder. They believed as easily as an animal does, for most creatures are forced to credit everything long before they are able to prove anything. We have arranged to label these faculties of imagination and prophecy among the lesser creatures Instinct, and with the label we have thrown overboard more of mystery than we could afford to live with. Later these may confront us again in our proper souls, and the wonder and terror so long overdue will compel our tardy obeisance.

At the end of amazement, as of all else, we go to sleep, and, within an hour of their meeting, the angels and the Mac Canns were stretched in one common unconsciousness.

The angels were asleep, their attitudes proclaimed it. Patsy was asleep, his nose, with the unpleasant emphasis of a cracked trumpet, pealed wheezy confirmation of his slumber. His daughter was asleep, for there by the brazier she lay, motionless as the ground itself.

Perhaps she was not asleep. Perhaps she was lying with her face to the skies, staring through the darkness at the pale, scarce stars, dreaming dreams and seeing visions, while, all around, down in the invisible road and across the vanished fields and the hills, night trailed her dusky robes and crushed abroad her poppy.

Whether she had slept or not she was the first to arise in the morning.

A pale twilight was creeping over the earth, and through it one could see chilly trees and shivering grass; the heavy clouds huddled together as though they were seeking warmth on those grisly heights; the birds had not yet left their nests; it was an hour of utter silence and uncomeliness; an hour for blind and despairing creatures to move forward spitefully, cursing themselves and the powers; an hour when imagination has no function, and hope would fly again to the darkness rather than remain in that livid wilderness, for this was not yet the thin child of the dawn, crowned with young buds and active as a wintry leaf; it was the abortion of the dawn, formless, heavy, and detestable.

Moving cautiously in that shade, Mary herself seemed no more than a shadow; she diminished thin and formless as a wraith, while she trod carefully to and fro from the cart to the hedge.

She sat down, unloosed her hair and commenced to brush it.

In this colourless light her hair had no colour, but was of astonishing length and thickness; it flowed about her like a cloak, and as she sat it rolled and crept on the grass. She did not often tend her hair thus. Sometimes she plaited it for the sake of convenience, so that windy days would not whip it into her eyes or lash her cheeks; sometimes, through sheer laziness, she did not even plait it, she rolled it into a great ball and drew a wide, masculine cap over its brightness; and now, before the day had broken, sitting in a ghastly lightness, which was neither light nor darkness, she was attending to her hair.

And this hair perplexed her, for she did not know what to do with it; she did not know whether it was to be seen or not seen; whether to braid it in two great ropes, or roll it carelessly or carefully above her head, or let it hang loosely about her shoulders held only at the nape with a piece of ribbon or stuff. An hesitation such as this was new to her; she had never had occasion for such forethought; it was strange and inquieting; more disturbing, indeed, than the visit at black of night of those tall strangers whose eyes and voices were so quiet, and whose appointments flashed in the firelight while they spoke to her father of the things in which travellers are interested.

She looked at them where they lay, but they were scarcely more than visible—a tangle of flowing cloths and great limbs fading away in the rank grasses and the obscurity, and to her mind the real wonder was not that they had come, but that they were still there, and that they were sleeping deeply and peacefully as she had slept so often, with her head pillowed on her arm and her limbs folded calmly between the earth and the sky.

CHAPTER IV

Her hair was not braided; it was tied at the neck with a piece of whitish cloth torn from some part of her clothing, and upon her shoulders it billowed and rolled in magnificent living abundance.

Very gently she moved to where her father lay on his back with his mouth open and his black chin jutting at the sky. He was breathing through his mouth, so he was not snoring any longer. She lifted the three or four sacks which covered him, and rocked his shoulders cautiously until he awakened.

Her father awakened exactly as she did, exactly as every open-air animal does; his eyes flew wide, instantly and entirely wakeful, and he looked at her with full comprehension of their adventure. He raised softly on an elbow and glanced to where the strangers were; then nodded to his daughter and rose noiselessly to his feet. She beckoned him and they stepped a few paces away so that they might talk in security.

Mary was about to speak but her father prevented her:

"Listen," he whispered, "the best thing we can do is to load the things into the cart, without making any noises, mind you! then we'll yoke the little ass as easy as anything, and then I'll get into the cart and I'll drive off as hard as ever I can pelt, and you can run beside the ass with a stick in your hand and you welting the devil out of him to make him go quick. I'm no good myself at the running, and that's why I'll get into the cart, but you can run like a hare, and that's why you'll wallop the beast."

"Mind now," he continued fiercely, "we don't know who them fellows are at all, and what would the priest say if he heard we were stravaiging the country with three big, buck angels, and they full of tricks maybe; so go you now and be lifting in the things and I'll give you good help myself."

"I'll do nothing of the kind," whispered Mary angrily, "and it wasn't for that I woke you up."

"Won't you, indeed?" said her father fiercely.

"What would they be thinking of us at all if they were to rouse and see us sneaking off in that way? I'm telling you now that I won't do it, and that you won't do it either, and if you make a move to the cart I'll give a shout that will waken the men."

"The devil's in you, you strap!" replied her father, grinding his teeth at her. "What call have we to be mixing ourselves up with holy angels that'll be killing us maybe in an hour or half an hour; and maybe they're not angels at all but men that do be travelling the land in a circus and they full of fun and devilment?"

"It's angels they are," replied his daughter urgently, "and if they're not angels itself they are rich men, for there's big rings of gold on their fingers, and every ring has a diamond in it, and they've golden chains across their shoulders, I'm telling you, and the stuff in their clothes is fit for the children of a king. It's rich and very rich they are."

Mac Cann rasped his chin with his thumb.

"Do you think they are rich folk?"

"I do, indeed."

"Then," said her father in an abstracted tone, "we won't say anything more about it."

After a moment he spoke again:

"What were you thinking about yourself?"

"I was thinking," she replied, "that when they waken up in a little while there won't be anything at all for them to eat and they strangers."

"Hum!" said her father.

"There's two cold potatoes in the basket," she continued, "and a small piece of bread, and there isn't anything more than that; so let you be looking around for something to eat the way we won't be put to shame before the men."

"It's easy talking!" said he; "where am I to look? Do you want me to pick red herrings out of the grass and sides of bacon off the little bushes?"

"We passed a house last night a mile down the road," said Mary; "go you there and get whatever you're able to get, and if you can't get anything buy it off the people in the house. I've three shillings in my pocket that I was saving for a particular thing, but I'll give them to you because I wouldn't like to be shamed before the strange men."

Her father took the money:

"I wish I knew that you had it yesterday," he growled, "I wouldn't have gone to sleep with a throat on me like a mid-summer ditch and it full of dust and pismires."

Mary pushed him down the road.

"Be back as quick as you are able, and buy every kind of thing that you can get for the three shillings."

She watched him stamping heavily down the road, and then she returned again to their encampment.

CHAPTER V

The visitors had not awakened.

Now the air was growing clearer; the first livid pallor of the dawn had changed to a wholesome twilight, and light was rolling like clear smoke over the land. The air looked cold, and it began to look sharp instead of muddy; now the trees and bushes stood apart; they seemed lonely and unlike living things which were cold and a little frightened in an immensity to which they were foreign and from which they had much to dread.

Of all unnatural things, if that word can be used in any context, there is none more unnatural than silence, there is none so terrifying; for silence means more than itself, it means also immobility; it is the symbol and signature of death, and from it no one knows what may come at an instant; for silence is not quietness; against it your watch must climb the tower and stare in vain; against it your picket must be set, and he will thrust a lance to the sound of his own pulses; he will challenge the beating of his own heart, and hear his own harness threatening him at a distance.

To walk in a forest when there is no wind to stir the branches and set the leaves tapping upon the boughs, this is terrifying; a lonely sea stretching beyond sight and upon which there is no ripple holds the same despair, and a grassy plain from whence there is no movement visible has too its desolating horror.

But these things did not haunt the girl. She did not heed the silence for she did not listen to it; she did not heed the immensity for she did not see it. In space and silence she had been cradled; they were her foster-parents, and if ever she looked or listened it was to see and hear something quite other than these. Now she did listen and look. She listened to the breathing of the sleepers, and soon, for she was a female, she looked to see what they were like.

She leaned softly over one. He was a noble old man with a sweeping, white beard and a great brow; the expression of his quiet features was that of a wise infant; her heart went out to him and she smiled at him in his sleep.

She trod to the next and bent again. He was younger, but not young; he looked about forty years of age; his features were regular and very determined; his face looked strong, comely as though it had been chiselled from a gracious stone; there was a short coal-black beard on his chin.

She turned to the third sleeper, and halted blushing. She remembered his face, caught on the previous night in one lightning peep while she slid away from their approach. It was from him she had fled in the night, and for him that her hair was now draping her shoulders in unaccustomed beauty.

She did not dare go near him; she was afraid that if she bent over him he would flash open his eyes and look at her, and, as yet, she could not support such a look. She knew that if she were stretched in sleep and he approached to lean across her, she would awaken at the touch of his eyes, and she would be ashamed and frightened.

She did not look at him.

She went again to her place and set to building a fire in the brazier, and, while she sat, a voice began to sing in the dawn; not loud, but very gently, very sweetly. It was so early for a bird to sing, and she did not recognise that tune although the sound of it was thrilling through all her body. Softly, more softly, O Prophetic Voice! I do not know your speech; I do not know what happiness you are promising; is it of the leaves you tell and of a nest that rocks high on a leafy spray; there your mate swings cooing to herself. She swings and coos; she is folded in peace, and the small, white clouds go sailing by and they do not fall.

So through unimagined ways went that song, lifting its theme in terms that she did not comprehend; but it was not a bird that sang to her, it was her own heart making its obscure music and lilting its secret, wild lyrics in the dawn.

CHAPTER VI

It was the donkey awakened them.

For some time he had been rolling along the ground in ecstasy; now his agitated legs were pointing at the sky while he scratched his back against little stones and clumps of tough clay; now he was lying flat rubbing his jowl against these same clumps. He stood up suddenly, shook himself, swung up his tail and his chin, bared his teeth, fixed his eye on eternity, and roared "hee-haw" in a voice of such sudden mightiness, that not alone did the sleepers bound from their slumbers, but the very sun itself leaped across the horizon and stared at him with its wild eye.

Mary ran and beat the ass on the nose with her fist, but whatever Mary did to the ass was understood by him as a caress, and he willingly suffered it—"hee-haw," said he again triumphantly, and he planted his big head on her shoulder and stared sadly into space.

He was thinking, and thought always makes an ass look sad, but what he was thinking about not even Mary knew; his eye was hazy with cogitation, and he looked as wise and as kindly as the eldest of the three angels; indeed, although he had never been groomed, he looked handsome also, for he had the shape of a good donkey; his muzzle and his paws were white, the rest of his body was black and his eyes were brown.

The angels arose and, much as the ass did they shook themselves; there was no further toilet than that practicable; they ran their hands through their abundant hair, and the two who had beards combed these also with their fingers—then they looked around them.

Now the birds were sweeping and climbing on the shining air; they were calling and shrieking and singing; fifty of them, and all of the same kind, came dashing madly together, and they all sang the one song, so loud, so exultant, the heaven and earth seemed to ring and ring again of their glee.

They passed, and three antic wings came tumbling and flirting together; these had no song or their happiness went far beyond all orderly sound; they squealed as they chased each other; they squealed as they dropped twenty sheer feet towards the ground, and squealed again as they recovered on a swoop, and as they climbed an hundred feet in three swift zig-zags, they still squealed without intermission, and then the three went flickering away off with the others.

There came a crow whose happiness was so intense that he was not able to move; he stood on the hedge for a long time, and all that time he was trying hard to compose himself to a gravity befitting the father of many families, but every few seconds he lost all control and bawled with fervour. He examined himself all over; he peeped under his feathers to see was his complexion good; he parted the plumage of his tail modishly; he polished his feet with his bill, and then polished his bill on his left thigh, and then he polished his left thigh with the back of his neck. "I'm a hell of a crow," said he, "and everybody admits it." He flew with admirable carelessness over the ass, and cleverly stole two claws and one beak full of hair; but in mid-air he laughed incautiously so that the hair fell out of his beak, and in grabbing at that portion he dropped the bits in his claws, and he got so excited in trying to rescue these before they reached the ground that his voice covered all the other sounds of creation.

The sun was shining; the trees waved their branches in delight; there was no longer murk or coldness in the air; it sparkled from every point like a vast jewel, and the brisk clouds arraying themselves in fleeces of white and blue raced happily aloft.

That was what the angels saw when they looked abroad; a few paces distant the cart was lying with its shafts up in the air, and a tumble of miscellaneous rubbish was hanging half in and half out of it; a little farther the ass, in a concentrated manner, was chopping grass as quickly as ever he could, and, naturally enough, eating it; for after thinking deeply we eat, and it is true wisdom to do so.

The eldest of the angels observed the donkey. He stroked his beard.

"One eats that kind of vegetable," said he.

The others observed also.

"And," that angel continued, "the time has come for us to eat."

The second eldest angel rolled his coal-black chin in his hand and his gesture and attitude were precisely those of Patsy Mac Cann.

"I am certainly hungry," said he.

He picked a fistful of grass and thrust some of it into his mouth, but after a moment of difficulty he removed it again.

"It is soft enough to eat," said he musingly, "but I do not care greatly for its taste."

The youngest angel made a suggestion.

"Let us talk to the girl," said he.

And they all moved over to Mary.

"Daughter," said the eldest of the three, "we are hungry," and he beamed on her so contentedly that all fear and diffidence fled from her on the instant.

She replied:

"My father has gone down the road looking for food; he will be coming back in a minute or two, and he'll be bringing every kind of thing that's nourishing."

"While we are waiting for him," said the angel, "let us sit down and you can tell us all about food."

"It is a thing we ought to learn at once," said the second angel.

So they sat in a half-circle opposite the girl, and requested her to give them a lecture on food.

She thought it natural they should require information about earthly matters, but she found, as all unpractised speakers do, that she did not know at what point to begin on her subject. Still, something had to be said, for two of them were stroking their beards, and one was hugging his knees, and all three were gazing at her.

"Everything," said she, "that a body can eat is good to eat, but some things do taste nicer than others; potatoes and cabbage are very good to eat, and so is bacon; my father likes bacon when it's very salt, but I don't like it that way myself; bread is a good thing to eat, and so is cheese."

"What do you call this vegetable that the animal is eating?" said the angel pointing to the ass.

"That isn't a vegetable at all, sir, that's only grass; every kind of animal eats it, but Christians don't."

"Is it not good to eat?"

"Sure, I don't know. Dogs eat it when they are sick, so it ought to be wholesome, but I never heard tell of any person that ate grass except they were dying of the hunger and couldn't help themselves, poor creatures! And there was a Jew once who was a king, and they do say that he used to go out with the cattle and eat the grass like themselves, and nobody says that he didn't get fat.

"But here's my father coming across the fields (which is a queer way for him to come, because he went away by the road), and I'm thinking that he has a basket under his arm and there will be food in it."

Chapter VII

It was true enough. Mac Cann was coming to them from a point at right angles to where he was expected.

Now and again he turned to look over his shoulder, and as he was taking advantage of dips in the ground, bushes, and such-like to shield his advance his daughter divined that something had occurred in addition to the purchase of food. She had often before observed her father moving with these precautionary tactics, and had many times herself shared and even directed a retreat which was full of interest.

When her father drew nigh he nodded meaningly at her, set down a basket and a bundle, and stood for a moment looking at these while he thumbed his chin.

"Faith!" said he, "the world is full of trouble, and that's a fact."

He turned to the strangers.

"And I'm telling you this, that if the world wasn't full of trouble there'd be no life at all for the poor. It's the only chance we get is when people are full of woe, God help them! and isn't that a queer thing?

"Mary," he turned, and his voice was full of careless pride, "try if there isn't some small thing or other in the basket, and let your honours sit down on the grass while the young girl is getting your breakfast."

So the angels and Patsy sat down peacefully on the grass, and Mary opened the basket.

There were two loaves of bread in it, a fine square of butter, a piece of cheese as big as a man's hand and four times as thick; there was a leg of mutton in the basket, and only a little bit had been taken off it, a big paper bag full of tea, a package of soft sugar, a bottle full of milk, a bottle half full of whisky, two tobacco pipes having silver bands on their middles, and a big bar of plug tobacco. Those were the things in the basket.

Mary's eyes and her mouth opened when she saw them, and

she blessed herself, but she made no sound; and when she turned her face towards the company there was no expression on it except that of hospitality.

She cut slices from each of these things and piled them on a large piece of paper in the centre of the men; then she sat herself down and they all prepared to eat.

The second angel turned courteously to Mac Cann.

"Will you kindly begin to eat," said he, "and by watching you we will know what to do."

"There can be nothing more uncomely," said the first angel, "than to see people acting in disaccord with custom; we will try to do exactly as you do, and although you may be troubled by our awkwardness you will not be shocked by a lapse from sacred tradition."

"Well!" said Patsy thoughtfully.

He stretched a hand towards the food.

"I'll stand in nobody's light, and teaching people is God's own work; this is the way I do it, your worships, and any one that likes can follow me up."

He seized two pieces of bread, placed a slice of cheese between them, and bit deeply into that trinity.

The strangers followed his actions with fidelity, and in a moment their mouths were as full as his was and as content.

Patsy paused between bites:

"When I've this one finished," said he, "I'll take two more bits of bread and I'll put a lump of meat between them, and I'll eat that."

"Ah!" said that one of the angels whose mouth chanced to be free.

Patsy's eye roved over the rest of the food.

"And after that," he continued, "we will take a bit of whatever is handy."

In a short time there was nothing left on the newspaper but soft sugar, butter, tea, and tobacco. Patsy was abashed.

"I did think that there was more than that," said he.

"I've had enough myself," he continued "but maybe your honours could eat more."

Two of the angels assured him that they were quite satisfied, but the youngest angel said nothing.

"I'm doubting that you had enough," said Patsy dubiously to him.

"I could eat more if I had it," returned that one with a smile.

Mary went to the cart and returned bearing two cold potatoes and a piece of bread, and she placed these before the young angel. He thanked her and ate these, and then he ate the package of soft sugar, and then he ate a little piece of butter, but he didn't care for it. He pointed to the plug of tobacco:

"Does this be eaten?" he enquired.

"It does not," said Patsy. "If you ate a bit of that you'd get a pain inside of your belly that would last you for a month. There's some people do smoke it, and there's others do chew it; but I smoke it and chew it myself, and that's the best way. There's two pipes there on the paper, and I've a pipe in my own pocket, so whichever of you would like a smoke can do exactly as I do."

With a big jack-knife he shredded pieces from the plug, and rolled these between his palms, then he carefully stuffed his pipe, pulled at it to see was it drawing well, lit the tobacco, and heaved a sigh of contentment. He smiled around the circle.

"That's real good," said he.

The strangers examined the pipes and tobacco with curiosity, but they did not venture to smoke, and they watched Patsy's beatific face with kindly attention.

Chapter VIII

Now at this moment Mary was devoured with curiosity. She wanted to know how her father had become possessed of the basketful of provisions. She knew that three shillings would not have purchased a tithe of these goods, and, as she had now no fear of the strangers, she questioned her parent.

"Father," said she, "where did you get all the good food?"

The angels had eaten of his bounty, so Mac Cann considered that he had nothing to fear from their side. He regarded them while he pulled thoughtfully at his pipe.

"Do you know," said he, "that the hardest thing in the world is to get the food, and a body is never done looking for it. We are after eating all that we got this morning, so now we'll have to search for what we'll eat to-night, and in the morning we'll have to look again for more of it, and the day after that, and every day until we are dead we'll have to go on searching for the food."

"I would have thought," said the eldest angel, "that of all problems food would be the simplest in an organized society."

This halted Mac Cann for a moment.

"Maybe you're right, sir," said he kindly, and he dismissed the interruption.

"I heard a man once, he was a stranger to these parts, and he had a great deal of the talk, he said that the folk at the top do grab all the food in the world, and that then they make every person work for them, and that when you've done a certain amount of work they give you just enough money to buy just enough food to let you keep on working for them. That's what the man said: a big, angry man he was, with whiskers on him like the whirlwind, and he swore he wouldn't work for any one. I'm thinking myself that he didn't work either. We were great friends, that man and me, for I don't do any work if I can help it; it's that I haven't got the knack for work and, God help me! I've a big appetite. Besides that, the work I'd be able to do in a day mightn't give me enough to eat, and wouldn't I be cheated then?"

"Father," said Mary, "where did you get all the good food this morning?"

"I'll tell you that. I went down to the bend of the road where the house is, and I had the three shillings in my hand. When I came to the house the door was standing wide open. I hit it a thump of my fist, but nobody answered me. 'God be with all here,' said I, and in I marched. There was a woman lying on the floor in one room, and her head had been cracked with a stick; and in the next room there was a man lying on the floor, and his head had been cracked with a stick. It was in that room I saw the food packed nice and tight in the basket that you see before you. I looked around another little bit, and then I came away, for, as they say, a wise man never found a dead man, and I'm wise enough no matter what I look like."

"Were the people all dead?" said Mary, horrified.

"They were not—they only got a couple of clouts. I'm thinking they are all right by this, and they looking for the basket, but, please God, they won't find it. But what I'd like to know is this, who was it hit the people with a stick, and then walked away without the food and the drink and the tobacco, for that's a queer thing."

He turned to his daughter.

"Mary, a cree, let you burn up that basket in the brazier, for I don't like the look of it at all, and it empty."

So Mary burned the basket with great care while her father piled their goods on the cart and yoked up the ass.

Meanwhile the angels were talking together, and after a short time they approached Mac Cann.

"If it is not inconvenient," said their spokesman, "we would like to remain with you for a time. We think that in your company we may learn more than we might otherwise do, for you seem to be a man of ability, and at present we are rather lost in this strange world."

"Sure," said Patsy heartily, "I haven't the least objection in the world, only, if you don't want to be getting into trouble, and if you'll take my advice, I'd say that ye ought to take off them kinds of clothes you're wearing and get into duds something like my own, and let you put your wings aside and your fine high crowns, the way folk won't be staring at you every foot of the road, for I'm telling you that it's a bad thing to have people looking after you when you go through a little village or a town, because you can never know who'll remember you afterwards, and you maybe not wanting to be remembered at all."

"If our attire," said the angel, "is such as would make us re-markable—"

"It is," said Patsy. "People would think you belonged to a circus, and the crowds of the world would be after you in every place."

"Then," replied the angel, "we will do as you say."

"I have clothes enough in this bundle," said Patsy, with a vague air. "I found them up there in the house, and I was think-ing of yourselves when I took them. Let you put them on, and we will tie up your own things in a sack and bury them here so that when you want them again you'll be able to get them, and then we can travel wherever we please and no person will say a word to us."

So the strangers retired a little way with the bundle, and there they shed their finery.

When they appeared again they were clad in stout, ordinary clothing. They did not look a bit different from Patsy Mac Cann, except that they were all taller men than he, but between his dilapidation and theirs there was very little to choose.

Mac Cann dug a hole beside a tree and carefully buried their property, then with a thoughtful air he bade Mary move ahead with the ass, while he and the angels stepped forward at the tailboard.

They walked then through the morning sunlight, and for a time they had little to say to each other.

CHAPTER IX

In truth Patsy Mac Cann was a very able person.

For forty-two years he had existed on the edges of a society which did not recognise him in any way, and, as he might him-self have put it he had not done so very badly at all.

He lived as a bird lives, or a fish, or a wolf. Laws were for other people, but they were not for him; he crawled under or vaulted across these ethical barriers, and they troubled him no more than as he had to bend or climb a little to avoid them—he discerned laws as something to be avoided, and it was thus he saw most things.

Religion and morality, although he paid these an extraordinary reverence, were not for him either; he beheld them from afar, and, however they might seem beautiful or foolish, he left them behind as readily as he did his debts, if so weighty a description may be given to his volatile engagements. He did not discharge these engagements; he elongated himself from them; between himself and a query he interposed distance, and at once that became foreign to him, for half a mile about himself was his frontier, and beyond that, wherever he was, the enemy lay.

He stood outside of every social relation, and within an organised humanity he might almost have been reckoned as a different species. He was very mobile, but all his freedom lay in one direction, and outside of that pasturage he could never go. For the average man there are two dimensions of space wherein he moves with a certain limited freedom; it is for him a horizontal and a perpendicular world; he goes up the social scale and down it, and in both these atmospheres there is a level wherein he can exercise himself to and fro, his journeyings being strictly limited by his business and his family. Between the place where he works and the place where he lives lies all the freedom he can hope for; within that range he must seek such adventures as he craves, and the sole expansion to which he can attain is upwards towards another social life if he be ambitious, or downward to the underworlds if he is bored. For Mac Cann there was no upward and no downward movements, he had plumbed to the very rocks of life, but his horizontal movements were bounded only by the oceans around the country, and in this gigantic underworld he moved with almost absolute freedom, and a knowledge which might properly be termed scientific.

In despite of his apparent outlawry he was singularly secure; ambition waved no littlest lamp at him; the one ill which could overtake him was death, which catches on every man; no enmity could pursue him to any wall, for he was sunken a whole sphere beneath malice as beneath benevolence. Physical ill-treatment might come upon him, but in that case it was his manhood and his muscle against another manhood and another muscle—the simplest best would win, but there was no glory for the conqueror nor any loot to be carried from the battle.

Casual warfares, such as these, had been frequent enough in his career, for he had fought stubbornly with every kind of man, and had afterwards medicined his wounds with the only unguents cheap enough for his usage—the healing balsams of time and patience. He had but one occupation, and it was an engrossing one—he hunted for food, and for it he hunted with the skill and pertinacity of a wolf or a vulture.

With what skill he did hunt! He would pick crumbs from the lank chaps of famine; he gathered nourishment from the empty air; he lifted it from wells and watercourses; he picked it off clothes lines and hedges; he stole so cleverly from the bees that they never felt his hand in their pocket; he would lift the eggs from beneath a bird, and she would think that his finger was a chicken; he would clutch a hen from the roost, and the housewife would think he was the yard dog, and the yard dog would think he was its brother.

He had a culture too, and if it was not wide it was profound; he knew wind and weather as few astronomers know it; he knew the habit of the trees and the earth; how the seasons moved, not as seasons, but as days and hours; he had gathered all the sweets of summer, and the last rigour of winter was no secret to him; he had fought with the winter every year of his life as one fights with a mad beast, he had held off that grizzliest of muzzles and escaped scatheless.

He knew men and women, and he knew them from an angle at which they seldom caught themselves or each other; he knew them as prey to be bitten and escaped from quickly. At them, charged with a thousand preoccupations, he looked with an eye in which there was a single surmise, and he divined them in a flash. In this quick vision he saw man, one expression, one attitude for all; never did he see a man or woman in their fullness, his microscopic vision caught only what it looked for, but he saw that with the instant clarity of the microscope. There were no complexities for him in humanity; there were those who gave and those who did not give; there were those who might be cajoled, and those who might be frightened. If there was goodness in a man he glimpsed it from afar as a hawk sees a mouse in the clover, and he swooped on that virtue and was away with booty. If there was evil in a man he passed it serenely as a sheep passes by a butcher, for evil did not affect him. Evil could never put a hand on him, and he was not evil himself.

If the denominations of virtue or vice must be affixed to his innocent existence, then these terms would have to be re-defined, for they had no meaning in his case; he stood outside these as he did outside of the social structure. But, indeed, he was not outside of the social structure at all; he was so far inside of it that he could never get out; he was at the very heart of it; he was held in it like a deer in an ornamental park, or a cork that bobs peacefully in a bucket, and in the immense, neglected pastures of civilisation he found his own quietude and his own wisdom.

All of the things he knew and all of the things that he had done were most competently understood by his daughter.

CHAPTER X

It is to be remarked that the angels were strangely like Patsy Mac Cann. Their ideas of right and wrong almost entirely coincided with his. They had no property and so they had no prejudices, for the person who has nothing may look upon the world as his inheritance, while the person who has something has seldom anything but that.

Civilisation, having built itself at hazard upon the Rights of Property, has sought on many occasions to unbuild itself again in sheer desperation of any advance, but from the great Ethic of Possession there never had been any escape, and there never will be until the solidarity of man has been really created, and until each man ceases to see the wolf in his neighbour.

Is there actually a wolf in our neighbour? We see that which we are, and our eyes project on every side an image of ourselves; if we look with fear that which we behold is frightful; if we look with love then the colours of heaven are repeated to us from the ditch and the dungeon. We invent eternally upon one another; we scatter our sins broadcast and call them our neighbours; let us scatter our virtues abroad and build us a city to live in.

For Mac Cann and his daughter there was no longer any strangeness in their companions. As day and night succeeded, as conversation and action supplemented each other on their journeys, so each of them began to unfold from the fleshy disguise, and in a short time they could each have spoken of the others to an inquiring stranger, giving, within bounds, reasonably exact information as to habit and mentality.

What conversations they had engaged in! Sitting now by a hedge close to a tiny chaotic village, compact of ugliness and stupidity, now at twilight as they camped in a disused quarry, leaning their shoulders against great splintered rocks, and hearing no sound but the magnified, slow trickle of water and the breeze that sung or screamed against razor edge of rock; or lying on the sheltered side of a pit of potatoes, they stared at the moon as she sailed on her lonely voyages, or watched the stars that glanced and shone from the drifting clouds; and as they lifted their eyes to these sacred voyagers in whose charge is the destiny of man they lifted their minds also and adored mutely that mind of which these are the thoughts made visible.

Sometimes they discussed the problems of man in a thousand

superficial relationships. The angels were wise, but in the vocabulary which they had to use wisdom had no terms. Their wisdom referred only to ultimates, and was the unhandiest of tools when dug into some immediate, curious problem. Before wisdom can be audible a new language must be invented, and they also had to unshape their definitions and re-translate these secular findings into terms wherein they could see the subject broadly, and they found that what they gained in breadth they lost in outline, and that the last generalisation, however logically it was framed, was seldom more than an intensely interesting lie when it was dissected again. No truth in regard to space and time can retain virtue for longer than the beating of an artery; it too has its succession, its sidereal tide, and while you look upon it, round and hardy as a pebble, behold, it is split and fissured and transformed.

Sometimes when it rained, and it rained often, they would seek refuge in a haystack, if one was handy; or they would creep into a barn and hide behind hills of cabbages or piles of farming tools; or they slid into the sheds among the cattle where they warmed and fed themselves against those peaceful flanks; or, if they were nigh a town and had been lucky that day, they would pay a few coppers to sleep on the well-trodden, earthen floor of a house.

As for the ass, he slept wherever he could. When there was rain he would stand with his tail against the wind sunken in a reverie so profound that he no longer seemed to feel the rain or the wind. From these abysses of thought he would emerge to the realisation that there was a sheltered side to a wall or a clump of heather, and he also would take his timely rest under·the stars of God.

What did they say to him? Down the glittering slopes they peer and nod; before his eyes the mighty pageant is unrolled in quiet splendour; for him too the signs are set. Does the Waterman care nothing for his thirst? Does the Ram not bless his increase? Against his enemies also the Archer will bend his azure bow and loose his arrows of burning gold.

On their journeyings they met with many people; not the folk who lived in the houses dotted here and there at great distances from each other on the curving roads, for with these people they had nothing to do, they had scarcely anything to say, and the housefolk looked on the strollers with a suspicion which was almost a fear. The language of these was seldom gracious, and often, on their approach, the man of the house was sent for and the dog was unchained.

But for the vagabonds these people did not count; Mac Cann and his daughter scarcely looked on them as human beings, and if he had generalised about them at all, he would have said that there was no difference between these folks and the trees that shaded their dwellings in leafy spray, that they were rooted in their houses, and that they had no idea of life other than the trees might have which snuff for ever the same atmosphere and look on the same horizon until they droop again to the clay they lifted from.

It was with quite other people they communed.

The wandering ballad singer with his wallet of songs slung at his ragged haunch; the travelling musician whose blotchy fiddle could sneeze out the ten strange tunes he had learned from his father and from his father's generations before him; the little band travelling the world carrying saplings and rushes from the stream which they wove cunningly into tables and chairs warranted not to last too long; the folk who sold rootless ferns to people from whose window-ledges they had previously stolen the pots to plant them in; the men who went roaring along the roads driving the cattle before them from fair to market and back again; the hairy tinkers with their clattering metals, who marched in the angriest of battalions and who spoke a language composed entirely of curses.

These, and an hundred varieties of these, they met and camped with and were friendly with, and to the angels these people were humanity, and the others were, they did not know what.

Chapter XI

It might be asked why Patsy Mac Cann permitted the strangers to remain with him.

Now that they were dressed like himself he had quite forgotten, or he never thought of their celestial character, and they were undoubtedly a burden upon his ingenuity. They ate as vigorously as he did, and the food which they ate he had to supply.

There were two reasons for this kindliness—He had always wished to be the leader of a troop. In his soul the Ancient Patriarch was alive and ambitious of leadership. Had his wife given him more children he would have formed them and their wives and children into a band, and the affairs of this little world would have been directed by him with pride and pleasure. He would have observed their goings-out and their comings-in; he would have apportioned praise and reproach to his little clann; he would have instructed them upon a multitude of things, and passed on to them the culture which he had gathered so hardily, and, when they arrived at the age of ingenuity, it would have still been his ambition to dash their arguments with his superior knowledge, or put the happy finish to any plan which they submitted for his approval; he would have taken the road, like a prince of old, with his tail, and he would have undertaken such raids and forays that his name and fame would ring through the underworld like the note of a trumpet.

He could not do this because he only had one child (the others had died wintry deaths) and she was a girl. But now heaven itself had blessed him with a following and he led it with skill and enjoyment. Furthermore, his daughter, of whom he stood in considerable awe, had refused flatly to desert the strangers whom Providence had directed to them.

She had constituted herself in some strange way the mother of the four men. She cooked for them, she washed and mended for them, and, when the necessity arose, she scolded them with the heartiest good-will.

Her childhood had known nothing of dolls, and so her youth made dolls of these men whom she dressed and fed. Sometimes her existence with them was peaceful and happy; at other times she almost went mad with jealous rage. Little by little she began to demand a domestic obedience which they very willingly gave her; so they were her men and no one else's, and the exercise of this power gave her a delight such as she had never known.

She was wise also, for it was only in domestic affairs that she claimed their fealty; with their masculine movements she did not interfere, nor did she interfere with the task and apportioning of the day, although her counsel was willingly listened to in these matters; but when night came, when the camp was selected, the little cart unloaded, and the brazier lit, then she stepped briskly to her kingdom and ruled like a chieftainess.

With her father she often had trouble: he would capitulate at the end, but not until he had set forth at length his distaste for her suggestions and his assurance that she was a strap. She seldom treated him as a father, for she seldom remembered that relationship; she loved him as one loves a younger brother, and she was angry with him as one can only be angry with a younger brother. Usually she treated him as an infant; she adored him, and, if he had permitted it, she would have beaten him soundly on many an occasion.

For she was a strong girl. She was big in build and bone, and she was beautiful and fearless. Framed in a rusty shawl her face leaped out instant and catching as a torch in darkness; under her clumsy garments one divined a body to be adored as a revelation; she walked carelessly as the wind walks, proudly as a young queen trained in grandeur. She could leap from where she stood, as a wild-cat that springs terribly from quietude; she could run as a deer runs, and pause at full flight like a carven statue. Each movement of hers was complete and lovely in itself; when she lifted a hand to her hair the free attitude was a marvel of composure; it might never have begun, and might never cease, it was solitary and perfect; when she bent to the brazier she folded to such an economy of content that one might have thought her half her size and yet perfect; she had that beauty which raises the mind of man to an ecstasy which is murderous if it be not artistic; and she was so conscious of her loveliness that she could afford to forget it, and so careless that she had never yet used it as a weapon or a plea.

She could not but be aware of her beauty, for her mirrors had tongues; they were the eyes of those she met and paused with. No man had yet said anything to her, saving in rough jest as to a child, but no woman could speak of anything else in her presence, and these exclamations drummed through all their talk.

She had been worshipped by many women, for to physical loveliness in their own sex women are the veriest slaves. They will love a man for his beauty, but a woman they will adore as a singularity, as something almost too good to be true, as something which may vanish even while they gaze at it. Prettiness they understand and like or antagonise, but they have credited beauty as a masculine trait; and as a race long sunken in slavery, and who look almost despairingly for a saviour, so the female consciousness prostrates itself before female beauty as before a messiah who will lead them to the unconscious horrible ambitions which are the goal of femininity. But, and it is humanity's guard against a solitary development, while women worship a beautiful woman the beauty does not care for them; she accepts their homage and flies them as one flies from the deadliest boredom; she is the widest swing of their pendulum, and must hurry again from the circumference to the centre with the violent speed of an outcast who sees from afar the smoke of his father's house and the sacred roof-tree.

There is a steadying influence; an irreconcilable desire and ambition; the desire of every woman to be the wife of a fool, her ambition to be the mother of a genius; but they postulate genius, it is their outlet and their justification for that leap at a tangent which they have already taken.

Out there they have discovered the Neuter. Is the Genius

always to be born from an unfertilised womb, or rather a self-unfertilised one? Singular Messiahs! scorners of paternity! claiming no less than the Cosmos for a father; taking from the solitary mother capacity for infinite suffering and infinite love, whence did ye gather the rough masculine intellect, the single eye, all that hardiness of courage and sensibility of self that made of your souls a battlefield, and of your memory a terror to drown love under torrents of horrid red! Deluded so far and mocked! No genius has yet sprung from ye but the Genius of War and Destruction, those frowning captains that have ravaged our vineyards and blackened our generations with the torches of their egotism.

To woman beauty is energy, and they would gladly take from their own sex that which they have so long accepted from man. They are economical; the ants and the bees are not more amazingly parsimonious than they, and, like the ants and the bees, their subsequent extravagance is a thing to marvel at. Food and children they will hoard, and when these are safeguarded their attitude to the life about them is ruinous. They will adorn themselves at the expense of all creation, and in a few years they crush from teeming life a species which nature has toiled through laborious ages to perfect. They adorn themselves, and too often adornment is the chief manifestation of boredom. They are world-weary, sex-weary, and they do not know what they want; but they want power, so that they may rule evolution once more as long ago they ruled it; their blood remembers an ancient greatness; they crave to be the queens again, to hold the sceptre of life in their cruel hands, to break up the mould which has grown too rigid for freedom, to form anew the chaos which is a womb, and which they conceive is their womb, and to create therein beauty and freedom and power. But the king whom they have placed on the throne has grown wise in watching them; he is their bone terribly separated, terribly endowed; he used their cruelty, their fierceness, as his armies against them and so the battle is set, and wild deeds may flare from the stars of rebellion and prophecy.

Mary, who could make women do anything for her, was entirely interested in making men bow to her will, and because, almost against her expectation they did bow, she loved them, and could not sacrifice herself too much for their comfort or even their caprice. It was the mother-spirit in her which, observing the obedience of her children, is forced in very gratitude to become their slave; for, beyond all things, a woman desires power, and, beyond all things, she is unable to use it when she gets it. If this power be given to her grudgingly she will exercise it mercilessly; if it is given kindly then she is bound by her nature to renounce authority, and to live happy ever after, but it must be given to her.

Chapter XII

It may be surprising to learn that the names of the angels were Irish names, but more than eight hundred years ago a famous Saint informed the world that the language spoken in heaven was Gaelic, and, presumably, he had information on the point. He was not an Irishman, and he had no reason to exalt Fodhla above the other nations of the earth, and, therefore, his statement may be accepted on its merits, the more particularly as no other saint had denied it, and every Irish person is prepared to credit it.

It was also believed in ancient times, and the belief was world-wide, that the entrance to heaven, hell, and purgatory yawned in the Isle of the Saints, and this belief also, although it has never been proved, has never been disproved, and it does assist the theory that Irish is the celestial language. Furthermore, Gaelic is the most beautiful and expressive fashion of speech in the whole world, and, thus, an artistic and utilitarian reinforcement can be hurried to the support of that theory should it ever be in danger from philologists with foreign axes to grind.

The names of the angels were Finaun and Càeltia and Art.

Finaun was the eldest angel; Caeltia was that one who had a small coal-black beard on his chin, and Art was the youngest of the three, and he was as beautiful as the dawn, than which there is nothing more beautiful.

Finaun was an Archangel when he was in his own place; Caeltia was a Seraph, and Art was a Cherub. An Archangel is a Councillor and a Guardian; a Seraph is one who accumulates knowledge; a Cherub is one who accumulates love. In heaven these were their denominations.

Finaun was wise, childish, and kind, and between him and the little ass which drew their cart there was a singular and very pleasant resemblance.

Caeltia was dark and determined, and if he had cropped his beard with a scissors, the way Patsy Mac Cann did, he would have resembled Patsy Mac Cann as closely as one man can resemble another.

Art was dark also, and young and swift and beautiful. Looking carelessly at him one would have said that, barring the colour, he was the brother of Mary Mac Cann, and that the two of them were born at a birth, and a good birth.

Mary extended to Finaun part of the affection which she already had for the ass, and while they were marching the roads these three always went together; the archangel would be on one side of the donkey and Mary would be on the other side, and (one may say so) the three of them never ceased talking for an instant.

The ass, it will be admitted, did not speak, but he listened with such evident intention that no one could say he was out of the conversation; his right-hand ear hearkened agilely to Mary; his left-hand ear sprang to attention when Finaun spoke, and when, by a chance, they happened to be silent at the one moment then both his ears drooped forward towards his nose, and so he was silent also. A hand from either side continually touched his muzzle caressingly, and at moments entirely unexpected he would bray affectionately at them in a voice that would have tormented the ears of any but a true friend.

Patsy Mac Cann and the seraph Caeltia used to march exactly at the tail of the cart, and they, also, talked a lot.

At first Patsy talked the most, for he had much information to impart, and the seraph listened with intent humility, but, after a while, Caeltia, having captured knowledge, would dispute and argue with great vivacity. They spoke of many things, but a person who listened closely and recorded these things would have found that they talked oftener about strong drinks than about anything else. Mac Cann used to speak longingly about strange waters which he had heard were brewed in foreign lands, potent brewings which had been described to him by emphatic sailormen with tarry thumbs; but at this stage Caeltia only spoke about porter and whisky, and was well contented to talk of these.

The cherub Art was used to promenade alone behind them all, but sometimes he would go in front and listen to the conversation with the ass; sometimes he would join the two behind and force them to consider matters in which they were not interested, and sometimes again he would range the fields on either side, or he would climb a tree, or he would go alone by himself shouting a loud song that he had learned at the fair which they had last journeyed to, or he would prance silently along the road as though his body was full of jumps and he did not know what to do with them, or he would trudge forlornly in a boredom so profound that one expected him to drop dead of it in his tracks.

So life fell into a sort of routine.

When they were camped for the night Caeltia and Art would always sit on one side of the brazier with Patsy Mac Cann sitting between them; on the other side of the brazier the archangel and Mary would sit; Finaun always sat very close to her when they had finished eating and were all talking together; he used to take her long plait of hair into his lap, and for a long time he would unplait and plait again the end of that lovely rope.

Mary liked him to do this, and nobody else minded it.

BOOK II: EILEEN NI COOLEY

CHAPTER XIII

Early in the morning the sun had been shining gloriously, and there was a thump of a wind blowing across the road that kept everything gay; the trees were in full leaf and every bough went jigging to its neighbour, but on the sky the clouds raced so fast that they were continually catching each other up and getting so mixed that they could not disentangle themselves again, and from their excessive gaiety black misery spread and the sun took a gloomy cast.

Mac Cann screwed an eye upwards like a bird and rubbed at his chin.

"There will be rain soon," said he, "and the country wants it."

"It will be a heavy rain," said his daughter.

"It will so," he replied; "let us be getting along now the way we'll be somewhere before the rain comes, for I never did like getting wetted by the rain, and nobody ever did except the people of the County Cork, and they are so used to it that they never know whether it's raining or whether it isn't."

So they encouraged the ass to go quicker and he did that.

As they hastened along the road they saw in front of them two people marching close together, and in a little time they drew close to these people.

"I know the look of that man's back," said Patsy, "but I can't tell you where I saw it. I've a good memory for faces, though, and I'll tell you all about him in a minute."

"Do you know the woman that is with him?" said Caeltia.

"You can't tell a woman by her back," replied Patsy, "and nobody could, for they all have the same back when they have a shawl on."

Mary turned her head to them:

"Every woman's back is different," said she, "whether there's a shawl on it or not, and I know from the way that woman is wearing her shawl that she is Eileen Ni Cooley and no one else."

"If that is so," said her father hastily, "let us be going slower the way we won't catch up on her. Mary, a grah, whisper a word in the ass's ear so that he won't be going so quick, for he is full of fun this day."

"I'll do that," said Mary, and she said "whoa," into the ear of the little ass, and he stopped inside the quarter of a pace.

"Do you not like that woman?" Caeltia enquired.

"She's a bad woman," replied Patsy.

"What sort of a bad woman is she?"

"She's the sort that commits adultery with every kind of man," said he harshly.

Caeltia turned over that accusation for a moment.

"Did she ever commit adultery with yourself?" said he.

"She did not," said Patsy, "and that's why I don't like her."

Caeltia considered that statement also, and found it reasonable:

"I think," said he, "that the reason you don't like that woman is because you like her too much."

"It's so," said Patsy, "but there is no reason for her taking on with every kind of man and not taking on with me at all."

He was silent for a moment.

"I tell you," said he furiously, "that I made love to that woman from the dawn to the dark, and then she walked off with a man that came down a little road."

"That was her right," said Caeltia mildly.

"Maybe it was, but for the weight of a straw I would have killed the pair of them that night in the dark place."

"Why didn't you?"

"She had me weakened. My knees gave under me when she walked away and there wasn't even a curse in my mouth."

Again he was silent, and again he broke into angry speech!

"I don't want to see her at all, for she torments me, so let the pair of them walk their road until they come to a ditch that is full of thorns and is fit for them to die in."

"I think," said Caeltia, "that the reason you don't want to see her is because you want to see her too much."

"It's so," growled Mac Cann, "and it's so too that you are a prying kind of a man and that your mouth is never at rest, so we'll go on now to the woman yonder, and let you talk to her with your tongue and your nimble questions."

Thereupon he rushed forward and kicked the ass so suddenly in the belly that it leaped straight off the ground and began to run before its legs touched earth again.

When they had taken a few dozen steps Mac Cann began to roar furiously:

"What way are you, Eileen Ni Cooley? What sort of a man is it that's walking beside yourself?"

And he continued roaring questions such as that until they drew on the people.

The folk stopped at his shouts.

The woman was big and thin and she had red hair. Her face was freckled all over so that one could only see her delicate complexion in little spots, and at the first glance the resemblance between herself and Finaun was extraordinary. In the sweep of the brow, the set of the cheek-bones, a regard of the eyes, that resemblance was seen, and then the look vanished in a poise of the head and came again in another one.

At the moment her blue eyes seemed the angriest that ever were in a woman's head. She stood leaning on a thick ash-plant and watched the advancing company, but she did not utter a word to them.

The man by her side was tall also and as thin as a pole; he was ramshackle and slovenly; there was not much pith in his body, for he was weak at the knees and his big feet splayed outwards at a curious angle; but his face was extraordinary intelligent; and when he was younger must have been beautiful. Drink and ill-health had dragged and carved his flesh, and nothing of comeliness remained to him but his eyes, which were timid and tender as those of a fawn, and his hands which had never done anything but fumble with women. He also leaned quietly on a cudgel and watched Patsy Mac Cann.

And it was to him that Patsy came. He did not look once at the woman, though all the time he never ceased shouting salutations and questions at her by her name.

He walked directly to the man, eyeing him intently.

"And how is yourself?" he roared with horrible heartiness. "It's a while since I saw you, and it was the pitch night that time."

"I'm all right," said the man.

"So you are," said Patsy, "and why wouldn't you be? Weren't you born in the wide lap of good luck, and didn't you stay there? Ah, it's the way that the men that come down little, narrow paths do have fortune, and the ones that tramp the wide roads do have nothing but their broken feet. Good luck to you, my soul, and long may you wave—Eh!"

"I didn't say a word," said the man.

"And there's a stick in your hand that would crack the skull of a mountain, let alone a man."

"It's a good stick," said the man.

"Would you be calling it the brother or the husband of the one that woman has in her happy hands?"

"I would be calling it a stick only," replied the man.

"That's the name for it surely," said Patsy, "for a stick hasn't got a soul any more than a woman has, and isn't that a great mercy and a great comfort, for heaven would be full of women and wood, and there would be no room for the men and the drink."

The red-haired woman strode to Patsy and, putting her hand against his breast, she gave him a great push:

"If you're talking," said she, "or if you're fighting, turn to myself, for the man doesn't know you."

Patsy did turn to her with a great laugh:

"It's the one pleasure of my life to have your hands on me," he gibed. "Give me another puck now, and a hard one, the way I'll feel you well."

The woman lifted her ash-plant threateningly and crouched towards him, but the look on his face was such that she let her hand fall again.

"You're full of fun," said Patsy, "and you always were, but

we're going to be the great friends from now on, yourself and myself and the man with the stick; we'll be going by short cuts everywhere in the world, and having a gay time."

"We're not going with you, Padraig," said the woman, "and whatever road you are taking this day the man and myself will be going another road."

"Whoo!" said Patsy, "there are roads everywhere, so you're all right, and there are men on every one of the roads."

Chapter XIV

While this conversation had been taking place the others stood in a grave semicircle, and listened intently to their words.

Caeltia, regarding the sky, intervened:

"The rain will be here in a minute, so we had better walk on and look for shelter."

Mac Cann detached his heavy regard from Eileen Ni Cooley, and swept the sky and the horizon.

"That is so," said he. "Let us go ahead now, for we've had our talk, and we are all satisfied."

"There is a broken-down house stuck up a bohereen," he continued. "It's only a few perches up this road, for I remember passing the place the last time I was this way; that place will give us shelter while the rain spills."

He turned his stubborn face to the woman:

"You can come with us if you like, and you can stay where you are if you like, or you can go to the devil," and, saying so, he tramped after his daughter.

The woman had just caught sight of Art the cherub, and was regarding him with her steady eyes.

"Whoo!" said she, "I'm not the one to be frightened and I never was, so let us all go along and talk about our sins in the wet weather."

They started anew on the road, Patsy's company in advance, and behind marched the woman and the man and Art the cherub.

The sun had disappeared; wild clouds were piling themselves in rugged hills along the sky, and the world was growing dull and chill. Against the grey atmosphere Art's face was a profile, an outline sharp and calm and beautiful.

Eileen Ni Cooley was regarding him curiously as they walked together, and the strange man, with a wry smile on his lips, was regarding her with a like curiosity.

She pointed towards Patsy Mac Cann, who was tramping vigorously a dozen yards ahead.

"Young boy," said she, "where did you pick up with the man yonder, for the pair of you don't look matched?"

Art had his hands in his pockets; he turned and looked at her tranquilly.

"Where did you pick up with that man," he nodded towards her companion, "and where did the man pick up with you, for you don't look matched either?"

"We're not," said the woman quickly; "we're not matched a bit. That man and myself do be quarrelling all day and all night, and threatening to walk away from each other every minute of the time."

The man stared at her.

"Is that how it is with us?" said he.

"It is," said she to Art, "that's the way it is with us, honey. The man and myself have no love for each other now, and we never had."

The man halted suddenly; he changed the cudgel to his left hand and thrust out his right hand to her.

"Put your own hand there," said he, "and shake it well, and then be going along your road."

"What are you talking about?" said she.

He replied, frowning sternly from his wild eyes:

"I wouldn't hold the grace of God if I saw it slipping from me, so put your hand into my hand and go along your road."

Eileen Ni Cooley put her hand into his with some awkwardness and turned away her head.

"There it is for you," said she.

Then the man turned about and flapped quickly along the path they had already travelled; his cudgel beat the ground with a sharp noise, and he did not once look back.

Before he had taken an hundred paces the rain came, a fine, noiseless drizzle.

"It will be heavy in a minute," said the woman, "let us run after the cart."

With a quick movement she tucked her shawl about her head and shoulders and started to run, and Art went after her in alternate long hops of each foot.

They had reached a narrow path running diagonally from the main road.

"Up this way," shouted Patsy, and the company trooped after him, leaving the ass and cart to the storm.

Two minutes' distance up the road stood a small, dismantled house. There was a black gape where the window had been, and there were holes in the walls. In these holes grass and weeds were waving as they were along the window-ledge. The roof was covered with a rusty thatch and there were red poppies growing on that.

Patsy climbed through the low window-space, and the others climbed in after him.

Chapter XV

Inside the house was an earthen floor, four walls, and plenty of air. There were breezes blowing in the empty house, for from whatever direction a wind might come it found entrance there. There were stones lying everywhere on the floor; some of them had dropped from the walls, but most had been jerked through the window by passing children. There were spider's webs in that house; the roof was covered with them, and the walls were covered with them too. It was a dusty house, and when it would be wet enough it would be a muddy house, and it was musty with disuse and desolation.

But the company did not care anything about dust or stones or spiders. They kicked the stones aside and sat on the floor in the most sheltered part of the place where there had once been a fireplace, and if a spider walked on any of them it was permitted.

Patsy produced a clay pipe and lit it, and Caeltia took a silver-mounted briar from his pocket and he lit that and smoked it.

Outside the rain suddenly began to fall with a low noise and the room grew dark. Within there was a brooding quietness, for none of the people spoke; they were all waiting for each other to speak.

Indeed, they had all been agitated when they came in, for the wrung face of Patsy and the savage eyes of Eileen Ni Cooley had whipped their blood. Tragedy had sounded her warning note on the air, and they were each waiting to see had they a part in the play.

But the sudden change of atmosphere wrought like a foreign chemical in their blood, the sound of the falling rain dulled their spirits, the must of that sleeping house went to their brains like an opiate, and the silence of the place folded them about, compelling them to a similar quietude.

We are imitative beings; we respond to the tone and colour of our environment almost against ourselves, and still have our links with the chameleon and the moth; the sunset sheds its radiant peace upon us and we are content; the silent mountain-top lays a finger on our lips and we talk in whispers; the clouds lend us of their gaiety and we rejoice. So for a few moments they sat wrestling with the dull ghosts of that broken house, the mournful phantasms that were not dead long enough to be happy, for death is sorrowful at first and for a long time, but afterwards the dead are contented and learn to shape themselves anew.

Patsy, drawing on his pipe, looked around the people.

"Eh!" he exclaimed with a heavy joviality, "where has the man got to, the man with the big stick? If he's shy let him come in, and if he's angry let him come in too."

Eileen Ni Cooley was sitting close beside Art. She had let her shawl droop from her head, and her hair was showing through the dusk like a torch.

"The man has gone away, Padraig," said she; "he got tired of the company, and he's gone travelling towards his own friends."

Patsy regarded her with shining eyes. The must of the house was no longer in his nostrils; the silence lifted from him at a bound.

"You are telling me a fine story, Eileen," said he, "tell me this too, did the man go away of his own will, or did you send him away?"

"It was a bit of both, Padraig."

"The time to get good news," said Patsy, "is when it's raining, and that is good news, and it's raining now."

"News need not be good or bad, but only news," she replied, "and we will leave it at that."

Caeltia spoke to her:

"Do you have a good life going by yourself about the country and making acquaintances where you please?"

"I have the life I like," she answered, "and whether it's good or bad doesn't matter."

"Tell me the reason you never let himself make love to you when he wants to make it?"

"He is a domineering man," said she, "and I am a proud woman, and we would never give in to each other. When one of us would want to do a thing the other one wouldn't do it, and there would be no living between us. If I said black he would say white, and if he said yes I would say no, and that's how we are."

"He has a great love for you."

"He has a great hate for me. He loves me the way a dog loves bones, and in a little while he'd kill me in a lonely place with his hands to see what I would look like and I dying."

She turned her face to Mac Cann:

"That's the kind of man you are to me, Padraig, although you're different to other people."

"I am not that sort of man, but it's yourself is like that. I tell you that if I took a woman with me I'd be staunch to her the way I was with the mother of the girl there, and if you were to come with me you wouldn't have any complaint from now on."

"I know every thing I'm talking about," she replied sternly, "and I won't go with you, but I'll go with the young man here beside me."

With the words she put her hand on Art's arm and kept it there.

Mary Mac Cann straightened up where she was sitting and became deeply interested.

Art turned and burst into a laugh as he looked critically at Eileen.

"I will not go with you," said he. "I don't care for you a bit."

She gave a hard smile and removed her hand from his arm.

"It's all the worse for me," said she, "and it's small harm to you, young boy."

"That's a new answer for yourself," said Patsy, grinning savagely.

"It is, and it's a new day for me, and a poor day, for it's the first day of my old age."

"You'll die in a ditch," cried Patsy, "you'll die in a ditch like an old mare with a broken leg."

"I will," she snarled, "when the time comes, but you'll never have the killing of me, Padraig."

Finaun was sitting beside Mary with her hand in his, but she snatched her hand away and flared so fiercely upon Eileen that the woman looked up.

"Don't be angry with me, Mary," said she; "I never did you any harm yet and I'll never be able to do it now, for there are years between us, and they're going to break my back."

Finaun was speaking, more, it seemed, to himself than to the company. He combed his white beard with his hand as he spoke, and they all looked at him.

"He is talking in his sleep," said Eileen pensively, "and he an old man, and a nice old man."

"My father," said Caeltia, in an apologetic voice; "there is no need to tell about that."

"There is every need, my beloved," replied Finaun with his slow smile.

"I would rather you did not," murmured Caeltia, lifting his hand a little.

"I ask your permission, my son," said Finaun gently.

Caeltia spread out his open palms and dropped them again.

"Whatever you wish to do is good, my father," and with a slight blush, he slid the pipe into his pocket.

Finaun turned to Eileen Ni Cooley:

"I will tell you a story," said he.

"Sure," said Eileen, "I'd love to hear you, and I could listen to a story for a day and a night."

Mac Cann pulled solemnly at his pipe and regarded Finaun who was looking at him peacefully from a corner.

"You're full of fun," said he to the archangel.

CHAPTER XVI

Said Finaun:

"While generation succeeds generation a man has to fight the same fight. At the end he wins, and he never has to fight that battle again, and then he is ready for Paradise.

"Every man from the beginning has one enemy from whom he can never escape, and the story of his lives is the story of his battles with that enemy whom he must draw into his own being, for an enemy can never be crushed, but every enemy can be won.

"Long before the foundations of this world were laid, when the voice was heard and the army of the voice went through the darkness, two people came into being with the universe that was their shell. They lived through myriad existences knowing star after star grow hot and cold in the broad sky, and they hated each other through the changing of the stars and the ebbing and flooding of their lives.

"At a time this one of them would be a woman and that other would be a man, and again in due period that one that had been a woman would be a man and the other would be a woman, that their battle might be joined in the intimacy which can only come through difference and the distance that is attraction.

"No one can say which of these did most harm to the other; no one can say which was the most ruthless, the most merciless, for they were born, as all enemies are, equal in being and in power.

"Through their lives they had many names and they lived in many lands, but their names in eternity were Finaun Mac Dea and Caeltia Mac Dea, and when the time comes, their name will be Mac Dea and nothing else: then they will become one in each other, and one in Infinite Greatness, and one in the unending life of Eternity which is God: but still, in world under world, in star under flaming star, they pursue each other with a hate which is slowly changing into love.

"It was not on earth, nor in any planet, that the beginning of love came to these two, it was in the hell that they had fashioned for themselves in terror and lust and cruelty. For, as they sat among their demons, a seed germinated in the soul of one, the seed of knowledge which is the parent of love and the parent of every terrible and beautiful thing in the worlds and the heavens.

"While that one looked on his companion, writhing like himself in torment, he grew conscious, and although he looked at the other with fury it was with a new fury, for with it came contempt, and they were no longer equal in power or in hate.

"Now, for the first time, that one in whom knowledge had been born desired to escape from his companion; he wished to get away so that he might never behold that enemy again; suddenly the other appeared to him hideous as a toad that couches in slime and spits his poison at random, but he could not escape, and he could never escape.

"As that one increased in knowledge so he increased in cruelty and power, so his lust became terrible, for now there was fear in his contempt because he could never escape. Many a time they fled from one another, but always, and however they fled, it was towards each other their steps were directed. At the feast, in the camp, and in the wilderness they found themselves and undertook anew the quarrel which was their blood and their being.

"And that other in whom knowledge had not awakened—He raged like a beast; he thought in blood and fever; his brains were his teeth and the nails of his hands. Cunning came creepingly to his aid against knowledge; he lay in wait for his enemy in gloomy places; he spread snares for him in the darkness and baited traps. He feigned humility to get closer to his vengeance, but he could not combat knowledge.

"Time and again he became the slave of that other, and as slave and master their battle was savagely joined, until at last knowledge stirred also in that mind and he grew conscious.

"Then the age-long enmity drew to its change. For him there was no contempt possible, the other was older than he and wiser, for to be wise is to be old; there was no vantage for contempt, but envy sharpened his sword, it salted his anger, and they fought anew and unceasingly.

"But now their hands were not seeking each other's throats with such frank urgency; they fought subterraneously, with smiles and polite words and decent observances, but they did not cease for an instant to strive and never did they forsake an advantage or lift up the one that had fallen.

"Again the change: and now they battled not in the name of hate but under the holy superscription of love; again and again, life after life, they harried and ruined each other; their desire for one another was a madness, and in that desire they warred more bitterly than before. They blasted each other's lives, they dashed their honour to the mud, they slew one another. Than this none of their battles had been so terrible. Here there was no let, no respite even for an instant. They knew each other with that superficial knowledge which seems so clear although it shows no more than the scum floating upon existence; they knew the scumminess of each other and exhausted to the dregs their abundant evil until of evil they could learn no further, and their lives, alternating in a fierce energy and a miserable weariness, came towards but could not come to stagnation.

"The horizon vanished from them; there were irons on the feet of the winds; the sun peered from a hood through a mask, and life was one room wherein dull voices droned dully, wherein something was for ever uttered and nothing was said, where hands were for ever lifted and nothing was done, where the mind smouldered and flared to lightning and no thought came from the spark.

"They had reached an end, and it was a precipice down which they must spin giddily to the murk, or else shape wings for themselves and soar from that completion, for completion is a consciousness, and once again they were powerfully aware of themselves. They were vice-conscious, and virtue did not abide in their minds than as a dream which was an illusion and a lie.

"Then, and this too was long ago! how long! how long! When the moon was young; when she gathered rosy clouds about her evening and sang at noon from bush and mountain-ledge; when she folded her breasts in dewy darkness and awakened with cries of joy to the sun; then she tended her flowers in the vale; she drove her kine to deep pasture: she sang to her multitudes of increase and happiness while her feet went in the furrow with the plough and her hand guided the sickle and the sheaf. Great love didst thou give when thou wast a mother, O Beautiful! who art now white as silver and hath ice upon thine ancient head.

"Again they lived and were wed.

"Which of them was which in that sad pilgrimage it is not now possible to know. Memory faints at the long talo of it, and they were so intermingled, so alike through all their difference that they were becoming one in the great memory. Again they took up the time-long burden, and again desire drew them wildly to the embrace which was much repugnance and very little love. So, behold these two, a man and a woman, walking through the pleasant light, taking each other's hands in a kindness that had no roots, speaking words of affection that their souls groaned the lie to.

"The woman was fair—she was fair as one star that shines on the void and is not abashed before immensity; she was beautiful as a green tree by a pool that bows peacefully to the sun; she was lovely as a field of mild corn waving to the wind in one slow movement. Together they plumbed their desire and found wickedness glooming at the bottom, and they were conscious of themselves and of all evil.

"There was a demon in the pit that they had digged, and always, when they founded anew their hell, he tormented them; he was the accumulation of their evil; age after age they re-created him until he showed gigantic and terrible as a storm, and as they lusted after each other so he lusted after them.

"On a time that Misery shaped itself as a man and came privily to the woman while she walked under heavy apple boughs in a garden. Their feet went to and fro closely together in the grass and their voices communed together, until one day the woman cried bitterly that there were no wings, and with the Spectre she leaped forthright to the chasm and went down shrieking a laughter that was woe. There she found herself and her demon and was the concubine of that one; and there, in the gulf and chasm of evil, she conjured virtue to her tortured soul and stole energy from the demon.

"She sat among the rocks of her place.

"Old Misery beside her laughed his laugh, and while she looked at him her eyes went backwards in her head, and when she looked again she saw differently, for in that space knowledge had put forth a bud and a blossom and she looked through knowledge. She saw herself and the demon and the man, and she prayed to the demon. As she prayed she gathered small blue flowers that peered sparsely among the crags, and she made a chaplet of these. She wove them with tears and sighs, and when the chaplet was made she put it to the demon's hand, praying him to bear it to the man.

"He did that for her because he loved to laugh at their trouble, and he divined laughter for his iron chaps.

"So the demon came terribly to the man as he walked under the swaying and lifting of green boughs in the long grass of an orchard, and he put the chaplet in the man's hand, saying:

" 'My concubine, your beloved, sends a greeting to you with her love and this garland of blue flowers which she has woven with her two hands in hell.'

"The man, looking on these flowers, felt his heart move within him like water.

" 'Bring her to me,' said he to the demon.

" 'I will not do so,' replied the Misery.

"And, suddenly, the man leaped on the Spectre. He locked his arms about that cold neck, and clung furiously with his knees.

" 'Then I will go to her with you,' said he.

"And together they went headlong down the pit, and as they fell they battled frightfully in the dark pitch."

CHAPTER XVII

Mac Cann was asleep, but when Finaun's voice ceased he awakened and stretched himself with a loud yawn.

"I didn't hear a word of that story," said he.

"I heard it," said Eileen Ni Cooley; "it was a good story."

"What was it about?"

"I don't know," she replied.

"Do you know what it was about, Mary?"

"I do not, for I was thinking about other things at the time." Finaun took her hand.

"There was no need for any of you to know what that story was about, excepting you only," and he looked very kindly at Eileen Ni Cooley.

"I listened to it," said she; "and it was a good story. I know what it was about, but I would not know how to tell what it was about."

"It must have been the queer yarn," said Patsy regretfully; "I wish I hadn't gone to sleep."

"I was awake for you," said Caeltia.

"What's the use of that?" said Patsy testily.

It was still raining.

The day was far advanced and evening was spinning her dull webs athwart the sky. Already in the broken house the light had diminished to a brown gloom, and their faces looked watchful and pale to each other as they crouched on the earthen floor. Silence was again seizing on them, and each person's eyes were focussing on the same object or point on the wall or the floor as their thoughts began to hold them.

Mac Cann roused himself.

"We are here for the night; that rain won't stop as long as there's a drop left in its can."

Mary bestirred herself also.

"I'll slip down to the cart and bring back whatever food is in it. I left every thing covered and I don't think they'll be too wet."

"Do that," said her father.

"There's a big bottle rolled up in a sack," he continued; "it's in a bucket at the front of the cart by the right shaft, and there's a little sup of whisky in the big bottle."

"I'll bring that too."

"You're a good girl," said he.

"What will I do with the ass this night?" said Mary.

"Hit him a kick," said her father.

Chapter XVIII

The ass stood quietly where he had been left.

Rain was pouring from him as though he were the father of rivers and supplied the world with running water. It dashed off his flanks; it leaped down his tail; it foamed over his forehead to his nose; and hit the ground from there with a thump.

"I'm very wet," said the ass to himself, "and I wish I wasn't."

His eyes were fixed on a brown stone that had a knob on its back. Every drop of rain that hit the stone jumped twice and then spattered to the ground. After a moment he spoke to himself again:

"I don't care whether it stops raining or not, for I can't be any wetter than I am, however it goes."

Having said this, he dismissed the weather and settled himself to think. He hung his head slightly and fixed his eyes afar off, and he stared distantly like that without seeing anything while he gathered and revolved his thoughts.

The first thing he thought about was carrots.

He thought of their shape, their colour, and the way they looked in a bucket. Some would have the thick end stuck up, and some would have the other end stuck up, and there were always bits of clay sticking to one end or the other. Some would be lying on their sides as though they had slipped quietly to sleep, and some would be standing in a slanting way as though they were leaning their backs against a wall and couldn't make up their minds what to do next. But, however they looked in the bucket, they all tasted alike, and they all tasted well. They are a companionable food; they make a pleasant, crunching noise when they are bitten, and so, when one is eating carrots, one can listen to the sound of one's eating and make a story from it.

Thistles make a swishing noise when they are bitten; they have their taste.

Grass does not make any noise at all; it slips dumbly to the sepulchre, and makes no sign.

Bread makes no sound when it is eaten by an ass; it has an interesting taste, and it clings about one's teeth for a long time.

Apples have a good smell and a joyful crunch, but the taste of sugar lasts longer in the mouth, and can be remembered for longer than anything else; it has a short, sharp crunch that is like a curse, and instantly it blesses you with the taste of it.

Hay can be eaten in great mouthfuls. It has a chip and a crack at the first bite, and then it says no more. It sticks out of one's mouth like whiskers, and you can watch it with your eye while it moves to and fro according as your mouth moves. It is a friendly food, and very good for the hungry.

Oats are not a food; they are a great blessing; they are a debauch; they make you proud, so that you want to kick the front out of a cart, and climb a tree, and bite a cow, and chase chickens.

Mary came running and unyoked him from the cart. She embraced him on the streaming nose. "You poor thing, you!" said she, and she took a large paper bag from the cart and held it to his muzzle. There was soft sugar in the bag, and half a pound of it clove to his tongue at the first lick.

As she went back to the house with the bundle of food the ass regarded her.

"You are a good girl," said the ass.

He shook himself and dissipated his thoughts; then he trotted briskly here and there on the path to see if there was anything worth looking for.

Chapter XIX

They shared the food: there was little of it, and some of it was wet; but they each had a piece of bread, a knuckle of cheese, and three cold potatoes.

Mary said there was something wrong with her, and she passed two of her cold potatoes to the cherub Art, who ate them easily.

"I wish you had given them to me," said her father.

"I'll give you one of mine," said Eileen Ni Cooley, and she thrust one across to him.

Mac Cann pushed it entire into his mouth, and ate it as one who eats in a trance: he stared at Eileen.

"Why did you give me your potato?" said he.

Eileen blushed until not a single freckle in her face was visible.

"I don't know," she answered.

"You don't seem to know anything at all this day," he complained. "You're full of fun," said he.

He lit his pipe, and, after pulling for a while at it, he handed it to the woman.

"Take a draw at the pipe," he commanded, "and let us be decent with each other."

Eileen Ni Cooley did take a draw at the pipe, but she handed it back soon.

"I never was much at the smoking," said she.

Caeltia had his pipe going at full blast. He was leaning against the wall with his eyes half closed, and was thinking deeply between puffs.

Finaun had a good grip on Mary's hair, which he was methodically plaiting and unloosening again. He was sunken in reverie.

Mary was peeping from beneath her lids at Art, and was at the same time watching everybody else to see that she was not observed.

Art was whistling to himself in a low tone, and he was looking fixedly at a spider.

The spider was hauling on a loose rope of his tent, and he was very leisurely. One would have thought that he was smoking also.

"What did you have for dinner?" said Art to the spider.

"Nothing, sir, but a little, thin, wisp of a young fly," said the spider.

He was a thick-set, heavy kind of spider, and he seemed to be middle-aged, and resigned to it.

"That is all I had myself," said Art. "Are the times bad with you now, or are they middling?"

"Not so bad, glory be to God! The flies do wander in through the holes, and when they come from the light outside to the darkness in here, sir, we catch them on the wall, and we crunch their bones."

"Do they like that?"

"They do not, sir, but we do. The lad with the stout, hairy

legs, down there beside your elbow, caught a blue-bottle yesterday; there was eating on that fellow, I tell you, and he's not all eaten yet, but that spider is always lucky, barring the day he caught the wasp."

"That was a thing he didn't like?" queried Art.

"Don't mention it to him, sir, he doesn't care to talk about it."

"What way are you going to fasten up your rope?" said Art.

"I'll put a spit on the end of it, and then I'll thump it with my head to make it stick."

"Well, good luck to yourself."

"Good luck to your honour."

Said Patsy to Caeltia, pointing to Finaun:

"What does he be thinking about then he gets into them fits?"

"He does be talking to the hierarchy," replied Caeltia.

"And who are themselves?"

"They are the people in charge of this world."

"Is it the kings and the queens and the Holy Pope?"

"No, they are different kinds of people."

Patsy yawned.

"What does he be talking to them about?"

"Every kind of thing," replied Caeltia, and yawned also. "They are asking him for advice now."

"What is he saying?"

"He is talking about love," said Caeltia.

"He is always talking about that," said Patsy.

"And," said Caeltia, "he is talking about knowledge."

"It's another word of his."

"And he is saying that love and knowledge are the same thing."

"I wouldn't put it past him," said Patsy.

For he was in a bad temper. Either the close confinement, or the dull weather, or the presence of Eileen Ni Cooley, or all of these, had made him savage.

He arose and began striding through the narrow room, kicking stones from one side of the place to the other and glooming fiercely at everybody. Twice he halted before Eileen Ni Cooley, staring at her, and twice, without a word said, he resumed his marching.

Suddenly he leaned his back against the wall facing her, and shouted:

"Well, Eileen a grah, the man went away from you, the man with the big stick and the lengthy feet. Ah! that's a man you'd be crying out for and you all by yourself in the night."

"He was a good man," said Eileen; "there was no harm in that man, Padraig."

"Maybe he used to be putting his two arms around you now and then beside a hedge and giving you long kisses on the mouth?"

"He used to be doing that."

"Aye did he, indeed, and he wasn't the first man to do that, Eileen."

"Maybe you're right, Padraig."

"Nor the twenty-first."

"You've got me here in the house, Padraig, and the people around us are your own friends."

Caeltia also had arisen to his feet and was staring morosely at Eileen. Suddenly he leaped to her, wrenched the shawl from her head with a wide gesture, and gripped her throat between his hands; as her head touched the ground she gasped, and then, and just as suddenly, he released her. He stood up, looking wildly at Patsy, who stared back at him grinning like a madman, then he stumbled across to Finaun and took his hands between his own.

"You must not hurt me, my dear," said Finaun, smiling gravely at him.

Mary had leaped to Art, whose arm she took, and they backed to the end of the room.

Eileen stood up; she arranged her dress and wrapped the shawl about her head again; she gazed fearlessly at Mac Cann.

"The house is full of your friends, Padraig, and there's nobody here with me at all; there's no man could want better than that for himself."

Patsy's voice was hoarse.

"You're looking for fight?"

"I'm looking for whatever is coming," she replied steadily.

"I'm coming, then," he roared, and he strode to her. He lifted his hands above his head, and brought them down so heavily on her shoulders that she staggered.

"Here I am," said he, staring into her face.

She closed her eyes.

"I knew it wasn't love you wanted, Padraig; it was murder you wanted, and you have your wish."

She was swaying under his weight as she spoke; her knees were giving beneath her.

"Eileen," said Patsy, in a small voice, "I'm going to tumble; I can't hold myself up, Eileen; my knees are giving way under me, and I've only got my arms around your neck."

She opened her eyes and saw him sagging against her, with his eyes half closed and his face gone white.

"Sure, Padraig!" said she.

She flung her arms about his body and lifted him, but the weight was too much, and he went down.

She crouched by him on the floor, hugging his head against her breast.

"Sure, listen to me, Padraig; I never did like any one in the world but yourself; there wasn't a man of them all was more to me than a blast of wind; you were the one I liked always. Listen to me now, Padraig. Don't I be wanting you day and night, and saying prayers to you in the darkness and crying out in the dawn; my heart is sore for you, so it is: there's a twist in us, O my dear. Don't you be minding the men; whatever they did it was nothing, it was nothing more than beasts playing in a field and not caring anything. We are beside one another for a minute now. When I would put my hand on my breast in the middle of a laugh it was you I was touching, and I do never stop thinking of you in any place under the sky."

They were kissing each other like lost souls; they babbled and clung to each other; they thrust one another's head back to stare at it, and pursued the head with their violent lips.

It was a time before they all got to sleep that night, but they did sleep at the end of it.

They stretched in the darkness with their eyes closed, and the night folded them around, separating each one from his fellow, and putting on each the enchantment of silence and blindness. They were no longer together although they were lying but a few inches apart; there was only the darkness that had no inches to it; the darkness that has no beginning and no end; that appears and disappears, calling hush as it comes and goes, and holding peace and terror in either invisible hand; there was no silver moon in the sky and no sparkle of white stars; there was only darkness and silence and the steady hushing of the rain.

When he awoke in the morning Mac Cann rolled urgently on his elbow and stared to where Eileen Ni Cooley had stretched herself for sleep—but she was not there, she was not anywhere.

He shouted, and the company sprang to their feet.

"She got out through the window," he roared.

"The devil damn the soul of her," said he.

from The Insurrection in Dublin

CHAPTER I

MONDAY

This has taken every one by surprise. It is possible, that, with the exception of their Staff, it has taken the Volunteers themselves by surprise; but, to-day, our peaceful city is no longer peaceful; guns are sounding, or rolling and crackling from different directions, and, although rarely, the rattle of machine guns can be heard also.

Two days ago war seemed very far away—so far, that I have covenanted with myself to learn the alphabet of music. Tom Bodkin had promised to present me with a musical instrument called a dulcimer—I persist in thinking that this is a species of guitar, although I am assured that it is a number of small metal plates which are struck with sticks, and I confess that this description of its function prejudices me more than a little against it. There is no reason why I should think dubiously of such an instrument, but I do not relish the idea of procuring music with a stick. With this dulcimer I shall be able to tap out our Irish melodies when I am abroad, and transport myself to Ireland for a few minutes, or a few bars.

In preparation for this present I had through Saturday and Sunday been learning the notes of the Scale. The notes and spaces on the lines did not trouble me much, but those above and below the line seemed ingenious and complicated to a degree that frightened me.

On Saturday I got the *Irish Times*, and found in it a long article by Bernard Shaw (reprinted from the *New York Times*). One reads things written by Shaw. Why one does read them I do not know exactly, except that it is a habit we got into years ago, and we read an article by Shaw just as we put on our boots in the morning—that is, without thinking about it, and without any idea of reward.

His article angered me exceedingly. It was called "Irish Nonsense talked in Ireland." It was written (as is almost all of his journalistic work) with that *bonhomie* which he has cultivated—it is his mannerism—and which is essentially hypocritical and untrue. *Bonhomie!* It is that man-of-the-world attitude, that shop attitude, that between-you-and-me-for-are-we-not-equal-and-cultured attitude, which is the tone of a card-sharper or a trick-of-the-loop man. That was the tone of Shaw's article. I wrote an open letter to him which I sent to the *New Age*, because I doubted that the Dublin papers would print it if I sent it to them, and I knew that the Irish people who read the other papers had never heard of Shaw, except as a trade-mark under which very good Limerick bacon is sold, and that they would not be interested in the opinions of a person named Shaw on any subject not relevant to bacon. I struck out of my letter a good many harsh things which I said of him, and hoped he would reply to it in order that I could furnish these acidities to him in a second letter.

That was Saturday.

On Sunday I had to go to my office, as the Director was absent in London, and there I applied myself to the notes and spaces below the stave, but relinquished the exercise, convinced that these mysteries were unattainable by man, while the knowledge that above the stave there were others and not less complex, stayed mournfully with me.

I returned home, and as novels (perhaps it is only for the duration of the war) do not now interest me I read for some time in Madame Blavatsky's "Secret Doctrine," which book interests me profoundly. George Russell was out of town or I would have gone round to his house in the evening to tell him what I thought about Shaw, and to listen to his own much finer ideas on that as on every other subject. I went to bed.

On the morning following I awoke into full insurrection and bloody war, but I did not know anything about it. It was Bank Holiday, but for employments such as mine there are not any holidays, so I went to my office at the usual hour, and after transacting what business was necessary I bent myself to the notes above and below the stave, and marvelled anew at the ingenuity of man. Peace was in the building, and if any of the attendants had knowledge or rumour of war they did not mention it to me.

At one o'clock I went to lunch. Passing the corner of Merrion Row I saw two small groups of people. These people were regarding steadfastly in the direction of St. Stephen's Green Park, and they spoke occasionally to one another with that detached confidence which proved they were mutually unknown. I also, but without approaching them, stared in the direction of the Green. I saw nothing but the narrow street which widened to the Park. Some few people were standing in tentative attitudes, and all looking in the one direction. As I turned from them homewards I received an impression of silence and expectation and excitement.

On the way home I noticed that many silent people were standing in their doorways—an unusual thing in Dublin outside of the back streets. The glance of a Dublin man or woman conveys generally a criticism of one's personal appearance, and is a little hostile to the passer. The look of each person as I passed was steadfast, and contained an enquiry instead of a criticism. I felt faintly uneasy, but withdrew my mind to a meditation which I had covenanted with myself to perform daily, and passed to my house.

There I was told that there had been a great deal of rifle firing all the morning, and we concluded that the Military recruits or Volunteer detachments were practising that arm. My return to business was by the way I had already come. At the corner of Merrion Row I found the same silent groups, who were still looking in the direction of the Green, and addressing each other occasionally with the detached confidence of strangers. Suddenly, and on the spur of the moment, I addressed one of these silent gazers.

"Has there been an accident?" said I.

I indicated the people standing about.

"What's all this for?"

He was a sleepy, rough-looking man about 40 years of age, with a blunt red moustache, and the distant eyes which one sees in sailors. He looked at me, stared at me as at a person from a different country. He grew wakeful and vivid.

"Don't you know?" said he.

And then he saw that I did not know.

"The Sinn Feiners have seized the City this morning."

"Oh!" said I.

He continued with the savage earnestness of one who has amazement in his mouth:

"They seized the City at eleven o'clock this morning. The Green there is full of them. They have captured the Castle. They have taken the Post Office."

"My God!" said I, staring at him, and instantly I turned and went running towards the Green.

In a few seconds I banished astonishment and began to walk. As I drew near the Green rifle fire began like sharply-cracking whips. It was from the further side. I saw that the Gates were closed and men were standing inside with guns on their shoulders. I passed a house, the windows of which were smashed in. As I went by a man in civilian clothes slipped me through the Park gates, which instantly closed behind him. He ran towards me, and I halted. He was carrying two small packets in his hand. He passed me hurriedly, and, placing his leg inside the broken window of the house behind me, he disappeared. Almost immediately another man in civilian clothes appeared from the broken window of another house. He also had something (I don't know what) in his hand. He ran urgently towards the gates, which opened, admitted him, and closed again.

In the centre of this side of the Park a rough barricade of carts and motor cars had been sketched. It was still full of gaps. Behind it was a halted tram, and along the vistas of the Green one saw other trams derelict, untenanted.

I came to the barricade. As I reached it and stood by the Shelbourne Hotel, which it faced, a loud cry came from the Park. The gates opened and three men ran out. Two of them held rifles with fixed bayonets. The third gripped a heavy revolver in his fist. They ran towards a motor car which had just turned the corner, and halted it. The men with bayonets took position instantly on either side of the car. The man with the revolver saluted, and I heard him begging the occupants to pardon him, and directing them to dismount. A man and woman got down. They were again saluted and requested to go to the sidewalk. They did so.

The man crossed and stood by me. He was very tall and thin, middle-aged, with a shaven, wasted face. "I want to get down to Armagh to-day," he said to no one in particular. The loose bluish skin under his eyes was twitching. The Volunteers directed the chauffeur to drive to the barricade and lodge his car in a particular position there. He did it awkwardly, and after three attempts, he succeeded in pleasing them. He was a big, brown-faced man, whose knees were rather high for the seat he was in, and they jerked with the speed and persistence of something moved with a powerful spring. His face was composed and fully under command, although his legs were not. He locked the car into the barricade, and then, being a man accustomed to be

NOTE—As I pen these words rifle shot is cracking from three different directions and continually. Three minutes ago there were two discharges from heavy guns. These are the first heavy guns used in the Insurrection, 25th April.

commanded, he awaited an order to descend. When the order came he walked directly to his master, still preserving all the solemnity of his features. These two men did not address a word to each other, but their drilled and expressionless eyes were loud with surprise and fear and rage. They went into the Hotel.

I spoke to the man with the revolver. He was no more than a boy, not more certainly than twenty years of age, short in stature, with close curling red hair and blue eyes—a kindly-looking lad. The strap of his sombrero had torn loose on one side, and except while he held it in his teeth it flapped about his chin. His face was sunburnt and grimy with dust and sweat.

This young man did not appear to me to be acting from his reason. He was doing his work from a determination implanted previously, days, weeks perhaps, on his imagination. His mind was—where? It was not with his body. And continually his eyes went searching widely, looking for spaces, scanning hastily the clouds, the vistas of the streets, for something that did not hinder him, looking away for a moment from the immediacies and rigours which were impressed where his mind had been.

When I spoke he looked at me, and I know that for some seconds he did not see me. I said:—

"What is the meaning of all this? What has happened?"

He replied collectedly enough in speech, but with that ramble and errancy clouding his eyes.

"We have taken the City. We are expecting an attack from the military at any moment, and those people," he indicated knots of men, women and children clustered towards the end of the Green, "won't go home for me. We have the Post Office, and the Railways, and the Castle. We have all the City. We have everything."

(Some men and two women drew behind me to listen.)

"This morning," said he, "the police rushed us. One ran at me to take my revolver. I fired but I missed him, and I hit a _____"

"You have far too much talk," said a voice to the young man.

I turned a few steps away, and glancing back saw that he was staring after me, but I know that he did not see me—he was looking at turmoil, and blood, and at figures that ran towards him and ran away—a world in motion and he in the centre of it astonished.

The men with him did not utter a sound. They were both older. One, indeed, a short, sturdy man, had a heavy white moustache. He was quite collected, and took no notice of the skies, or the spaces. He saw a man in rubbers placing his hand on a bicycle in the barricade, and called to him instantly: "Let that alone."

The motorist did not at once remove his hand, whereupon the white-moustached man gripped his gun in both hands and ran violently towards him. He ran directly to him, body to body, and, as he was short and the motorist was very tall, stared fixedly up in his face. He roared up at his face in a mighty voice.

"Are you deaf? Are you deaf? Move back!"

The motorist moved away, pursued by an eye as steady and savage as the point of the bayonet that was level with it.

Another motor car came round the Ely Place corner of the Green and wobbled at the sight of the barricade. The three men who had returned to the gate roared "Halt," but the driver made a tentative effort to turn his wheel. A great shout of many voices came then, and the three men ran to him.

"Drive to the barricade," came the order.

The driver turned his wheel a point further towards escape, and instantly one of the men clapped a gun to the wheel and blew the tyre open. Some words were exchanged, and then a shout:

"Drive it on the rim, drive it."

The tone was very menacing, and the motorist turned his car slowly to the barricade and placed it in.

For an hour I tramped the City, seeing everywhere these knots of watchful strangers speaking together in low tones, and it sank into my mind that what I had heard was true, and that the City was in insurrection. It had been promised for so long, and had been threatened for so long. Now it was here. I had seen it in the Green, others had seen it in other parts—the same men clad in dark green and equipped with rifle, bayonet, and bandolier, the same silent activity. The police had disappeared from the streets. At that hour I did not see one policeman, nor did I see one for many days, and men said that several of them had been shot earlier in the morning; that an officer had been shot on Portobello Bridge, that many soldiers had been killed, and that a good many civilians were dead also.

Around me as I walked the rumour of war and death was in the air. Continually and from every direction rifles were crackling and rolling; sometimes there was only one shot, again it would be a roll of firing crested with single, short explosions, and sinking again to whip-like snaps and whip-like echoes; then for a moment silence, and then again the guns leaped in the air.

The rumour of positions, bridges, public places, railway stations, Government offices, having been seized was persistent, and was not denied by any voice.

I met some few people I knew. P. H., T. M., who said: "Well!" and thrust their eyes into me as though they were rummaging me for information.

But there were not very many people in the streets. The greater part of the population were away on Bank Holiday, and did not know anything of this business. Many of them would not know anything until they found they had to walk home from Kingstown, Dalkey, Howth, or wherever they were.

I returned to my office, decided that I would close it for the day. The men were very relieved when I came in, and were more relieved when I ordered the gong to be sounded. There were some few people in the place, and they were soon put out. The outer gates were locked, and the great door, but I kept the men on duty until the evening. We were the last public institution open; all the others had been closed for hours.

I went upstairs and sat down, but had barely reached the chair before I stood up again, and began to pace my room, to and fro, to and fro; amazed, expectant, inquiet; turning my ear to the shots, and my mind to speculations that began in the middle, and were chased from there by others before they had taken one thought forward. But then I took myself resolutely and sat me down, and I pencilled out exercises above the stave, and under the stave; and discovered suddenly that I was again marching the floor, to and fro, to and fro, with thoughts bursting about my head as though they were fired on me from concealed batteries.

At five o'clock I left. I met Miss P., all of whose rumours coincided with those I had gathered. She was in exceeding good humour and interested. Leaving her I met Cy ————, and we turned together up to the Green. As we proceeded, the sound of firing grew more distinct, but when we reached the Green it died away again. We stood a little below the Shelbourne Hotel, looking at the barricade and into the Park. We could see nothing. Not a Volunteer was in sight. The Green seemed a desert. There were only the trees to be seen, and through them small green vistas of sward.

Just then a man stepped on the footpath and walked directly to the barricade. He stopped and gripped the shafts of a lorry lodged near the centre. At that instant the Park exploded into life and sound; from nowhere armed men appeared at the railings, and they all shouted at the man.

"Put down that lorry. Let out and go away. Let out at once."

These were the cries. The man did not let out. He halted with the shafts in his hand, and looked towards the vociferous palings. Then, and very slowly, he began to draw the lorry out of the barricade. The shouts came to him again, very loud, very threatening, but he did not attend to them.

"He is the man that owns the lorry," said a voice beside me.

Dead silence fell on the people around while the man slowly drew his cart down by the footpath. Then three shots rang out in succession. At the distance he could not be missed, and it was obvious they were trying to frighten him. He dropped the shafts and instead of going away he walked over to the Volunteers.

"He has nerve," said another voice behind me.

The man walked directly towards the Volunteers, who, to the number of about ten, were lining the railings. He walked slowly, bent a little forward, with one hand raised and one finger up as though he were going to make a speech. Ten guns were pointing at him, and a voice repeated many times:

"Go and put back that lorry or you are a dead man. Go before I count four. One, two, three, four,—"

A rifle spat at him, and in two undulating movements the man sank on himself and sagged to the ground.

I ran to him with some others, while a woman screamed unmeaningly, all on one strident note. The man was picked up and carried to a hospital beside the Arts Club. There was a hole in the top of his head, and one does not know how ugly blood can look until it has been seen clotted in hair. As the poor man was being carried in, a woman plumped to her knees in the road and began not to scream but to screech.

At that moment the Volunteers were hated. The men by whom I was and who were lifting the body, roared into the railings:—

"We'll be coming back for you, damn you."

From the railings there came no reply, and in an instant the place was again desert and silent, and the little green vistas were slumbering among the trees.

No one seemed able to estimate the number of men inside the Green, and through the day no considerable body of men had been seen, only those who held the gates, and the small parties of threes and fours who arrested motors and carts for their barricades. Among these were some who were only infants—one boy seemed about twelve years of age. He was strutting the centre of the road with a large revolver in his small fist. A motor car came by him containing three men, and in the shortest of time he had the car lodged in his barricade, and dismissed its stupefied occupants with a wave of his armed hand.

The knots were increasing about the streets, for now the Bank Holiday people began to wander back from places that were not distant, and to them it had all to be explained anew. Free movement was possible everywhere in the City, but the constant crackle of rifles restricted somewhat that freedom. Up to one o'clock at night belated travellers were straggling into the City, and curious people were wandering from group to group still trying to gather information.

I remained awake until four o'clock in the morning. Every five minutes a rifle cracked somewhere, but about a quarter to twelve sharp volleying came from the direction of Portobello Bridge, and died away after some time. The windows of my flat listen out towards the Green, and obliquely towards Sackville Street. In another quarter of an hour there were volleys from Stephen's Green direction, and this continued with intensity for about twenty-five minutes. Then it fell into a sputter of fire and ceased.

I went to bed about four o'clock convinced that the Green had been rushed by the military and captured, and that the rising was at an end.

That was the first day of the insurrection.

From the Foreword

There is a reference in the earlier pages of this record to a letter which I addressed to Mr. George Bernard Shaw and published in the *New Age*. This was a thoughtless letter, and subsequent events have proved that it was unmeaning and ridiculous. I have since, through the same hospitable journal, apologised to Mr. Shaw, but have let my reference to the matter stand as an indication that electricity was already in the air. Every statement I made about him in that letter and in this book was erroneous; for, afterwards, when it would have been politic to run for cover, he ran for the open, and he spoke there like the valiant thinker and great Irishman that he is.

from Irish Fairy Tales

THE STORY OF TUAN MAC CAIRILL

Chapter I

Finnian, the Abbot of Moville, went southwards and eastwards in great haste. News had come to him in Donegal that there were yet people in his own province who believed in gods that he did not approve of, and the gods that we do not approve of are treated scurvily, even by saintly men.

He was told of a powerful gentleman who observed neither Saint's day nor Sunday.

"A powerful person!" said Finnian.

"All that," was the reply.

"We shall try this person's power," said Finnian.

"He is reputed to be a wise and hardy man," said his informant.

"We shall test his wisdom and his hardihood."

"He is," that gossip whispered—"he is a magician."

"I will magician him," cried Finnian angrily. "Where does that man live?"

He was informed, and he proceeded to that direction without delay.

In no great time he came to the stronghold of the gentleman who followed ancient ways, and he demanded admittance in order that he might preach and prove the new God, and exorcise

and terrify and banish even the memory of the old one; for to a
god grown old Time is as ruthless as to a beggarman grown old.

But the Ulster gentleman refused Finnian admittance.

He barricaded his house, he shuttered his windows, and in a
gloom of indignation and protest he continued the practices of
ten thousand years, and would not hearken to Finnian calling at
the window or to Time knocking at his door.

But of those adversaries it was the first he redoubted.

Finnian loomed on him as a portent and a terror; but he had
no fear of Time. Indeed he was the foster-brother of Time, and
so disdainful of the bitter god that he did not even disdain him;
he leaped over the scythe, he dodged under it, and the sole occasions on which Time laughs is when he chances on Tuan, the son
of Cairill, the son of Muredac Red-neck.

CHAPTER II

Now Finnian could not abide that any person should resist
both the Gospel and himself, and he proceeded to force the
stronghold by peaceful but powerful methods. He fasted on the
gentleman, and he did so to such purpose that he was admitted
to the house; for to an hospitable heart the idea that a stranger
may expire on your doorstep from sheer famine cannot be
tolerated. The gentleman, however, did not give in without a
struggle: he thought that when Finnian has grown sufficiently
hungry he would lift the siege and take himself off to some place
where he might get food. But he did not know Finnian. The great
abbot sat down on a spot just beyond the door, and composed
himself to all that might follow from his action. He bent his gaze
on the ground between his feet, and entered into a meditation
from which he would only be released by admission or death.

The first day passed quietly.

Often the gentleman would send a servitor to spy if that de-
serter of the gods was still before his door, and each time the
servant replied that he was still there.

"He will be gone in the morning," said the hopeful master.

On the morrow the state of siege continued, and through that day the servants were sent many times to observe through spy-holes.

"Go," he would say, "and find out if the worshipper of new gods has taken himself away."

But the servants returned each time with the same information.

"The new druid is still there," they said.

All through that day no one could leave the stronghold. And the enforced seclusion wrought on the minds of the servants, while the cessation of all work banded them together in small groups that whispered and discussed and disputed. Then these groups would disperse to peep through the spy-hole at the patient, immobile figure seated before the door, wrapped in a meditation that was timeless and unconcerned. They took fright at the spectacle, and once or twice a woman screamed hysterically, and was bundled away with a companion's hand clapped on her mouth, so that the ear of their master should not be affronted.

"He has his own troubles," they said. "It is a combat of the gods that is taking place."

So much for the women; but the men also were uneasy. They prowled up and down, tramping from the spy-hole to the kitchen, and from the kitchen to the turreted roof. And from the roof they would look down on the motionless figure below, and speculate on many things, including the staunchness of man, the qualities of their master, and even the possibility that the new gods might be as powerful as the old. From these peepings and discussions they would return languid and discouraged.

"If," said one irritable guard, "if we buzzed a spear at the persistent stranger, or if one slung at him with a jagged pebble!"

"What!" his master demanded wrathfully, "is a spear to be thrown at an unarmed stranger? And from this house!"

And he soundly cuffed that indelicate servant.

"Be at peace all of you," he said, "for hunger has a whip, and he will drive the stranger away in the night."

The household retired to wretched beds; but for the master of the house there was no sleep. He marched his halls all night, going often to the spy-hole to see if that shadow was still sitting in the shade, and pacing thence, tormented, preoccupied, refusing even the nose of his favourite dog as it pressed lovingly into his closed palm.

On the morrow he gave in.

The great door was swung wide, and two of his servants carried Finnian into the house, for the saint could no longer walk or stand upright by reason of the hunger and exposure to which he had submitted. But his frame was tough as the unconquerable spirit that dwelt within it, and in no long time he was ready for whatever might come of dispute or anathema.

Being quite re-established he undertook the conversion of the master of the house, and the siege he laid against that notable intelligence was long spoken of among those who are interested in such things.

He had beaten the disease of Mugain; he had beaten his own pupil the great Colm Cille; he beat Tuan also, and just as the latter's door had opened to the persistent stranger, so his heart opened, and Finnian marched there to do the will of God, and his own will.

Chapter III

One day they were talking together about the majesty of God and His love, for although Tuan had now received much instruction on this subject he yet needed more, and he laid as close a siege on Finnian as Finnian had before that laid on him. But man works outwardly and inwardly. After rest he has energy, after energy he needs repose; so, when we have given instruction for a time, we need instruction, and must receive it or the spirit faints and wisdom herself grows bitter.

Therefore Finnian said: "Tell me now about yourself, dear heart."

But Tuan was avid of information about the True God.

"No, no," he said, "the past has nothing more of interest for me, and I do not wish anything to come between my soul and its instruction; continue to teach me, dear friend and saintly father."

"I will do that," Finnian replied, "but I must first meditate deeply on you, and must know you well. Tell me your past, my beloved, for a man is his past, and is to be known by it."

But Tuan pleaded:

"Let the past be content with itself, for man needs forgetfulness as well as memory."

"My son," said Finnian, "all that has ever been done has been done for the glory of God, and to confess our good and evil deeds is part of instruction; for the soul must recall its acts and abide by them, or renounce them by confession and penitence. Tell me your genealogy first, and by what descent you occupy these lands and stronghold, and then I will examine your acts and your conscience."

Tuan replied obediently:

"I am known as Tuan, son of Cairill, son of Muredac Red-neck, and these are the hereditary lands of my father."

The saint nodded.

"I am not as well acquainted with Ulster genealogies as I should be, yet I know something of them. I am by blood a Leinsterman," he continued.

"Mine is a long pedigree," Tuan murmured.

Finnian received that information with respect and interest.

"I also," he said, "have an honourable record."

His host continued:

"I am indeed Tuan, the son of Starn, the son of Sera, who was brother to Partholon."

"But," said Finnian in bewilderment, "there is an error here, for you have recited two different genealogies."

"Different genealogies, indeed," replied Tuan thoughtfully, "but they are my genealogies."

"I do not understand this," Finnian declared roundly.

"I am now known as Tuan mac Cairill," the other replied, "but in the days of old I was known as Tuan mac Starn, mac Sera."

"The brother of Partholon," the saint gasped.

"That is my pedigree," Tuan said.

"But," Finnian objected in bewilderment, "Partholon came to Ireland not long after the Flood."

"I came with him," said Tuan mildly.

The saint pushed his chair back hastily, and sat staring at his host, and as he stared the blood grew chill in his veins, and his hair crept along his scalp and stood on end.

Chapter IV

But Finnian was not one who remained long in bewilderment. He thought on the might of God and he became that might, and was tranquil.

He was one who loved God and Ireland, and to the person who could instruct him in these great themes he gave all the interest of his mind and the sympathy of his heart.

"It is a wonder you tell me, my beloved," he said. "And now you must tell me more."

"What must I tell?" asked Tuan resignedly.

"Tell me of the beginning of time in Ireland, and of the bearing of Partholon, the son of Noah's son."

"I have almost forgotten him," said Tuan. "A greatly bearded, greatly shouldered man he was. A man of sweet deeds and sweet ways."

"Continue, my love," said Finnian.

"He came to Ireland in a ship. Twenty-four men and twenty-four women came with him. But before that time no man had come to Ireland, and in the western parts of the world no human being lived or moved. As we drew on Ireland from the sea the country seemed like an unending forest. Far as the eye could reach, and in whatever direction, there were trees; and from these there came the unceasing singing of birds. Over all that land the sun shone warm and beautiful, so that to our sea-weary eyes, our wind-tormented ears, it seemed as if we were driving on Paradise.

"We landed and we heard the rumble of water going gloomily through the darkness of the forest. Following the water we came to a glade where the sun shone and where the earth was warmed, and there Partholon rested with his twenty-four couples, and made a city and a livelihood.

"There were fish in the rivers of Eirè, there were animals in her coverts. Wild and shy and monstrous creatures ranged in her plains and forests. Creatures that one could see through and walk through. Long we lived in ease, and we saw new animals grow,—the bear, the wolf, the badger, the deer, and the boar.

"Partholon's people increased until from twenty-four couples there came five thousand people, who lived in amity and contentment although they had no wits."

"They had no wits!" Finnian commented.

"They had no need of wits," Tuan said.

"I have heard that the first-born were mindless," said Finnian. "Continue your story, my beloved."

"Then, sudden as a rising wind, between one night and a morning, there came a sickness that bloated the stomach and purpled the skin, and on the seventh day all of the race of Partholon were dead, save one man only."

"There always escapes one man," said Finnian thoughtfully.

"And I am that man," his companion affirmed.

Tuan shaded his brow with his hand, and he remembered backwards through incredible ages to the beginning of the world and the first days of Eirè. And Finnian, with his blood again running chill and his scalp crawling uneasily, stared backwards with him.

Chapter V

"Tell on, my love," Finnian murmured.

"I was alone," said Tuan. "I was so alone that my own shadow frightened me. I was so alone that the sound of a bird in flight, or the creaking of a dew-drenched bough, whipped me to cover as a rabbit is scared to his burrow.

"The creatures of the forest scented me and knew I was alone. They stole with silken pad behind my back and snarled when I faced them; the long, grey wolves with hanging tongues and staring eyes chased me to my cleft rock; there was no creature so weak but it might hunt me; there was no creature so timid but it might outface me. And so I lived for two tens of years and two years, until I knew all that a beast surmises and had forgotten all that a man had known.

"I could pad as gently as any; I could run as tirelessly. I could be invisible and patient as a wild cat crouching among leaves; I could smell danger in my sleep and leap at it with wakeful claws; I could bark and growl and clash with my teeth and tear with them."

"Tell on, my beloved," said Finnian, "you shall rest in God, dear heart."

"At the end of that time," said Tuan, "Nemed the son of Agnoman came to Ireland with a fleet of thirty-four barques, and in each barque there were thirty couples of people."

"I have heard it," said Finnian.

"My heart leaped for joy when I saw the great fleet rounding the land, and I followed them along scarped cliffs, leaping from rock to rock like a wild goat, while the ships tacked and swung seeking a harbour. There I stooped to drink at a pool, and I saw myself in the chill water.

"I saw that I was hairy and tufty and bristled as a savage boar; that I was lean as a stripped bush; that I was greyer than a badger; withered and wrinkled like an empty sack; naked as a fish; wretched as a starving crow in winter; and on my fingers and toes there were great curving claws, so that I looked like nothing that was known, like nothing that was animal or divine. And I sat by the pool weeping my loneliness and wildness and my stern old age; and I could do no more than cry and lament between the earth and the sky, while the beasts that tracked me listened from behind the trees, or crouched among bushes to stare at me from their drowsy covert.

"A storm arose, and when I looked again from my tall cliff I saw that great fleet rolling as in a giant's hand. At times they were pitched against the sky and staggered aloft, spinning gustily there like wind-blown leaves. Then they were hurled from these dizzy tops to the flat, moaning gulf, to the glassy, inky horror that swirled and whirled between ten waves. At times a wave leaped howling under a ship, and with a buffet dashed it into air, and chased it upwards with thunder stroke on stroke, and followed again, close as a chasing wolf, trying with hammering on hammering to beat in the wide-wombed bottom and suck out the frightened lives through one black gape. A wave fell on a ship and sunk it down with a thrust, stern as though a whole sky had tumbled at it, and the barque did not cease to go down until it crashed and sank in the sand at the bottom of the sea.

"The night came, and with it a thousand darknesses fell from the screeching sky. Not a round-eyed creature of the night might pierce an inch of that multiplied gloom. Not a creature dared creep or stand. For a great wind strode the world lashing its league-long whips in cracks of thunder, and singing to itself, now in a world-wide yell, now in an ear-dizzying hum and buzz; or with a long snarl and whine it hovered over the world searching for life to destroy.

"And at times, from the moaning and yelping blackness of the sea, there came a sound—thin-drawn as from millions of miles away, distinct as though uttered in the ear like a whisper of confidence—and I knew that a drowning man was calling on his God as he thrashed and was battered into silence, and that a blue-lipped woman was calling on her man as her hair whipped round her brows and she whirled about like a top.

"Around me the trees were dragged from earth with dying groans; they leaped into the air and flew like birds. Great waves whizzed from the sea: spinning across the cliffs and hurtling to the earth in monstrous clots of foam; the very rocks came trundling and sidling and grinding among the trees; and in that rage, and in that horror of blackness I fell asleep, or I was beaten into slumber."

Chapter VI

"There I dreamed, and I saw myself changing into a stag in dream, and I felt in dream the beating of a new heart within me, and in dream I arched my neck and braced my powerful limbs.

"I awoke from the dream, and I was that which I had dreamed.

"I stood a while stamping upon a rock, with my bristling head swung high, breathing through wide nostrils all the savour of the world. For I had come marvellously from decrepitude to strength. I had writhed from the bonds of age and was young again. I smelled the turf and knew for the first time how sweet that smelled. And like lightning my moving nose sniffed all things to my heart and separated them into knowledge.

"Long I stood there, ringing my iron hoof on stone, and learning all things through my nose. Each breeze that came from the right hand or the left brought me a tale. A wind carried me the tang of wolf, and against that smell I stared and stamped. And on a wind there came the scent of my own kind, and at that I belled. Oh, loud and clear and sweet was the voice of the great stag. With what ease my lovely note went lilting. With what joy I heard the answering call. With what delight I bounded, bounded, bounded, light as a bird's plume, powerful as a storm, untiring as the sea.

"Here now was ease in ten-yard springings, with a swinging head, with the rise and fall of a swallow, with the curve and flow and urge of an otter of the sea. What a tingle dwelt about my heart! What a thrill spun to the lofty points of my antlers! How the world was new! How the sun was new! How the wind caressed me!

"With unswerving forehead and steady eye I met all that came. The old, lone wolf leaped sideways, snarling, and slunk away. The lumbering bear swung his head of hesitations and thought again; he trotted his small red eye away with him to a near-by brake. The stags of my race fled from my rocky forehead, or were pushed back and back until their legs broke under them and I trampled them to death. I was the beloved, the well known, the leader of the herds of Ireland.

"And at times I came back from my boundings about Eirè, for the strings of my heart were drawn to Ulster; and, standing away, my wide nose took the air, while I knew with joy, with terror, that men were blown on the wind. A proud head hung to the turf then, and the tears of memory rolled from a large, bright eye.

"At times I drew near, delicately, standing among thick leaves or crouched in long grown grasses, and I stared and mourned as I looked on men. For Nemed and four couples had been saved from that fierce storm, and I saw them increase and multiply until four thousand couples lived and laughed and were riotous in the sun, for the people of Nemed had small minds but great activity. They were savage fighters and hunters.

"But one time I came, drawn by that intolerable anguish of memory, and all of these people were gone: the place that knew them was silent: in the land where they had moved there was nothing of them but their bones that glinted in the sun.

"Old age came on me there. Among these bones weariness crept into my limbs. My head grew heavy, my eyes dim, my knees jerked and trembled, and there the wolves dared chase me.

"I went again to the cave that had been my home when I was an old man.

"One day I stole from the cave to snatch a mouthful of grass, for I was closely besieged by wolves. They made their rush, and I barely escaped from them. They sat beyond the cave staring at me.

"I knew their tongue. I knew all that they said to each other, and all that they said to me. But there was yet a thud left in my forehead, a deadly trample in my hoof. They did not dare come into the cave.

"'To-morrow,' they said, 'we will tear out your throat, and gnaw on your living haunch.'"

Chapter VII

"Then my soul rose to the height of Doom, and I intended all that might happen to me, and agreed to it.

"'To-morrow,' I said, 'I will go out among ye, and I will die,' and at that the wolves howled joyfully, hungrily, impatiently.

"I slept, and I saw myself changing into a boar in dream, and I felt in dream the beating of a new heart within me, and in dream I stretched my powerful neck and braced my eager limbs. I awoke from my dream, and I was that which I had dreamed.

"The night wore away, the darkness lifted, the day came; and from without the cave the wolves called to me:

"'Come out, O Skinny Stag. Come out and die.'

"And I, with joyful heart, thrust a black bristle through the hole of the cave, and when they saw that wriggling snout, those curving tusks, that red fierce eye, the wolves fled yelping, tumbling over each other, frantic with terror; and I behind them, a wild cat for leaping, a giant for strength, a devil for ferocity; a madness and gladness of lusty, unsparing life; a killer, a champion, a boar who could not be defied.

"I took the lordship of the boars of Ireland.

"Wherever I looked among my tribes I saw love and obedience: whenever I appeared among the strangers they fled away. And the wolves feared me then, and the great, grim bear went bounding on heavy paws. I charged him at the head of my troop and rolled him over and over; but it is not easy to kill the bear, so deeply is his life packed under that stinking pelt. He picked himself up and ran, and was knocked down, and ran again blindly, butting into trees and stones. Not a claw did the big bear flash, not a tooth did he show, as he ran whimpering like a baby, or as he stood with my nose rammed against his mouth, snarling up into his nostrils.

"I challenged all that moved. All creatures but one. For men had again come to Ireland. Semion, the son of Stariath, with his people, from whom the men of Domnann and the Fir Bolg and the Galiuin are descended. These I did not chase, and when they chased me I fled.

"Often I would go, drawn by my memoried heart, to look at them as they moved among their fields; and I spoke to my mind in bitterness:

"When the people of Partholon were gathered in counsel my voice was heard; it was sweet to all who heard it, and the words I spoke were wise. The eyes of women brightened and softened when they looked at me. They loved to hear him when he sang who now wanders in the forest with a tusky herd."

CHAPTER VIII

"Old age again overtook me. Weariness stole into my limbs, and anguish dozed into my mind. I went to my Ulster cave and dreamed my dream, and I changed into a hawk.

"I left the ground. The sweet air was my kingdom, and my bright eye stared on a hundred miles. I soared, I swooped; I hung, motionless as a living stone, over the abyss; I lived in joy and slept in peace, and had my fill of the sweetness of life.

"During that time Beothach, the son of Iarbonel the Prophet, came to Ireland with his people, and there was a great battle between his men and the children of Semion. Long I hung over that combat, seeing every spear that hurtled, every stone that whizzed from a sling, every sword that flashed up and down, and the endless glittering of the shields. And at the end I saw that the victory was with Iarbonel. And from his people the Tuatha Dè and the Andè came, although their origin is forgotten, and learned people, because of their excellent wisdom and intelligence, say that they came from heaven.

"These are the people of Faery. All these are the gods.

"For long, long years I was a hawk. I knew every hill and

stream; every field and glen of Ireland. I knew the shape of cliffs and coasts, and how all places looked under the sun or moon. And I was still a hawk when the sons of Mil drove the Tuatha Dè Danann under the ground, and held Ireland against arms or wizardry; and this was the coming of men and the beginning of genealogies.

"Then I grew old, and in my Ulster cave close to the sea I dreamed my dream, and in it I became a salmon. The green tides of ocean rose over me and my dream, so that I drowned in the sea and did not die, for I awoke in deep waters, and I was that which I dreamed.

"I had been a man, a stag, a boar, a bird, and now I was a fish. In all my changes I had joy and fulness of life. But in the water joy lay deeper, life pulsed deeper. For on land or air there is always something excessive and hindering; as arms that swing at the sides of a man, and which the mind must remember. The stag has legs to be tucked away for sleep, and untucked for movement; and the bird has wings that must be folded and pecked and cared for. But the fish has but one piece from his nose to his tail. He is complete, single and unencumbered. He turns in one turn, and goes up and down and round in one sole movement.

"How I flew through the soft element: how I joyed in the country where there is no harshness: in the element which upholds and gives way; which caresses and lets go, and will not let you fall. For man may stumble in a furrow; the stag tumble from a cliff; the hawk, wing-weary and beaten, with darkness around him and the storm behind, may dash his brains against a tree. But the home of the salmon is his delight, and the sea guards all her creatures."

CHAPTER IX

"I became the king of the salmon, and, with my multitudes, I ranged on the tides of the world. Green and purple distances were under me: green and gold the sunlit regions above. In these latitudes I moved through a world of amber, myself amber and gold; in those others, in a sparkle of lucent blue, I curved, lit like a living jewel: and in these again, through dusks of ebony all mazed with silver, I shot and shone, the wonder of the sea.

"I saw the monsters of the uttermost ocean go heaving by; and the long lithe brutes that are toothed to their tails: and below, where gloom dipped down on gloom, vast, livid tangles that coiled and uncoiled, and lapsed down steeps and hells of the sea where even the salmon could not go.

"I knew the sea. I knew the secret caves where ocean roars to ocean; the floods that are icy cold, from which the nose of a salmon leaps back as at a sting; and the warm streams in which we rocked and dozed and were carried forward without motion. I swam on the outermost rim of the great world, where nothing was but the sea and the sky and the salmon; where even the wind was silent, and the water was clear as clean grey rock.

"And then, far away in the sea, I remembered Ulster, and there came on me an instant, uncontrollable anguish to be there. I turned, and through days and nights I swam tirelessly, jubilantly; with terror wakening in me, too, and a whisper through my being that I must reach Ireland or die.

"I fought my way to Ulster from the sea.

"Ah, how that end of the journey was hard! A sickness was racking in every one of my bones, a languor and weariness creeping through my every fibre and muscle. The waves held me back and held me back; the soft waters seemed to have grown hard; and it was as though I were urging through a rock as I strained towards Ulster from the sea.

"So tired I was! I could have loosened my frame and been swept away; I could have slept and been drifted and wafted away; swinging on grey-green billows that had turned from the land and were heaving and mounting and surging to the far blue water.

"Only the unconquerable heart of the salmon could brave that end of toil. The sound of the rivers of Ireland racing down to the sea came to me in the last numb effort: the love of Ireland bore me up: the gods of the rivers trod to me in the white-curled breakers, so that I left the sea at long, long last; and I lay in sweet water in the curve of a crannied rock, exhausted, three parts dead, triumphant."

CHAPTER X

"Delight and strength came to me again, and now I explored all the inland ways, the great lakes of Ireland, and her swift brown rivers.

"What a joy to lie under an inch of water basking in the sun, or beneath a shady ledge to watch the small creatures that speed like lightning on the rippling top. I saw the dragon-flies flash and dart and turn, with a poise, with a speed that no other winged thing knows: I saw the hawk hover and stare and swoop: he fell like a falling stone, but he could not catch the king of the salmon: I saw the cold-eyed cat stretching along a bough level with the water, eager to hook and lift the creatures of the river. And I saw men.

"They saw me also. They came to know me and look for me. They lay in wait at the waterfalls up which I leaped like a silver flash. They held out nets for me; they hid traps under leaves; they made cords of the colour of water, of the colour of weeds— but this salmon had a nose that knew how a weed felt and how a string—they drifted meat on a sightless string, but I knew of the hook; they thrust spears at me, and threw lances which they drew back again with a cord.

"Many a wound I got from men, many a sorrowful scar.

"Every beast pursued me in the waters and along the banks; the barking, black-skinned otter came after me in lust and gust and swirl; the wild cat fished for me; the hawk and the steep-winged, spear-beaked birds dived down on me, and men crept on me with nets the width of a river, so that I got no rest. My life became a ceaseless scurry and wound and escape, a burden and anguish of watchfulness—and then I was caught."

<h3 style="text-align:center">CHAPTER XI</h3>

"The fisherman of Cairill, the King of Ulster, took me in his net. Ah, that was a happy man when he saw me! He shouted for joy when he saw the great salmon in his net.

"I was still in the water as he hauled delicately. I was still in the water as he pulled me to the bank. My nose touched air and spun from it as from fire, and I dived with all my might against the bottom of the net, holding yet to the water, loving it, mad with terror that I must quit that loveliness. But the net held and I came up.

"'Be quiet, King of the River,' said the fisherman, 'give in to Doom,' said he.

"I was in air, and it was as though I were in fire. The air pressed on me like a fiery mountain. It beat on my scales and scorched them. It rushed down my throat and scalded me. It weighed on me and squeezed me, so that my eyes felt as though they must burst from my head, my head as though it would leap from my body, and my body as though it would swell and expand and fly in a thousand pieces.

"The light blinded me, the heat tormented me, the dry air made me shrivel and gasp; and, as he lay on the grass, the great salmon whirled his desperate nose once more to the river, and leaped, leaped, leaped, even under the mountain of air. He could leap upwards, but not forwards, and yet he leaped, for in each rise he could see the twinkling waves, the rippling and curling waters.

"'Be at ease, O King,' said the fisherman. 'Be at rest, my beloved. Let go the stream. Let the oozy marge be forgotten, and the sandy bed where the shades dance all in green and gloom, and the brown flood sings along.'

"And as he carried me to the palace he sang a song of the

river, and a song of Doom, and a song in praise of the King of the Waters.

"When the king's wife saw me she desired me. I was put over a fire and roasted, and she ate me. And when time passed she gave birth to me, and I was her son and the son of Cairill the king. I remember warmth and darkness and movement and unseen sounds. All that happened I remember, from the time I was on the gridiron until the time I was born. I forget nothing of these things."

"And now," said Finnian, "you will be born again, for I shall baptize you into the family of the Living God."

So far the story of Tuan, the son of Cairill.

No man knows if he died in those distant ages when Finnian was Abbot of Moville, or if he still keeps his fort in Ulster, watching all things, and remembering them for the glory of God and the honour of Ireland.

THE LITTLE BRAWL AT ALLEN

Chapter I

"I think," said Cairell Whiteskin, "that although judgment was given against Fionn, it was Fionn had the rights of it."

"He had eleven hundred killed," said Conán amiably, "and you may call that the rights of it if you like."

"All the same—" Cairell began argumentatively.

"And it was you that commenced it," Conán continued.

"Ho! Ho!" Cairell cried. "Why, you are as much to blame as I am."

"No," said Conán, "for you hit me first."

"And if we had not been separated—" the other growled.

"Separated!" said Conán, with a grin that made his beard poke all around his face.

"Yes, separated. If they had not come between us I still think—"

"Don't think out loud, dear heart, for you and I are at peace by law."

"That is true," said Cairell, "and a man must stick by a judgement. Come with me, my dear, and let us see how the youngsters are shaping in the school. One of them has rather a way with him as a swordsman."

"No youngster is any good with a sword," Conán replied.

"You are right there," said Cairell. "It takes a good ripe man for that weapon."

"Boys are good enough with slings," Conán continued, "but except for eating their fill and running away from a fight, you can't count on boys."

The two bulky men turned towards the school of the Fianna.

It happened that Fionn mac Uail had summoned the gentlemen of the Fianna and their wives to a banquet. Everybody came, for a banquet given by Fionn was not a thing to be missed. There was Goll mor mac Morna and his people; Fionn's son Oisín and his grandson Oscar. There was Dermod of the Gay Face, Caelte mac Ronán—but indeed there were too many to be told of, for all the pillars of war and battle-torches of the Gael were there.

The banquet began.

Fionn sat in the Chief Captain's seat in the middle of the fort; and facing him, in the place of honour, he placed the mirthful Goll mac Morna; and from these, ranging on either side, the nobles of the Fianna took each the place that fitted his degree and patrimony.

After good eating, good conversation; and after good conversation, sleep—that is the order of a banquet; so when each person had been served with food to the limit of desire the butlers carried in shining and jewelled drinking-horns, each having its tide of smooth, heady liquor. Then the young heroes grew merry and audacious, the ladies became gentle and kind, and the poets became wonders of knowledge and prophecy. Every eye beamed in that assembly, and on Fionn every eye was turned continually in the hope of a glance from the great, mild hero.

Goll spoke to him across the table enthusiastically.

"There is nothing wanting to this banquet, O Chief," said he.

And Fionn smiled back into that eye which seemed a well of tenderness and friendship.

"Nothing is wanting," he replied, "but a well-shaped poem."

A crier stood up then, holding in one hand a length of coarse iron links and in the other a chain of delicate, antique silver. He shook the iron chain so that the servants and followers of the household should be silent, and he shook the silver one so that the nobles and poets should hearken also.

Fergus, called True-Lips, the poet of the Fianna-Finn, then sang of Fionn and his ancestors and their deeds. When he had finished Fionn and Oisín and Oscar and mac Lugac of the Terrible Hand gave him rare and costly presents, so that every person wondered at their munificence, and even the poet, accustomed to the liberality of kings and princes, was astonished at his gifts.

Fergus then turned to the side of Goll mac Morna, and he sang of the Forts, the Destructions, the Raids, and the Wooings of clann-Morna; and as the poems succeeded each other, Goll grew more and more jovial and contented.

When the songs were finished Goll turned in his seat.

"Where is my runner?" he cried.

He had a woman runner, a marvel for swiftness and trust. She stepped forward.

"I am here, royal captain."

"Have you collected my tribute from Denmark?"

"It is here."

And, with help, she laid beside him the load of three men of doubly refined gold. Out of this treasure, and from the treasure of rings and bracelets and torques that were with him, Goll mac Morna paid Fergus for his songs, and, much as Fionn had given, Goll gave twice as much.

But, as the banquet proceeded, Goll gave, whether it was to harpers or prophets or jugglers, more than any one else gave, so that Fionn became displeased, and as the banquet proceeded he grew stern and silent.

Chapter II [1]

The wonderful gift-giving of Goll continued, and an uneasiness and embarrassment began to creep through the great banqueting hall.

Gentlemen looked at each other questioningly, and then spoke again on indifferent matters, but only with half of their minds. The singers, the harpers, and jugglers submitted to that constraint, so that every person felt awkward and no one knew what should be done or what would happen, and from that doubt dulness came, with silence following on its heels.

There is nothing more terrible than silence. Shame grows in that blank, or anger gathers there, and we must choose which of these is to be our master.

That choice lay before Fionn, who never knew shame.

"Goll," said he, "how long have you been taking tribute from the people of Lochlann?"

"A long time now," said Goll.

And he looked into an eye that was stern and unfriendly.

"I thought that my rent was the only one those people had to pay," Fionn continued.

"Your memory is at fault," said Goll.

"Let it be so," said Fionn. "How did your tribute arise?"

"Long ago, Fionn, in the days when your father forced war on me."

"Ah!" said Fionn.

"When he raised the High King against me and banished me from Ireland."

"Continue," said Fionn, and he held Goll's eye under the great beetle of his brow.

[1] This version of the death of Uail is not correct. Also Cnocha is not in Lochlann but in Ireland.

"I went into Britain," said Goll, "and your father followed me there. I went into White Lochlann (Norway) and took it. Your father banished me thence also."

"I know it," said Fionn.

"I went into the land of the Saxons and your father chased me out of that land. And then, in Lochlann, at the battle of Cnocha, your father and I met at last, foot to foot, eye to eye, and there, Fionn!"

"And there, Goll?"

"And there I killed your father."

Fionn sat rigid and unmoving, his face stony and terrible as the face of a monument carved on the side of a cliff.

"Tell all your tale," said he.

"At that battle I beat the Lochlannachs. I penetrated to the hold of the Danish king, and I took out of his dungeon the men who had lain there for a year and were awaiting their deaths. I liberated fifteen prisoners, and one of them was Fionn."

"It is true," said Fionn.

Goll's anger fled at the word.

"Do not be jealous of me, dear heart, for if I had twice the tribute I would give it to you and to Ireland."

But at the word jealous the Chief's anger revived.

"It is an impertinence," he cried, "to boast at this table that you killed my father."

"By my hand," Goll replied, "if Fionn were to treat me as his father did I would treat Fionn the way I treated Fionn's father."

Fionn closed his eyes and beat away the anger that was rising within him. He smiled grimly.

"If I were so minded, I would not let that last word go with you, Goll, for I have here an hundred men for every man of yours."

Goll laughed aloud.

"So had your father," he said.

Fionn's brother, Cairell Whiteskin, broke into the conversation with a harsh laugh.

"How many of Fionn's household has the wonderful Goll put down?" he cried.

But Goll's brother, bald Conán the Swearer, turned a savage eye on Cairell.

"By my weapons," said he, "there were never less than an hundred-and-one men with Goll, and the least of them could have put you down easily enough."

"Ah!" cried Cairell. "And are you one of the hundred-and-one, old scaldhead?"

"One indeed, my thick-witted, thin-livered Cairell, and I undertake to prove on your hide that what my brother said was true and that what your brother said was false."

"You undertake that," growled Cairell, and on the word he loosed a furious buffet at Conán, which Conán returned with a fist so big that every part of Cairell's face was hit with the one blow. The two then fell into grips, and went lurching and punching about the great hall. Two of Oscar's sons could not bear to see their uncle being worsted, and they leaped at Conán, and two of Goll's sons rushed at them. Then Oscar himself leaped up, and with a hammer in either hand he went battering into the *mélée*.

"I thank the gods," said Conán, "for the chance of killing yourself, Oscar."

These two encountered then, and Oscar knocked a groan of distress out of Conán. He looked appealingly at his brother Art og mac Morna, and that powerful champion flew to his aid and wounded Oscar. Oisín, Oscar's father, could not abide that; he dashed in and quelled Art Og. Then Rough Hair mac Morna wounded Oisín and was himself tumbled by mac Lugac, who was again wounded by Gara mac Morna.

The banqueting hall was in tumult. In every part of it men were giving and taking blows. Here two champions with their arms round each other's necks were stamping round and round in a slow, sad dance. Here were two crouching against each other, looking for a soft place to hit. Yonder a big-shouldered person lifted another man in his arms and threw him at a small group that charged him. In a retired corner a gentleman stood in a thoughtful attitude while he tried to pull out a tooth that had been knocked loose.

"You can't fight," he mumbled, "with a loose shoe or a loose tooth."

"Hurry up with that tooth," the man in front of him grumbled, "for I want to knock out another one."

Pressed against the wall was a bevy of ladies, some of whom were screaming and some laughing and all of whom were calling on the men to go back to their seats.

Only two people remained seated in the hall.

Goll sat twisted round watching the progress of the brawl critically, and Fionn, sitting opposite, watched Goll.

Just then Faelan, another of Fionn's sons, stormed the hall with three hundred of the Fianna, and by this force all Goll's people were put out of doors, where the fight continued.

Goll looked then calmly on Fionn.

"Your people are using their weapons," said he.

"Are they?" Fionn inquired as calmly, and as though addressing the air.

"In the matter of weapons——!" said Goll.

And the hard-fighting pillar of battle turned to where his arms hung on the wall behind him. He took his solid, well-balanced sword in his fist, over his left arm his ample, bossy shield, and, with another side-look at Fionn, he left the hall and charged irresistibly into the fray.

Fionn then arose. He took his accoutrements from the wall also and strode out. Then he raised the triumphant Fenian shout and went into the combat.

That was no place for a sick person to be. It was not the corner which a slender-fingered woman would choose to do up her hair; nor was it the spot an ancient man would select to think quietly in, for the tumult of sword on sword, of axe on shield, the roar of the contending parties, the crying of wounded men, and the screaming of frightened women destroyed peace, and over all was the rallying cry of Goll mac Morna and the great shout of Fionn.

Then Fergus True-Lips gathered about him all the poets of the Fianna, and they surrounded the combatants. They began to chant and intone long, heavy rhymes and incantations, until the rhythmic beating of their voices covered even the noise of war, so that the men stopped hacking and hewing, and let their weapons drop from their hands. These were picked up by the poets and a reconciliation was effected between the two parties.

But Fionn affirmed that he would make no peace with clann-Morna until the matter had been judged by the king, Cormac mac Art, and by his daughter Ailve, and by his son Cairbre of Ana Lifé, and by Fintan the chief poet. Goll agreed that the affair should be submitted to that court, and a day was appointed, a fortnight from that date, to meet at Tara of the Kings for judgement. Then the hall was cleansed and the banquet recommenced.

Of Fionn's people eleven hundred of men and women were dead, while of Goll's people eleven men and fifty women were dead. But it was through fright the women died, for not one of them had a wound or a bruise or a mark.

CHAPTER III

At the end of a fortnight Fionn and Goll and the chief men of the Fianna attended at Tara. The king, his son and daughter, with Flahri, Feehal, and Fintan mac Bocna sat in the place of judgement, and Cormac called on the witnesses for evidence.

Fionn stood up, but the moment he did so Goll mac Morna arose also.

"I object to Fionn giving evidence," said he.

"Why so?" the king asked.

"Because in any matter that concerned me Fionn would turn a lie into truth and the truth into a lie."

"I do not think that is so," said Fionn.

"You see, he has already commenced it," cried Goll.

"If you object to the testimony of the chief person present, in what way are we to obtain evidence?" the king demanded.

"I," said Goll, "will trust to the evidence of Fergus True-Lips. He is Fionn's poet, and will tell no lie against his master; he is a poet, and will tell no lie against any one."

"I agree to that," said Fionn.

"I require, nevertheless," Goll continued, "that Fergus should swear before the Court, by his gods, that he will do justice between us."

Fergus was accordingly sworn, and gave his evidence.

He stated that Fionn's brother Cairell struck Conán mac Morna, that Goll's two sons came to help Conán, that Oscar went to help Cairell, and with that Fionn's people and the clann-Morna rose at each other, and what had started as a brawl ended as a battle with eleven hundred of Fionn's people and sixty-one of Goll's people dead.

"I marvel," said the king in a discontented voice, "that, considering the numbers against them, the losses of clann-Morna should be so small."

Fionn blushed when he heard that.

Fergus replied:

"Goll mac Morna covered his people with his shield. All that slaughter was done by him."

"The press was too great," Fionn grumbled. "I could not get at him in time or——"

"Or what?" said Goll with a great laugh.

Fionn shook his head sternly and said no more.

"What is your judgement?" Cormac demanded of his fellow-judges.

Flahri pronounced first.

"I give damages to clann-Morna."

"Why?" said Cormac.

"Because they were attacked first."

Cormac looked at him stubbornly.

"I do not agree with your judgement," he said.

"What is there faulty in it?" Flahri asked.

"You have not considered," the king replied, "that a soldier owes obedience to his captain, and that, given the time and the place, Fionn was the captain and Goll was only a simple soldier."

Flahri considered the king's suggestion.

"That," he said, "would hold good for the white-striking or blows of fists, but not for the red-striking or sword-strokes."

"What is your judgement?" the king asked Feehal.

Feehal then pronounced:

"I hold that clann-Morna were attacked first, and that they are to be free from payment of damages."

"And as regards Fionn?" said Cormac.

"I hold that on account of his great losses Fionn is to be exempt from payment of damages, and that his losses are to be considered as damages."

"I agree in that judgement," said Fintan.

The king and his son also agreed, and the decision was imparted to the Fianna.

"One must abide by a judgement," said Fionn.

"Do you abide by it?" Goll demanded.

"I do," said Fionn.

Goll and Fionn then kissed each other, and thus peace was made. For, notwithstanding the endless bicker of these two heroes, they loved each other well.

Yet, now that the years have gone by, I think the fault lay with Goll and not with Fionn, and that the judgement given did not consider everything. For at that table Goll should not have given greater gifts than his master and host did. And it was not right of Goll to take by force the position of greatest gift-giver of the Fianna, for there was never in the world one greater at giving gifts, or giving battle, or making poems than Fionn was.

That side of the affair was not brought before the Court. But perhaps it was suppressed out of delicacy for Fionn, for if Goll could be accused of ostentation, Fionn was open to the uglier charge of jealousy. It was, nevertheless, Goll's forward and imp-ish temper which commenced the brawl, and the verdict of time must be to exonerate Fionn and to let the blame go where it is merited.

There is, however, this to be added and remembered, that whenever Fionn was in a tight corner it was Goll that plucked him out of it; and, later on, when time did his worst on them all and the Fianna were sent to hell as unbelievers, it was Goll mac Morna who assaulted hell, with a chain in his great fist and three iron balls swinging from it, and it was he who attacked the hosts of great devils and brought Fionn and the Fianna-Finn out with him.

THE CARL OF THE DRAB COAT

CHAPTER I

One day something happened to Fionn, the son of Uail; that is, he departed from the world of men, and was set wandering in great distress of mind through Faery. He had days and nights there and adventures there, and was able to bring back the memory of these.

That, by itself, is wonderful, for there are few people who remember that they have been to Faery or aught of all that happened to them in that state.

In truth we do not go to Faery, we become Faery, and in the beating of a pulse we may live for a year or a thousand years. But when we return the memory is quickly clouded, and we seem to have had a dream or seen a vision, although we have verily been in Faery.

It was wonderful, then, that Fionn should have remembered all that happened to him in that wide-spun moment, but in this tale there is yet more to marvel at; for not only did Fionn go to Faery, but the great army which he had marshalled to Ben

Edair [1] were translated also, and neither he nor they were aware that they had departed from the world until they came back to it.

Fourteen battles, seven of the reserve and seven of the regular Fianna, had been taken by the Chief on a great march and manœuvre. When they reached Ben Edair it was decided to pitch camp so that the troops might rest in view of the warlike plan which Fionn had imagined for the morrow. The camp was chosen, and each squadron and company of the host were lodged into an appropriate place, so there was no overcrowding and no halt or interruption of the march; for where a company halted that was its place of rest, and in that place it hindered no other company, and was at its own ease.

When this was accomplished the leaders of battalions gathered on a level, grassy plateau overlooking the sea, where a consultation began as to the next day's manœuvres, and during this discussion they looked often on the wide water that lay wrinkling and twinkling below them.

A roomy ship under great press of sail was bearing on Ben Edair from the east.

Now and again, in a lull of the discussion, a champion would look and remark on the hurrying vessel; and it may have been during one of these moments that the adventure happened to Fionn and the Fianna.

"I wonder where that ship comes from?" said Conán idly.

But no person could surmise anything about it beyond that it was a vessel well equipped for war.

As the ship drew by the shore the watchers observed a tall man swing from the side by means of his spear shafts, and in a little while this gentleman was announced to Fionn, and was brought into his presence.

A sturdy, bellicose, forthright personage he was indeed. He was equipped in a wonderful solidity of armour, with a hard, carven helmet on his head, a splendid red-bossed shield swinging

[1] The Hill of Howth.

on his shoulder, a wide-grooved, straight sword clashing along his thigh. On his shoulders under the shield he carried a splendid scarlet mantle; over his breast was a great brooch of burnt gold, and in his fist he gripped a pair of thick-shafted, unburnished spears.

Fionn and the champions looked on this gentleman, and they admired exceedingly his bearing and equipment.

"Of what blood are you, young gentleman?" Fionn demanded, "and from which of the four corners of the world do you come?"

"My name is Cael of the Iron," the stranger answered, "and I am son to the King of Thessaly."

"What errand has brought you here?"

"I do not go on errands," the man replied sternly, "but on the affairs that please me."

"Be it so. What is the pleasing affair which brings you to this land?"

"Since I left my own country I have not gone from a land or an island until it paid tribute to me and acknowledged my lordship."

"And you have come to this realm—" cried Fionn, doubting his ears.

"For tribute and sovereignty," growled that other, and he struck the haft of his spear violently on the ground.

"By my hand," said Conán, "we have never heard of a warrior, however great, but his peer was found in Ireland, and the funeral songs of all such have been chanted by the women of this land."

"By my hand and word," said the harsh stranger, "your talk makes me think of a small boy or of an idiot."

"Take heed, sir," said Fionn, "for the champions and great dragons of the Gael are standing by you, and around us there are fourteen battles of the Fianna of Ireland."

"If all the Fianna who have died in the last seven years were added to all that are now here," the stranger asserted, "I would treat all of these and those grievously, and would curtail their limbs and their lives."

"It is no small boast," Conán murmured, staring at him.

"It is no boast at all," said Cael, "and, to show my quality and standing, I will propose a deed to you."

"Give out your deed," Fionn commanded.

"Thus," said Cael with cold savagery. "If you can find a man among your fourteen battalions who can outrun or outwrestle or outfight me, I will take myself off to my own country, and will trouble you no more."

And so harshly did he speak, and with such a belligerent eye did he stare, that dismay began to seize on the champions, and even Fionn felt that his breath had halted.

"It is spoken like a hero," he admitted after a moment, "and if you cannot be matched on those terms it will not be from a dearth of applicants."

"In running alone," Fionn continued thoughtfully, "we have a notable champion, Caelte mac Ronán."

"This son of Ronán will not long be notable," the stranger asserted.

"He can outstrip the red deer," said Conán.

"He can outrun the wind," cried Fionn.

"He will not be asked to outrun the red deer or the wind," the stranger sneered. "He will be asked to outrun me," he thundered. "Produce this runner, and we shall discover if he keeps as great heart in his feet as he has made you think."

"He is not with us," Conán lamented.

"These notable warriors are never with us when the call is made," said the grim stranger.

"By my hand," cried Fionn, "he shall be here in no great time, for I will fetch him myself."

"Be it so," said Cael.

"And during my absence," Fionn continued, "I leave this as a compact, that you make friends with the Fianna here present, and that you observe all the conditions and ceremonies of friendship."

Cael agreed to that.

"I will not hurt any of these people until you return," he said.

Fionn then set out towards Tara of the Kings, for he thought Caelte mac Ronán would surely be there; "and if he is not there," said the champion to himself, "then I shall find him at Cesh Corran of the Fianna."

CHAPTER II

He had not gone a great distance from Ben Edair when he came to an intricate, gloomy wood, where the trees grew so thickly and the undergrowth was such a sprout and tangle that one could scarcely pass through it. He remembered that a path had once been hacked through the wood, and he sought for this. It was a deeply scooped, hollow way, and it ran or wriggled through the entire length of the wood.

Into this gloomy drain Fionn descended and made progress, but when he had penetrated deeply in the dank forest he heard a sound of thumping and squelching footsteps, and he saw coming towards him a horrible, evil-visaged being; a wild, monstrous, yellow-skinned, big-boned giant, dressed in nothing but an ill-made, mud-plastered, drab-coloured coat, which swaggled and clapped against the calves of his big bare legs. On his stamping feet there were great brogues of boots that were shaped like, but were bigger than, a boat, and each time he put a foot down it squashed and squirted a barrelful of mud from the sunk road.

Fionn had never seen the like of this vast person, and he stood gazing on him, lost in a stare of astonishment.

The great man saluted him.

"All alone, Fionn!" he cried. "How does it happen that not one Fenian of the Fianna is at the side of his captain?"

At this inquiry Fionn got back his wits.

"That is too long a story and it is too intricate and pressing to be told, also I have no time to spare now."

"Yet tell it now," the monstrous man insisted.

Fionn, thus pressed, told of the coming of Cael of the Iron, of the challenge the latter had issued, and that he, Fionn, was off to Tara of the Kings to find Caelte mac Ronán.

"I know that foreigner well," the big man commented.

"Is he the champion he makes himself out to be?" Fionn inquired.

"He can do twice as much as he said he would do," the monster replied.

"He won't outrun Caelte mac Ronán," Fionn asserted.

The big man jeered.

"Say that he won't outrun a hedgehog, dear heart. This Cael will end the course by the time your Caelte begins to think of starting."

"Then," said Fionn, "I no longer know where to turn, or how to protect the honour of Ireland."

"I know how to do these things," the other man commented with a slow nod of the head.

"If you do," Fionn pleaded, "tell it to me upon your honour."

"I will do that," the man replied.

"Do not look any further for the rusty-kneed, slow-trotting son of Ronán," he continued, "but ask me to run your race, and, by this hand, I will be first at the post."

At this the Chief began to laugh.

"My good friend, you have work enough to carry the two tons of mud that are plastered on each of your coat-tails, to say nothing of your weighty boots."

"By my hand," the man cried, "there is no person in Ireland but myself can win that race. I claim a chance."

Fionn agreed then.

"Be it so," said he. "And now, tell me your name?"

"I am known as the Carl of the Drab Coat."

"All names are names," Fionn responded, "and that also is a name."

They returned then to Ben Edair.

Chapter III

When they came among the host the men of Ireland gathered about the vast stranger; and there were some who hid their faces in their mantles so that they should not be seen to laugh, and there were some who rolled along the ground in merriment, and there were others who could only hold their mouths open and crook their knees and hang their arms and stare dumbfoundedly upon the stranger, as though they were utterly dazed.

Cael of the Iron came also on the scene, and he examined the stranger with close and particular attention.

"What in the name of the devil is this thing?" he asked of Fionn.

"Dear heart," said Fionn, "this is the champion I am putting against you in the race."

Cael of the Iron grew purple in the face, and he almost swallowed his tongue through wrath.

"Until the end of eternity," he roared, "and until the very last moment of doom I will not move one foot in a race with this greasy, big-hoofed, ill-assembled resemblance of a beggarman."

But at this the Carl burst into a roar of laughter, so that the eardrums of the warriors present almost burst inside of their heads.

"Be reassured, my darling, I am no beggarman, and my quality is not more gross than is the blood of the most delicate prince in this assembly. You will not evade your challenge in that way, my love, and you shall run with me or you shall run to your ship with me behind you. What length of course do you propose, dear heart?"

"I never run less than sixty miles," Cael replied sullenly.

"It is a small run," said the Carl, "but it will do. From this place to the Hill of the Rushes, Slieve Luachra of Munster, is exactly sixty miles. Will that suit you?"

"I don't care how it is done," Cael answered.

"Then," said the Carl, "we may go off to Slieve Luachra now, and in the morning we can start our race there to here."

"Let it be done that way," said Cael.

These two set out then for Munster, and as the sun was setting they reached Slieve Luachra and prepared to spend the night there.

CHAPTER IV

"Cael, my pulse," said the Carl, "we had better build a house or a hut to pass the night in."

"I'll build nothing," Cael replied, looking on the Carl with great disfavour.

"No!"

"I won't build house or hut for the sake of passing one night here, for I hope never to see this place again."

"I'll build a house myself," said the Carl, "and the man who does not help in the building can stay outside of the house."

The Carl stumped to a near-by wood, and he never rested until he had felled and tied together twenty-four couples of big timber. He thrust these under one arm and under the other he tucked a bundle of rushes for his bed, and with that one load he rushed up a house, well thatched and snug, and with the timber that remained over he made a bonfire on the floor of the house.

His companion sat at a distance regarding the work with rage and aversion.

"Now Cael, my darling," said the Carl, "if you are a man help me to look for something to eat, for there is game here."

"Help yourself," roared Cael, "for all that I want is not to be near you."

"The tooth that does not help gets no helping," the other replied.

In a short time the Carl returned with a wild boar which he had run down. He cooked the beast over his bonfire and ate one half of it, leaving the other half for his breakfast. Then he lay down on the rushes, and in two turns he fell asleep.

But Cael lay out on the side of the hill, and if he went to sleep that night he slept fasting.

It was he, however, who awakened the Carl in the morning.

"Get up, beggarman, if you are going to run against me."

The Carl rubbed his eyes.

"I never get up until I have had my fill of sleep, and there is another hour of it due to me. But if you are in a hurry, my delight, you can start running now with a blessing. I will trot on your track when I waken up."

Cael began to race then, and he was glad of the start, for his antagonist made so little account of him that he did not know what to expect when the Carl would begin to run.

"Yet," said Cael to himself, "with an hour's start the beggarman will have to move his bones if he wants to catch on me," and he settled down to a good, pelting race.

Chapter V

At the end of an hour the Carl awoke. He ate the second half of the boar, and he tied the unpicked bones in the tail of his coat. Then with a great rattling of the boar's bones he started.

It is hard to tell how he ran or at what speed he ran, but he went forward in great two-legged jumps, and at times he moved in immense one-legged, mud-spattering hops, and at times again, with wide-stretched, far-flung, terrible-tramping, space-destroying legs he ran.

He left the swallows behind as if they were asleep. He caught up on a red deer, jumped over it, and left it standing. The wind was always behind him, for he outran it every time; and he caught up in jumps and bounces on Cael of the Iron, although Cael was running well, with his fists up and his head back and his two legs flying in and out so vigorously that you could not see them because of that speedy movement.

Trotting by the side of Cael, the Carl thrust a hand into the tail of his coat and pulled out a fistful of red bones.

"Here, my heart, is a meaty bone," said he, "for you fasted all night, poor friend, and if you pick a bit off the bone your stomach will get a rest."

"Keep your filth, beggarman," the other replied, "for I would rather be hanged than gnaw on a bone that you have browsed."

"Why don't you run, my pulse?" said the Carl earnestly; "why don't you try to win the race?"

Cael then began to move his limbs as if they were the wings of a fly, or the fins of a little fish, or as if they were the six legs of a terrified spider.

"I am running," he gasped.

"But try and run like this," the Carl admonished, and he gave a wriggling bound and a sudden outstretching and scurrying of shanks, and he disappeared from Cael's sight in one wild spatter of big boots.

Despair fell on Cael of the Iron, but he had a great heart.

"I will run until I burst," he shrieked, "and when I burst, may I burst to a great distance, and may I trip that beggarman up with my burstings and make him break his leg."

He settled then to a determined, savage, implacable trot.

He caught up on the Carl at last, for the latter had stopped to eat blackberries from the bushes on the road, and when he drew nigh, Cael began to jeer and sneer angrily at the Carl.

"Who lost the tails of his coat?" he roared.

"Don't ask riddles of a man that's eating blackberries," the Carl rebuked him.

"The dog without a tail and the coat without a tail," cried Cael.

"I give it up," the Carl mumbled.

"It's yourself, beggarman," jeered Cael.

"I am myself," the Carl gurgled through a mouthful of blackberries, "and as I am myself, how can it be myself? That is a silly riddle," he burbled.

"Look at your coat, tub of grease!"

The Carl did so.

"My faith," said he, "where are the two tails of my coat?"

"I could smell one of them and it wrapped around a little tree thirty miles back," said Cael, "and the other one was dishonouring a bush ten miles behind that."

"It is bad luck to be separated from the tails of your own coat," the Carl grumbled. "I'll have to go back for them. Wait here, beloved, and eat blackberries until I come back, and we'll both start fair."

"Not half a second will I wait," Cael replied, and he began to run towards Ben Edair as a lover runs to his maiden or as a bee flies to his hive.

"I haven't had half my share of blackberries either," the Carl lamented as he started to run backwards for his coat-tails.

He ran determinedly on that backward journey, and as the path he had travelled was beaten out as if it had been trampled by an hundred bulls yoked neck to neck, he was able to find the two bushes and the two coat-tails. He sewed them on his coat.

Then he sprang up, and he took to a fit and a vortex and an exasperation of running for which no description may be found. The thumping of his big boots grew as continuous as the pattering of hailstones on a roof, and the wind of his passage blew trees down. The beasts that were ranging beside his path dropped dead from concussion, and the steam that snored from his nose blew birds into bits and made great lumps of cloud fall out of the sky.

He again caught up on Cael, who was running with his head down and his toes up.

"If you won't try to run, my treasure," said the Carl, "you will never get your tribute."

And with that he incensed and exploded himself into an eye-blinding, continuous, waggle and complexity of boots that left Cael behind him in a flash.

"I will run until I burst," sobbed Cael, and he screwed agitation and despair into his legs until he hummed and buzzed like a blue-bottle on a window.

Five miles from Ben Edair the Carl stopped, for he had again come among blackberries.

He ate of these until he was no more than a sack of juice, and when he heard the humming and buzzing of Cael of the Iron he mourned and lamented that he could not wait to eat his fill. He took off his coat, stuffed it full of blackberries, swung it on his shoulders, and went bounding stoutly and nimbly for Ben Edair.

CHAPTER VI

It would be hard to tell of the terror that was in Fionn's breast and in the hearts of the Fianna while they attended the conclusion of that race.

They discussed it unendingly, and at some moment of the day a man upbraided Fionn because he had not found Caelte the son of Ronán as had been agreed on.

"There is no one can run like Caelte," one man averred.

"He covers the ground," said another.

"He is light as a feather."

"Swift as a stag."

"Lunged like a bull."

"Legged like a wolf."

"He runs!"

These things were said to Fionn, and Fionn said these things to himself.

With every passing minute a drop of lead thumped down into every heart, and a pang of despair stabbed up to every brain.

"Go," said Fionn to a hawk-eyed man, "go to the top of this hill and watch for the coming of the racers." And he sent lithe men with him so that they might run back in endless succession with the news.

The messengers began to run through his tent at minute intervals calling "nothing," "nothing," "nothing," as they paused and darted away.

And the words, "nothing, nothing, nothing," began to drowse into the brains of every person present.

"What can we hope from that Carl?" a champion demanded savagely.

"Nothing," cried a messenger who stood and sped.

"A clump!" cried a champion.

"A hog!" said another.

"A flat-footed,"

"Little-winded,"

"Big-bellied,"

"Lazy-boned,"

"Pork!"

"Did you think, Fionn, that a whale could swim on land, or what did you imagine that lump could do?"

"Nothing," cried a messenger, and was sped as he spoke.

Rage began to gnaw in Fionn's soul, and a red haze danced and flickered before his eyes. His hands began to twitch and a desire crept over him to seize on champions by the neck, and to shake and worry and rage among them like a wild dog raging among sheep.

He looked on one, and yet he seemed to look on all at once.

"Be silent," he growled. "Let each man be silent as a dead man."

And he sat forward, seeing all, seeing none, with his mouth drooping open, and such a wildness and bristle lowering from that great glum brow that the champions shivered as though already in the chill of death, and were silent.

He rose and stalked to the tent-door.

"Where to, O Fionn?" said a champion humbly.

"To the hill-top," said Fionn, and he stalked on.

They followed him, whispering among themselves, and keeping their eyes on the ground as they climbed.

Chapter VII

"What do you see?" Fionn demanded of the watcher.

"Nothing," that man replied.

"Look again," said Fionn.

The eagle-eyed man lifted a face, thin and sharp as though it had been carven on the wind, and he stared forward with an immobile intentness.

"What do you see?" said Fionn.

"Nothing," the man replied.

"I will look myself," said Fionn, and his great brow bent forward and gloomed afar.

The watcher stood beside, staring with his tense face and unwinking, lidless eye.

"What can you see, O Fionn?" said the watcher.

"I can see nothing," said Fionn, and he projected again his grim, gaunt forehead. For it seemed as if the watcher stared with his whole face, aye, and with his hands; but Fionn brooded weightedly on distance with his puckered and crannied brow.

They looked again.

"What can you see?" said Fionn.

"I see nothing," said the watcher.

"I do not know if I see or if I surmise, but something moves," said Fionn. "There is a trample," he said.

The watcher became then an eye, a rigidity, an intense out-thrusting and ransacking of thin-spun distance. At last he spoke.

"There is a dust," he said.

And at that the champions gazed also, straining hungrily afar, until their eyes became filled with a blue darkness and they could no longer see even the things that were close to them.

"I," cried Conán triumphantly, "I see a dust."

"And I," cried another.

"And I."

"I see a man," said the eagle-eyed watcher.

And again they stared, until their straining eyes grew dim with tears and winks, and they saw trees that stood up and sat down, and fields that wobbled and spun round and round in a giddy swirling world.

"There *is* a man," Conán roared.

"A man there is," cried another.

"And he is carrying a man on his back," said the watcher. "It is Cael of the Iron carrying the Carl on his back," he groaned.

"The great pork!" a man gritted.

"The no-good!" sobbed another.

"The lean-hearted,"

"Thick-thighed,"

"Ramshackle,"

"Muddle-headed,"

"Hog!" screamed a champion.

And he beat his fists angrily against a tree.

But the eagle-eyed watcher watched until his eyes narrowed and became pin-points, and he ceased to be a man and became an optic.

"Wait," he breathed, "wait until I screw into one other inch of sight."

And they waited, looking no longer on that scarcely perceptible speck in the distance, but straining upon the eye of the watcher as though they would penetrate it and look through it.

"It is the Carl," he said, "carrying something on his back, and behind him again there is a dust."

"Are you sure?" said Fionn in a voice that rumbled and vibrated like thunder.

"It is the Carl," said the watcher, "and the dust behind him is Cael of the Iron trying to catch him up."

Then the Fianna gave a roar of exultation, and each man seized his neighbour and kissed him on both cheeks; and they gripped hands about Fionn, and they danced round and round in a great circle, roaring with laughter and relief, in the ecstasy which only comes where grisly fear has been and whence that bony jowl has taken itself away.

CHAPTER VIII

The Carl of the Drab Coat came bumping and stumping and clumping into the camp, and was surrounded by a multitude that adored him and hailed him with tears.

"Meal!" he bawled, "meal for the love of the stars!"

And he bawled, "Meal, meal!" until he bawled everybody into silence.

Fionn addressed him.

"What for the meal, dear heart?"

"For the inside of my mouth," said the Carl, "for the recesses and crannies and deep-down profundities of my stomach. Meal, meal!" he lamented.

Meal was brought.

The Carl put his coat on the ground, opened it carefully and revealed a store of blackberries, squashed, crushed, mangled, democratic, ill-looking.

"The meal!" he groaned, "the meal!"

It was given to him.

"What of the race, my pulse?" said Fionn.

"Wait, wait," cried the Carl. "I die, I die for meal and black-berries."

Into the centre of the mess of blackberries he discharged a barrel of meal, and he mixed the two up and through, and round and down, until the pile of white-black, red-brown slibber-slobber reached up to his shoulders. Then he commenced to paw and impel and project and cram the mixture into his mouth, and between each mouthful he sighed a contented sigh, and during every mouthful he gurgled an oozy gurgle.

But while Fionn and the Fianna stared like lost minds upon the Carl, there came a sound of buzzing, as if a hornet or a queen of the wasps or a savage, steep-winged griffin was hovering about them, and looking away they saw Cael of the Iron charging on them with a monstrous extension and scurry of his legs. He had a sword in his hand, and there was nothing in his face but red-ness and ferocity.

Fear fell like night around the Fianna, and they stood with slack knees and hanging hands waiting for death. But the Carl lifted a pawful of his oozy slop and discharged this at Cael with such a smash that the man's head spun off his shoulders and hopped along the ground. The Carl then picked up the head and threw it at the body with such aim and force that the neck part of the head jammed into the neck part of the body and stuck there, as good a head as ever, you would have said, but that it had got twisted the wrong way round. The Carl then lashed his opponent hand and foot.

"Now, dear heart, do you still claim tribute and lordship of Ireland?" said he.

"Let me go home," groaned Cael, "I want to go home."

"Swear by the sun and moon, if I let you go home, that you will send to Fionn, yearly and every year, the rent of the land of Thessaly."

"I swear that," said Cael, "and I would swear anything to get home."

The Carl lifted him then and put him sitting into his ship. Then he raised his big boot and gave the boat a kick that drove it seven leagues out into the sea, and that was how the adventure of Cael of the Iron finished.

"Who are you, sir?" said Fionn to the Carl.

But before answering the Carl's shape changed into one of splendour and delight.

"I am ruler of the Shí of Rath Cruachan," he said.

Then Fionn mac Uail made a feast and a banquet for the jovial god, and with that the tale is ended of the King of Thessaly's son and the Carl of the Drab Coat.

❦ ❦
❦

from Deirdre

Deirdre, the "Troubler," her lover Naoise (pronounced Neesh-eh)
and his younger brothers Ainnle and Ardan have returned to
Ireland after seven years' exile in Scotland. Deirdre's prophetic
fears are confirmed. Instead of being received into the palace of
Conachúr, Emperor of Ulster, whose bride Deirdre was to have
been and whose pretence at forgiveness has lured them back,
they are lodged "for the night" at the fortress of the Red Branch.
With them are Buinne and Iollann, the sons of their protector
Fergus mac Roy, detained from accompanying them himself by
an unwelcome feast of sharks. The late-arriving Conall Cearnach
is Naoise's cousin, also a grandson of the old magician Cathfa,
Conachúr's father.

BOOK II

Chapter XII

"What do you hear, Ardan?"
"Big feet, and a big lot of them."
"The doors are well secured?"
"Every bolt is drawn."
"And the door we arranged for is left with only one bolt shot?"

255

"Yes. It is a quick, well-oiled bolt. It will open and close again like lightning."

There came a loud command, and, in a moment, a thundering knock.

Naoise strode to the door.

"Who goes there?"

"The king's men."

"What do you want?"

"We want the woman who is with you."

"Is that all you want?"

"And we want Naoise, the son of Uisneac."

"They are both here," said Naoise.

"Open this door," the voice commanded.

"Ah, no," Naoise laughed, "why should we do your business, honest man?"

There was no reply for a moment, but the rumble of conversation could be heard, then the voice came again.

"You others, Ainnle and Ardan and the sons of Fergus, open this door and you shall go free."

Naoise looked gravely at his companions.

"That is the necessary second part," said Buinne, hitching his sword-belt round.

Naoise's brothers took no notice, but their faces grew savage and their eyes narrowed and sparkled.

"Iollann and Deirdre, keep an eye on the windows," Naoise warned.

Iollann dangled a sling in his hand and Deirdre held another with a copper bolt in it.

"If," said the voice, "the woman Deirdre comes out we will go away."

"Watch the windows," Naoise warned; "they are talking to keep us occupied."

Deirdre's arm swung viciously, and a wild yell told that the bolt had gone home.

"I thought so," said Naoise. "They cannot get in through the windows because of the bars, but they could manage to fly an arrow through, although it would be an awkward shot."

"Why," said Ainnle, "we could go to sleep here!"

A series of thundering knocks came on the door.

"A ram!" said Buinne.

"Half-an-hour of that might bring even these doors down," said Naoise.

He turned to his companions.

"Ardan, yours will be the first sortie. They will not be prepared, lad, for it is very awkward to work a ram and to keep guard at the same time. Do not mind the men with the ram; they will be unarmed. But behind them there will be a mass of men. You know how deep a fighter can penetrate! It depends on his own weight. The instant you touch that weight fight backwards. When you are two yards from the door Ainnle will shout. Turn then and run. I shall have the door closed on you almost before you are through. The moment the door slams, you, Buinne, push in the bottom bolt. I shall slide the middle one with my right hand and will be reaching for the top one with my left. You are ready! Ardan, listen to me. The men immediately in front of you will give back a step until they start to come on. Fight, therefore, to the right, sidewards, and with the point all the time. Keep your left covered with the shield, and if there is a press cut with its cutting edges. The moon is high and you will be able to see. No foolhardiness, boy! The moment you touch weight fight backwards, and then sweep broadly with the edge, and, when Ainnle shouts, run."

He turned again.

"Buinne, stand to the bolts. Iollann, Ainnle, Deirdre, place yourselves so, and sling the ramsmen or they may cumber his retreat."

Under the thundering batter of the ram and the savage roaring of the invaders the bolts were half drawn.

"Ready all!" said Naoise. "Ready, Ardan?"

Ardan hunched the shield to his left side and crouched, staring.

"Good boy!" said Naoise. "Now, Buinne—Pull!"

They heaved the great door wide and Ardan went through it like an arrow.

"Sling, children," said Naoise. "Keep me informed, Ainnle. I must stick behind the door."

"He is at them, and well in. . . . Ah!" said Ainnle, and he slung shrewdly. "He has forgotten to thrust and is cutting. My thanks, Iollann, for that bolt. His shield work is excellent, brother, but he will out. There is his limit, if he knows it. He is fighting back, and now he is thrusting where he should use the sweeping blade for a retreat! That ramsman, Iollann! This one for me, and you sister, for the crouching man. I shall shout now."

"Ardan!" he roared.

The boy dropped his combat as a dog drops a toad. In three seconds he was through the doorway, and in four the door had slammed.

Naoise towered long and lean over his young brother.

"Good lad!" he said. "Well done, Ardan!"

"I killed a million," said Ardan.

A savage, raging yell came from without.

"They will begin to warm to it now," said Naoise, "and we must keep them occupied. It is your turn, Ainnle. Give your sling to Ardan."

Ainnle whizzed at one window and Deirdre at another. Two loud shouts were heard.

"Whether they are hit or not their skulls are cracked by the fall," said Naoise, "but the windows do not matter. Come to this door."

"Why cannot I go out?" said Buinne.

"You and I are the heaviest metal, my heart, and when the real fighting commences we shall have plenty to do. This is only a little fun for the boys. Ainnle, listen carefully. You will slip out by this door, and will run, and fight as you run. Range where you please, but run always. In five minutes—do not delay,

Ainnle—make for yonder door. This one will be shut, and the slingsmen will be inside that door to cover your retreat. Is it understood?"

Ainnle nodded, and made his blade whistle through the air. He heaved the shield from his back to his shoulder.

"The instant you are in, Ainnle, fly to this door again, while we close the other behind you. Open all the bolts but one; Buinne will help, and I and Iollann will dart out for five minutes. I wish to see what arrangements they are making."

"Are you protecting my brother?" said Buinne savagely.

"No, my heart, I am giving him a run and spying their dispositions."

"I claim this combat," said the rough young man.

"You shall have one immediately afterwards. You and I together will make the tour of this fortress, shoulder to shoulder, Buinne. Will not that content you?" Naoise laughed.

"I was beginning to feel lonely," said Buinne. "We shall have a pleasant run."

"Ten minutes for our run," said Naoise. "Ready, Ainnle?"

His brother nodded.

"Run straight out, thirty feet out if you can. Double then as you please. Remember the door you are to come in by, and do all the damage you can. If you are in difficulty give our call."

"I could not get into difficulty in five minutes," Ainnle smiled.

"Ready, Buinne? Pull!"

Ainnle sped out, and the door slammed on him like thunder.

The uproar without had been terrific, but now it redoubled, and at times a long scream topped the noise as spray tops a wave.

"We cannot see our brother," said Deirdre nervously.

"We know his work," Naoise replied. "He is as safe for five minutes as if he were in bed."

"Your combat, Naoise!" she breathed.

"It will be the easiest of them all. There will be a rough companion with me. Run all to the other door," he cried. "Iollann!

Deirdre! Ardan! Your slings! The bolts, Buinne! Pull, my soul!"

Far out in the moonlight Ainnle was coursing like a deer. The moon flashed on his blade and on his shield. Men ran from him, and men ran to head him off, and into the middle of these he went diving like a fish. A band from the right came rushing for the open door.

"Out, Buinne, for ten seconds, and back when he is through."

Naoise and Buinne leaped out with whirling weapons. There was a clatter of shields, a medley of shouts and curses, and in ten seconds they were in again and the door was closed.

"You opened a minute too early," said Ainnle. "I was all right."

"You did some damage?"

"Not badly."

"You didn't kill as many as I did," said Ardan.

"Pooh!" Ainnle retorted. "No one could kill as many as you except Cúchulinn."

"Let us arrange the next sortie," said Naoise.

Chapter XIII

Conachúr had come to the Red Branch, and a great roar of cheering greeted him. He strode to the captain of his troop.

"Well, my soul?"

"We have begun, majesty."

"How is it going?"

"Excellently," said the captain. "We have lost about forty men already."

Conachúr stared at him.

"How did that happen?"

"It happened because of the king's royal decision to lodge these men in a fortress."

"You have five hundred men here!"

"When they are all killed," said the captain sourly, "we can call out another five hundred."

"What is the difficulty?" his master growled.

"A fortress with six doors. They leap in and out of these doors the way frogs leap in a pool. While we are using the ram on this door they make a sally by another door, this door, any door— and they are the devil's own fighters! We don't know where to expect them, and any one of those within is the equal of ten of our men in fighting, and the superior of them all in tricks. I am to have them out before morning—it is the king's orders, but I don't know how it is to be done."

"Ram all the doors," said Conachúr.

"I have but one ram. I can get others to-morrow."

"To-morrow will be too late," said the king furiously. "We shall have half Ulster on our backs to-morrow."

"I want scaling ladders, grapnels," said the officer angrily. "This work has been thrown on us at a moment's notice and we are not prepared for it. I can get them out in a day, but not in a night."

"Attack a door with your ram," snarled Conachúr, "and guard your other doors."

"I am doing that," said the captain, "and my men, I fear, are beginning to love the work."

He returned to his place, and in a few minutes the thud and batter of the ram was heard again. Conachúr strode there and watched the work with savage impatience. The captain returned and stood by him.

"You put good doors in the Red Branch, majesty," he said cheerfully, "an hour of that ramming will begin to make them quiver."

A shout arose, but it was multiplied from every side by the roaring soldiery, and one could not tell from which direction danger came.

"They have popped out somewhere," said the captain. "In bout two minutes they will pop in again, somewhere—they know but we don't, and in those two minutes we will lose five men or twenty."

"Stick to the ram," Conachúr roared. "Keep at that door, my men."

A wild yelling came from the side and a burst of men came pell-mell round the corner. Weapons were striking everywhere and anywhere.

"Which are our men and which are theirs?" said the captain. "Ours don't know in this light which is friend and which is enemy. *They* know," he said bitterly, "but we are killing each other."

Two figures detached themselves in the moonlight. They were bounding like great cats, and wherever there was a mass they bounded into it, burst through it, and leaped on.

"Ho, Conachúr!" a voice called, "do you remember Naoise?"

"Ho, traitor king!" another boomed. "Do you remember Fergus?"

"It is Naoise and Buinne this time," said the captain.

The two figures leaped at the ramsmen. The ram was dropped, and the unarmed crew fled yelling. The door that was being battered opened and shut, and the two figures were gone.

"That's how it's done!" said the captain.

"Get to the ram!" Conachúr roared.

Chapter XIV

"The king himself is there," said Naoise.

"Let us hunt him," cried Ardan in savage glee.

"He will move about," Naoise replied. "We would never know where he is, and we should only waste time. We have but to hold out until the morning, and we can do it with ease. Why!" he cried, "we have forgotten our days of travel; Fergus himself may be here to-morrow."

"He will travel day and night, and by chariot where we came on foot," said Iollann. "He may be here in the morning."

Naoise nodded joyfully.

"He will have choked whatever is in it out of Borach's throat long before this," Iollann continued, "and he will be an angry man." ·

"If he came, even alone," said Naoise, "that rabble would fly."

"They will fly before he comes," Ardan boasted, "for it's my turn to go out now, and I shall show them a trick or two."

"It's two by two now, babe," said Ainnle, "so we are going out together."

"That man," Ardan mourned, "is trying to cheat me of my fame. Fight for me, Deirdreen! Back me up, Naoise!"

"Hark to them battering," said Iollann.

"How angry some people get," Ardan giggled.

"Let us make a full sortie," Buinne cried. "We five could eat those soldiers."

"One must be left for the door," Naoise replied. "Ardan—"

"No door for me!" said Ardan violently.

"Ainnle," said Naoise, "our lives will depend on the doorman."

"I shall go out the next time all by myself," Ainnle bargained.

His brother nodded, while Ardan danced for joy.

"Pooh!" Ainnle gibed. "He thinks he is Cúchulinn!"

Ardan squared up and began to shoulder him and to speak very roughly.

"And I am better than Cúchulinn," he concluded.

Ainnle seized his head and gave him three kisses.

"Little brother!" he said, "you are even better than I."

"You are a good brother," said Ardan. "I shall not divorce you," and he returned the three kisses.

"Are we ready all?" said Naoise. "Then let us arrange this sally."

"It shall be in two parties. Buinne and—" he halted for one moment, "Buinne and Ardan, Iollann and myself."

"You trust Ardan to me!" said Buinne shortly.

"Why not?" said Naoise.

Deirdre was staring at her husband with a fixed, white stare, and Naoise's throat went suddenly dry. He strode to her.

"What is it?" he murmured.

"I have no vision," she whispered. "I do not know."

"You still think—?"

"I know it," she said, "but I do not know when."

He closed his eyes and turned again.

"We go through this door. Once out, you turn to the left, Buinne, and I to the right and away each on a grand half circle. When we meet we form in line and charge back to this same door; six feet between each man for sword-play; Buinne and I on the outside."

"I shall be quite on the outside," said Buinne.

"As you will, friend," said Naoise. "Get to the bolts, Ainnle. You two will watch over each other?" he said, but it was at Buinne he looked.

"I shall bring him back," said the gruff man.

"If one of Buinne's hairs is touched," Ardan boasted, "I shall give him one of my own hairs instead of it."

"You are ready, Ainnle?"

"How shall I know when to open the door?" Ainnle roared.

"My wits are going!" said Naoise. "We shall fight in silence, and when you hear our battle-cry open the door at that instant."

"Wait!" said Buinne. "Heavier blades are wanted for this sortie. It should be two-handed work at the edge of a thirty-foot line, and the shields must be left behind."

"My wits are indeed going!" said Naoise.

"I shall bring him back," said Buinne. "I take him under my protection," he growled.

"You two," said Naoise, "keep your shields. Buinne and I take the great swords, and we leave our armour off for speed. The outside men must run twice as quick as the inside ones," he explained to Buinne.

Buinne nodded and began to unlace his battle-coats. Deirdre flew to help him, and she looked at him with such soft affection that the youth marvelled. Naoise was bending the great blade that he got from Manannan mac Lir, the God of the Sea.

"Now, Ainnle, the door! Buinne is out first, I second, Iollann and Ardan together. Ready! . . . Pull!"

They were gone.

Ainnle and Deirdre slammed the door, and he stood with his back leaning against it, staring as it were inwardly, and listening with every pore of his body. Deirdre threw her arms about his neck.

"Oh Ainnle! dear Ainnle!"

"It is lonely here," he muttered.

Her head dropped on his breast.

"Do not faint, sister, the door has yet to be opened, and you must help with the bolts."

"Hear those clowns roaring!"

"If our own men would but shout once," she moaned.

"I should open the door immediately," he smiled, "and this noble combat would have a stupid end."

"To-morrow will never come," she moaned.

"Do not make my teeth chatter," said Ainnle.

"We must attend to the door," he continued. "I shall draw the top bolt now. Crouch down with your hands on the bottom one, and, when the shout comes, draw it; I will draw the middle one, and when I say, 'Pull,' drag with me on the door. It is almost too heavy for one man to move, but between us—and they will push from the outside."

Deirdre crouched at his knees. A vast confusion of noise began to draw nigh.

"They are coming back," said Ainnle. "Draw your bolt now, sister, and take hold of the knob."

Above the infernal uproar there came the shout they knew.

"Pull!" he roared.

The door gave, a great push from without helped it, and the four leaped through. A blade leaped in behind them and was snapped in pieces as Ainnle, and a shoulder helping, smashed to the door.

Buinne was panting heavily.

"That deserves a rest," he said.

And the other three began with one voice to narrate the sortie to the two who had been within.

Chapter XV

Buinne stood up.

"Naoise," he said sternly.

"My soul?" said Naoise.

"You interfered in my combat."

"Your end of the line was almost too heavy for any man, dear heart."

"You did it twice."

"Thirty feet out is a great distance. All the press was in your path. I did but lighten it when my own front was easy."

"I will accept no man's assistance," said Buinne.

"We are comrades," Naoise replied gently. "We give and take help."

"Did I call for help?" the other growled.

Naoise's great chest rose, but his voice was calm.

"No man will ever hear you call for help, Buinne."

"Let no man give what is not called for."

"But for that help, Buinne, you would now be dead."

"I was not fit for the end of the line?" said Buinne harshly.

"You are young yet, comrade, but in two years you will have the speed and smash that such a post calls for."

"Your speed! your smash!" said the sardonic Buinne.

"The world knows," Ainnle interposed, "that the four greatest champions of Ireland are Cúchulinn, Fergus, Conall, and Naoise."

"And Ainnle," Buinne completed with a grin.

The young man turned his dancing length of whipcord and his narrowed brow on Buinne.

"I, myself—" he said gently.

"And so could I," said Ardan.

"Do not quarrel," Naoise interrupted. "In two years Buinne will be the equal of any man you have named. Hush," he said.

He bent his head sideward and hearkened in amazement. The others listened, with their eyes turned questioningly on each other. They listened to nothing, for the ram had ceased and there was a silence of the dead without.

In a few moments there came a gentle tapping, then a louder knocking at the door.

Naoise stood before it, frowning.

"Who goes there?"

"The herald."

"What do you want?"

"Parley."

"Say what you have to say, herald."

"If the woman Deirdre is put out through this door the troops will march away."

"And what then?"

"No vengeance will be for ever exacted against the sons of Uisneac."

"There is no answer," said Naoise.

"I have yet a message," said the voice.

"Deliver it."

"It is for the ear of the sons of Fergus."

Buinne strode forward.

"Deliver it," he said.

"There is no quarrel," said the herald, "between the king and Fergus mac Roy. The king's love for Fergus is such that he wishes at any cost to save his two sons from a death that is certain."

"Well?" said Buinne.

"The king says that if these young men retire from the combat he will bestow a lordship on them."

"What lordship?"

"A cantred of land greater than that which Fergus himself has, and the king's friendship."

Buinne looked under steep red brows at Naoise.

"I shall go out," he said.

He turned to his brother.

"You will come out with me."

"I shall not," said Iollann.

His brother stamped a foot.

"My father is my chief," said Iollann. "What he orders I do. I cannot protect the sons of Uisneac as he commanded, but I can fight beside them."

Buinne turned.

"Herald," he roared, "tell Conachúr that I shall go out to him."

His hand went to the door, but Naoise stepped forward.

"Do not touch a bolt," he commanded. "You shall go out by the door I choose. That door," he pointed, and strode to it. "Iollann, Ainnle, stand so with the spears, Ardan, Deirdre, sling from this point. Buinne stand so, one foot beyond the swing of the door."

"We may meet again, Naoise," said Buinne.

"If we meet in the press, Buinne, I may perhaps spare you for the sake of my brother Iollann. Ready, Buinne! When the door is opened I shall count three. Be gone ere the last count or I shall smash you to a pulp."

Naoise gave one mighty heave, and counted. Then Buinne was gone and the door had closed again.

"I claim this sortie," said Iollann, as the ram recommenced on the door.

"It is my turn," said Ainnle, "but we will go together, my friend."

"I wish to go alone, and bring honour back to the name of Fergus. I am a better fighter than you think," he insisted.

"You are a good fighter in truth," said Naoise, "but a solitary venture is now dangerous. They are more accustomed to the light and to our methods, for there is nothing to vary in them. We must emerge by a door, and they are watching every door like hawks. But before you go, Iollann, there is one work we must do for safety's sake. Listen carefully, my dear ones."

Chapter XVI

"This is endless," Conachúr gritted. "Has that Buinne come out yet?"

"The men will shout when he appears."

"Bring him here and we will get their dispositions from him."

"There is nothing to get, majesty. Their plan is the simplest. They have six doors: they choose one to come out by and one to get in by. That is the whole plan."

"Post men in such a way that when one does come out he will not be able to get in again through that door or any other door. Send for reinforcements and put fifty men against each door. . . . Those ramsmen have women's shoulders," he growled. "They would beat a mud wall down in a month."

"It must give shortly," said the captain, "but there will be no entrance when the door is down."

"No?" said Conachúr.

"They will have the inside barricaded, and our men will not dare that narrow, black, impeded passage. We could leave an hundred dead in that doorway and be no farther."

"There is Buinne," the captain continued, as a shout came from the side.

"Buinne," said Conachúr, "you will fight for me?"

"My lordship, Conachúr?" said the gruff young man.

"It shall be as I said, and more," said the king. (It was given as promised, and was known for long as Dal Buinne, but it is now called Slieve Fuad.)

Buinne told what he could of the defence, but, as the captain had foreseen, there was nothing to tell.

"This door," said Conachúr, "will be down shortly. Have they barricaded it on the inside?"

"They have not," said Buinne.

The captain became active and violent.

"Ah!" he cried, "there is always something forgotten."

"Get at the ram, you there," he roared. "Put your shoulders into it."

He turned to the king.

"We have them!" he said.

Conachúr, with his eyes gleaming and a savage smile curling his lips, strode towards the rammers, but as he moved the door swung open and four men leaped from its yawning blackness. In a second two of the ramsmen were dead, and the rest were flying wildly, bustling the very king in their passage.

"By my hand!" the captain gurgled.

Two of the assaulters lifted the ram and trotted with it through the door. The other two made an onslaught of such ferocity that the soldiers were appalled. Then one fled back through the door, which instantly slammed, and the other sped like lightning around the building.

"After him!" roared Conachúr.

But the captain remained where he was, howling and dancing with rage.

"I've lost my ram," he bawled. "I've lost my ram."

"We have you, Iollann!" said Conachúr. "Traitor to your king!" he growled.

"Traitor to your friends," Iollann retorted.

"Deliver yourself to me," said Conachúr, "and you shall be spared."

"I came out for a purpose," said Iollann. "I demand single combat."

"There are no gentlemen here," Conachúr replied, "except your brother, so your claim cannot be granted."

"I shall cuff him," said Buinne, "but I will not fight him," and he strode away.

"I shall take this combat," said a voice.

Conachúr turned and saw his own son, Fiachra, standing there, and his heart sank.

"You have no arms," he said harshly.

"You will lend me yours," said Fiachra.

Conachúr stared on the fierce circle that surrounded him. He stared at Iollann, who stood with his back to the Red Branch swinging his blade, and he knew that the combat must take place.

"Iollann and I were born on the same night," said Fiachra. "It is an equal combat."

Conachúr took off his own battle-coats and gave them to Fiachra. He gave him his shield, the enchanted Aicean, and his green sword.

"Fight, then," he said, "and remember my teaching. Remember my shield work and my thrust."

They fought then, but at the first stroke from Iollann the great shield roared; for that virtue was in the Bright-Rim, to roar when the man it covered was struck at, and in answer to its roar the Three Waves of Ireland, the Wave of Tua, the Wave of Clíona, and the Wave of Rury roared in reply, and thereby all Ireland knew that a king was in danger.

Away in the palace Conall Cearnach sat drinking, listening to some great brawl, as he thought. He heard the roaring of Aicean, and leaped to his feet.

"The king is in danger!" he said.

He seized his weapons and fled from the palace of Macha, and came on the great combat.

In the dim light he thought it was Conachúr himself was behind the shield, and from the daring and mighty onslaught of the opponent he saw there was no time to lose. He burst his blue-green spear through the press and through the back of Iollann.

Iollann staggered to the wall of the Red Branch.

Who has struck me from behind?" he said.

"I, Conall Cearnach."

"Great and horrible is the deed you have done, Conall."

"Who are you?" Conall demanded.

"I am Iollann the Fair, sent by my father to protect the sons of Uisneac."

"By my hand," said Conall fiercely, "I shall undo some of
what I have done," and with one side twist of the sword he lifted
the head from Fiachra.

"Help me to that door, Conall," said Iollann. "The sons of
Uisneac are within."

The appalled soldiery shrank back, and on Conall's arm they
came to the door. There Iollann gave his shout. A feeble one it
was, but it was heard and the door opened. Iollann staggered in.

"Fight bravely, Naoise!" he said, and with that he sank on the
floor, and he was dead.

Outside the Red Branch Conachúr ran hither and thither like
a man enraged by madness.

CHAPTER XVII

"We are yet three," said Naoise. "Draw the bolts, Ainnle, for
one sortie of friendship. We have no doorman, for Deirdre could
not close or open the door by herself. You and I, Ainnle. Be
quiet, Ardan! Come, my brother, and put all your arm into the
blade. We will come in by the door we go out of. This door! Be
ready for our shout, Ardan!"

They went out and returned with red weapons, and for a long
time they sat in the dim flare of a torch watching by their dead
comrade.

"He was a brave boy," said Deirdre.

"He did not obey my order," her husband sighed. "I do not
know what he did."

"I smell—smoke," said Ainnle suddenly.

"I have smelled something for a long time," said Deirdre, "but
I could not think what it was. I am weary because of the death
of this good friend."

But little by little the vast building became full of smoke, and
in a while a fierce roar and crackling was heard also.

Naoise was again the hardy leader.

"They have fired the fortress! We do not know what happened

while Iollann was away, but Conachúr has reached the end of the world. Who could have foretold that he would fire the Red Branch! We must prepare for all that can happen."

"We are not dead yet," said Ardan.

"What do you counsel, brother?" said Ainnle.

"Sit down, there is less smoke on the floor."

A ruddy glare could be seen by each window.

"Fire is laid all round the building. We must make our plans quickly."

Ainnle turned gleefully to his younger brother.

"You shall run after all, my poor friend."

"In good truth," Ardan grinned, "I thought in Scotland that I should never want to run again, but I feel now that we have been staying too long in the one place. After all," he said complacently, "I am a man of action."

"And, of course," Ainnle gibed, "no one can run as quickly as you can."

"No one," said Ardan, "except Deirdre."

"Listen," said Naoise. "We have still more than a chance. We can run. Scotland trained us in that certainly, and if we can surprise but forty yards on the men without, we will outrun their best in twenty minutes."

"Where shall we run to?"

"We shall take the road to our own lordship. If Lavarcham's message has been sent our kinsmen should be marching at this moment on Emain. But," he said, and pointed, "we cannot wait for them."

They looked in silence.

A huge, golden flame licked screaming through the window, wavered hither and thither like some blindly savage tongue, and roared out again.

"It was ten feet long and three feet thick," said Ardan in a whisper.

"In ten minutes we will go," said Naoise.

"What arms?"

"Shield and spear, brother. Strip off all armour. We must run lightly."

"I shall be out first," he continued. "Give me twenty seconds before you follow, Ainnle, I can make room in twenty seconds. You will run ten paces to the left of the door. Deirdre and Ardan will run immediately into our interval; turn all to the right, and at my shout, run. Single file; Ainnle at the end. If I shout 'halt,' you two turn about and protect the rear. When I shout 'run,' drop every combat and fly. You, Deirdre, take Iollann's shield."

"And his spear," said Deirdre.

"Keep actually at my back, beloved, and each time we halt drop flat on the ground."

He was shouting his instructions now, for the voice of the fire was like the steady rage and roar of the sea, and through every window monstrous sheets of flame were leaping and crashing.

"This door," said Naoise. "A kiss for every one," he called. "We shall win yet. Pull, Ainnle!"

"The door is red hot," said Ainnle.

"Back for a mantle; two. Now grip. Pull! Give me twenty seconds, Ainnle."

He leaped across fire and disappeared.

The others leaped after him, with a wild yell from Ardan.

Conachúr sent a flying messenger to the palace.

"Bring Cathfa back with you," he ordered. "Tell him I want him. Say that the king beseeches him to come."

The captain of his troop stood by.

"Alas for the Red Branch!" he said mournfully.

"All that can be destroyed and be rebuilt," said Conachúr. "I shall rebuild the Red Branch."

He was in terrible distress and agitation.

"The morn is nigh," he said.

And he strode unhappily to and fro, with his eyes on the ground and his mind warring.

Far to the east a livid gleam appeared. The darkness of a summer night, which is yet a twilight, was shorn of its soft beauty, and in the air there moved imperceptibly and voluminously a spectral apparition of dawn. A harsh, grey, iron-bound upper-world brooded on a chill and wrinkled earth. The king's eyes and the eyes of his captain scanned each other from colourless, bleak faces. There was no hue in their garments; their shields were dull as death; and their hands, each clutching a weapon, seemed like the knotted claws of goblins.

A slow, sad exhalation came from the king's grey lips, like the plaint of some grim merman of the sea, rising away and alone amid the chop and shudder of his dismal waters.

"The fire is catching," the captain murmured. "Hark to that crackling!"

"We shall have light," the king murmured. "The Red Branch will flame."

"Within . . . !" said the captain moodily, and he looked with stern mournfulness on the vast pile.

"They must soon come out," he muttered.

"Your men are posted?"

"Every door is held. When they pop out this time—"

"They will have no place to pop into," said Conachúr. "I have them," he growled; and he threw his hand in the air and gripped it, as though in that blanched fist he held all that could never escape from him.

"They will fight," said the captain, "and they are woeful fighters."

"You are nervous, man," said Conachúr.

"At this hour and after this night," said the captain, "our men could fly from those three like scared rabbits."

"I fear that," said Conachúr.

"They may get away," said the captain.

Conachúr advanced on him so savagely and with such a writhe of feature that the man fell back.

"Dog!" said Conachúr. "If they escape I shall take your head."

"They are surrounded," the captain stammered; "they cannot escape."

"They can escape," Conachúr roared. "You know they can escape. Your men are cowards and idiots, and what are you? Oh, am I not a thwarted man! Am I not a forsaken king! Where is Cathfa? Where is the druid?" he cried.

"Majesty," the captain implored, "do not curse us. The great magician is coming."

The magician indeed had come.

"What has set you raging, Conachúr?" he asked.

"Father," said Conachúr. "If you do not assist me I am lost."

The old, old man looked at him.

"Tell me your tale, son. Whom have you locked up in fire?"

"The sons of Uisneac are there," said Conachúr. "They will escape me," he said.

"They are my grandchildren," said Cathfa.

"It is the woman with them. It is Deirdre I want. She was mine. She was stolen from me. I am not myself without her. I am a dead man while she is with Naoise."

"What do you fear from boys roared round by flame?"

"They may escape with her. When they come out my men may run from them. If they escape this time, father, I am dead."

"If I help you, Conachúr—!"

"I shall do anything you ask. Nothing you can demand will be too much for Conachúr."

"It is the woman you want?"

"The woman only."

"It is not the blood of these boys you lust for?"

"The woman, father, only the woman."

"I shall help you, Conachúr. Do not lay one finger on my daughter's sons, the sons of your young sister."

"They are out," the captain said, as a great roar came from the soldiers.

Conachúr moved to that direction.

"Quick, quick," he said, twitching his father's mantle in his impatience. "They will escape me."

"They shall not escape me," Cathfa answered. "There is no need for haste."

They were out, indeed, and, like two grim lions or woeful griffins of the air Naoise and Ainnle were raging in that press. Into their interval leaped Ardan, with but one eye peeping from the shield and a deadly hand thrusting from the rim. Back and forth they leaped with resistless savagery. Men flew at them and from them. Everywhere was a wild yelling of orders and the wilder screaming of stricken men. But over all Naoise's voice came pealing—

"Up, Deirdre. Run!"

She was at his back in an instant: the shield covering her side, her spear darting viciously by his right elbow, and a venturesome man dropped squealing. Five feet behind Ardan was leaping like a cat, all eyes and points, and ten paces behind him Ainnle was bounding.

"Halt," roared Naoise.

Deirdre was again on the ground. Ardan ranged tigerishly to right and left, while Ainnle whirled on the pursuers in ten-foot bounds.

Conachúr had arrived with Cathfa. Men were falling before them at the rate of three a second. So dreadful was Naoise's onslaught in the front that none would face him. Men tumbled over each other when he charged.

"The men will run away in a second," said the captain.

"Get into the *mêlée*, coward," roared Conachúr. . . . "Cathfa—!" he implored.

The officer whizzed out his blade and leaped forward. In three seconds he was dead, and five who followed him were rolling in their agony along the ground.

Naoise's voice came in a wild shout.

"Up, Deirdre. Run!"

The four were again in line. The men in front melted to either side of that dreadful file.

"Run!" said Naoise. "We are out!"

In front of him there was but Conachúr and Cathfa. Conachúr drew his great sword and stood crouching; and at him, with a dreadful smile, Naoise came on. Cathfa moved two paces to the front and stared fixedly at Naoise. He extended his two arms widely—

Naoise dropped on one knee, rose again, leaped high in the air and dropped again on his knee. Deirdre fell to the ground and rose up gasping. Ardan rolled over on his back, tossed his shield away, and came slowly up again, beating the air with his hands. Ainnle went half way down, rose again, and continued his advance on tiptoe.

A look of dismay and rage came on Naoise's face. He moved with extraordinary slowness to Deirdre and lifted her to his shoulder.

"We are lost," he said. "That magician—!"

"Keep on swimming," Ardan giggled. "There was never water here before, but the whole sea has risen around our legs, and we may paddle to Uisneac."

The arms dropped from their hands, and, in fact, they swam.

Not for a minute or two did the soldiers dare advance, and then they did so cautiously. They picked up the fallen weapons, and then only did they lay hands on the raging champions.

Cathfa dropped his arms to his sides.

"We are taken," said Naoise. "Our run is ended."

from In the Land of Youth

PART I
THE FEAST OF SAMHAIN

CHAPTER I

It was decided that the evening meal should be eaten on the lawn before the palace. A tent had been set under a tree and a fire was built in front of it. Torches were tied to the branches of the tree, and others were fixed to stakes driven into the ground; so there was plenty of light; and in the ring cast by these flares there was great animation.

But beyond this circle, where the smoke went drifting in grey billows, night was already brooding, and minute by minute the darkness became deep and deeper.

No stars were visible. There was no sky to be seen. There was nothing for the eye to rest on. And if a man had placed his hand before his face he would not have been able to see his hand.

Little by little the last loitering couples were driven from dusk vistas to the centre of the lawn; and little by little the merry talk became grave, and the loud voices were hushed. Soon there was no one moving outside the circle of light except servants who had to draw water from the well, or perform other outdoor duties.

Even these did not move abroad, for this was the month of

Samhain,[1] and the one night of the year in which whoever has the will and the courage may go to Faery.[2]

The servants even did not stir without. They had accumulated all the water which could possibly be used that night. The store-houses, the piggeries, the sheep-cotes and hen-roosts had been closed for the night; and around each of these, and all around Cruachan Ai, and all about every hamlet in Ireland, incantations had been uttered, and magical circles drawn against the Masters of Magic.

While waiting for the meats to be brought, Ailill lay in the opening of the tent staring beyond the fire at that great black-ness. Maeve was at the back of the tent sharing nuts that had been stewed in honey between three royally clamorous children, and exchanging apples with Fergus mac Roy, and glances also which were meant for no other eye than his. Other people also were stretched about the tent, chattering aimlessly and all im-patient for their supper.

"The meal will be ready soon," said Maeve. "It is late because of the games, but it will be ready very soon now."

Or she would detail his future to an impatient champion:

"There is roast meat and boiled, my dear. There is fish stewed in milk, and birds boiled with spices. There are puddings of minced flesh and sweet bread. There is white thin milk, and thick yellow milk. There are many different kinds of broth. There is wine from far countries, and mead, my love, made by myself from the honey gathered by my own bees in the flowers that grow about Cruachan. And after that there is ale, and red-cheeked apples.

"It will be ready very soon, my darlings."

CHAPTER II

"I wonder would any man dare go abroad to-night," said Ailill, as he stared against the darkness. "I seem to hear already the

---

[1] Samhain: pronounced "Sow'in."
[2] Now "All-Hallows" Eve.

brisk tread of the people of Dana moving out there beyond the light."

"I hear something," a companion averred.

"You hear the wind stirring in lazy branches," said a third.

"Was *that* the wind?"

"It was a ferret."

"Was it so?" Ailill queried. "If you will go to the hill where the outlaws were hanged yesterday, and if you will tie a withy round the foot of one of the hanging men, I will give you a present."

"I'll do that."

But in two minutes the man returned, saying that he heard things moving and did not care to go farther.

"I thought you would come back, my pulse," said Ailill.

Two others ventured, and returned terrified.

"The night is dark, and there are demons about," said Maeve, "no man would go out on the eve of Samhain, even for a prize."

Then Nera stepped forward.

"What prize are you offering, Majesty?"

"This gold-hilted sword," the King replied, looking at him mockingly.

"I will go," said Nera.

"Go, with my love," said the King, "but," as Nera stepped from the tent, "I shall expect you back in a minute, dear heart."

"I will come for my prize," said Nera.

He walked through the flare of the torches, and the company watched him go.

He came to the end of the lawn where the light began to fail, and, as he walked, he looked closely at what light was left.

Here the light was golden, and here it became grey, and here, a step farther, it became blue or purple, and here, but two paces beyond, it was no longer a colour; it was a blackness, an invisibility.

It would be wrong to say that the young man was not afraid. Given the night and the deed that he had undertaken, any man might have shown the fear which he kept hidden. But his will was set, and he knew that, even if he could not go on, he would not turn back; so he bent his mind inflexibly on the hill before him, and on the swinging figures which he had to meet.

The man whose mind is thus set is conscious of himself to that extent, but in other and curious ways he has ceased to be quite his own master, for while the mind is concentrated and engaged on one sole matter we are blind and deaf to all others, and we may be interfered with beyond our knowledge.

Nera turned to look over his shoulder, and, when he saw the tent, now curiously distant and precise, and the figures that moved unhurriedly about it, it was as though he were peeping into or at another world.

Then he set out with long, strong paces in the direction of the hill. But he kept his sword in his hand and his buckler on his arm.

Chapter III

He knew his way to the hill. Indeed, he had been there on the previous day when these malefactors were swung, and he remembered that they had been a troublesome couple.

One of them had said:

"It is not often that notable miscreants are ended, and everybody has a right to look on wonders. There are not enough women present," he complained.

The other outlaw contented himself with a criticism of all that was done for him, and of the looks and qualities of his guard. When the rope had been fixed on his neck he yawned so widely that it was disarranged, and had to be settled again.

"Keep your yawns to yourself," said the captain of the guard, "and please to let my men do their duty."

"I'm sleepy," the outlaw objected.

"Even if you are," said the captain of the guard, "you need not hinder my men."

"One must be polite in company," said the outlaw, "so I'll do my best not to yawn until you have finished with me."

He did his best.

The other rogue remarked that he had become thirsty standing all that time.

"There is nothing here to drink," the captain returned.

"It doesn't matter," the rogue answered. "It just struck me, and I mentioned it."

Nera remembered these men, and he remembered in especial the face of the thirsty man—a long, hatchet-face, with a great nose on it, and a close-curling beard on the chin. He had seemed to be thinking deeply and discontentedly at the last moment, and had obviously dismissed what was happening about him for more private imaginings.

As he walked the face of this man appeared before him with such suddenness that he almost drove at it with his sword; but, recognising at the same instant that it was merely his imagination at play, he banished the phantom and went on.

Although he knew the way so well it was nevertheless not easy to keep to it in that darkness, and he paused a few times to reconstruct the path he had already come, and to calculate from it the direction in which he should continue.

He had not far to go.

Barely five minutes' march lay between the lawn of Royal Cruachan and the place towards which he was bent, and, given only a general direction, he could not miss the hill.

He passed through a bushy place which swished and crackled about his ears; came out on turf that sank and rose with its clear elastic noise; and then he came on the rising ground which told that the hill had begun.

He held the sword thrust in front of him as he trod upwards, not to ward off goblins, but so that he might feel if a tree was in his path or a boulder.

There were not many trees to be sure, but there were huge outcropping rocks carved to every kind of edge and knob and projection that one could think of, and if a man stumbled against one of these his skull could be broken, or his shin bone might get a crack that would leave him hopping for a month.

CHAPTER IV

He came to the top of the hill, and found that, careful as he had been, he had yet moved somewhat from the direct path, and was some score of yards east of the point he aimed for.

Up here it was not so dark as it had been among the trees and boulders below. Or perhaps the fact that he was on an eminence tended to make him look upwards and catch such rays of light as there might be.

While walking below he had kept his eyes to the ground, following, although not seeing, his feet; and adding, thus, to the darkness that descended from the atmosphere the deeper blackness which arose from the ground. Or it might be that his eyes had become more accustomed to darkness, and, although he could not exactly see, he could, as it were, surmise; for he began to distinguish between the various darknesses that lay about him, and was aware of gradations among these dusks.

Here there was the black of ebony—it was a boulder.

Here was a sketchy incomplete blackness—it was a bush.

Beyond was not a blackness but a darkness, and that was space.

Beneath him there was a velvet gloom, and that was the ground.

And above there was a darkness, not to be described, but to be thought of, as a movement, and that was the sky.

He moved to the right searching for the one tree which grew on the hill, and, after a cautious exploration, he found it, and stood listening to the slow creakings which told that this was indeed his tree.

As he moved forward a foot tapped him gently on the mouth, and he leaped back with his sword uplifted, staring blindly, and listening with all his blood.

Then he smiled to himself, rattled the sword into its scabbard, and, putting his hand resolutely forward, he laid hold of that foot.

CHAPTER V

He took the withy he had prepared out of his belt and began to fix it on the foot, but the thing was too elastic, and each time that he thought he had it right it sprang open.

From above his head, out of and into darkness, there came a hoarse and bubbling whisper, a rusty stammering that thudded his heart most out of his breast and his soul all but out of his body.

"You'll never tie it that way," said the voice. "Put a peg into it, decent man, or stick your brooch through it if you have no peg."

Nera almost let go the foot, but a savage obstinacy came on him, and he bit with his upper teeth on his lower lip until he nigh bit it in two.

"Very well," said he to the voice, "I'll stick my brooch in."

He did so, and the withy held.

"You are not dead?" said he to the man above him.

"Not out and out," the man replied.

"How does it happen that you are still alive?"

"It happened this way," replied that creaky and rusty tone; "when they were hanging me I was very thirsty, and ever since I have been too thirsty to die."

"It is a hard case," said Nera.

"Well," said he then, "I'll be moving, for I'm going to get a prize for what I did tonight to your foot."

"It was a good manly job," said the voice.

"It was," Nera admitted, "considering the kind of thing I had to do, and the sort of night in which I had to do it."

"But," said the voice above, "prove to me that you are really a courageous man."

"How would I prove that?" Nera asked.

"Take me down off this tree and carry me to some place where I can get a drink."

"You've been sentenced to be hanged," Nera replied, "and you've got to hang."

"That's all right," the voice answered, "I don't want to dodge Doom. You could bring me back after I got the drink, and you could hang me up again."

"I don't like the job," said Nera.

"I wouldn't like it myself," the voice replied, "but it would be a charitable act, and a valorous one."

"That is true," said Nera, "and I'll do what you ask."

"For," he continued, "there never was a man in the world before was asked to do the like; and there isn't a man in the world but myself would do it."

Nera then began to climb the tree.

Chapter VI

"Is this you, decent man?" Nera inquired as he fumbled at a knot.

"It is not," the voice answered. "That's my comrade, and he has been dead for a day and a half."

"This is yourself anyhow," said Nera.

"You're right now," the voice replied.

"I'm afraid," said Nera, as he worked over him, "I'm afraid I shall have to let you fall on the ground; you are too heavy for me to hold with one hand."

"Don't bother about that," said the voice, "I can stand anything except the thirst."

Nera let him drop then, and he got a great fall.

"You'll have to carry me on your back," said the man, "for although I'm not dead enough to be buried I'm too dead to walk."

"I've done that much," said Nera, "and now I'll do whatever I have to do."

He packed the man on to his back and started away looking for a house where a drink could be got.

"What is it like to be hanged?" he asked as he plodded along.

"Nothing is as bad as they make it out," the man answered; "but I'm terribly thirsty, and I can't think of anything else."

They came to a house, and Nera knocked at the door. It was opened by a woman, and the visitor marched in with the man on his back.

The woman gave one look at Nera, and one at the stretched neck and twisted jowl that was waggling on Nera's shoulder, then she gave a low squeal and vanished out of the house.

A man strode to them truculently:

"What are you looking for, gentles?" said he.

Then he caught sight of that fishy eye peering by Nera's ear.

"The devil," said he, and he went through the door in a standing jump.

Three children crawled hastily under a bed in the corner and never another sound came from them. And an old woman, who was sitting by the fire with a mutton-bone in her fist, stared at them with her eyes open and her mouth open, and a long monotonous squawk tumbling off the end of her tongue the way water tumbles off a ledge.

There were three buckets of water standing by the wall. Nera propped his man against the door, and held one of the buckets to his lips. He drank a bucket dry. Then he drank the other two buckets dry.

"That's not a bad drink," said Nera, "and if you're not satisfied 'tis because nothing will satisfy you. Come back to your torment, my soul."

He picked up the malefactor, hunched him on to his back, and went out of the house with him and back to the hill.

As he strung him up he asked:

"Do you feel any better now, my darling?"

"I feel splendid," said the outlaw. "I'll be dead in a jiffey."

Nera left him then, swinging easily and buoyantly, and he took the road back to Cruachan of the Dun Ramparts, for he was impatient to get his prize.

CHAPTER VII

"I have been a good while away," said Nera to himself. "No man can say I was afraid, for I shouldn't have stayed out so long, and on the night of Samhain, if I had been afraid."

He thought also that it would be a fine thing to own a gold-hilted sword, and he wondered if the blade would be as good as the blade of his own weapon was; for, after all, it is not the hilt that is important in a sword.

Musing thus, he came in good time to Cruachan, and on the skirt of the lawn, just beyond the fringe of light, he halted.

There was far more light coming from the lawn than there had been when he went away.

Not only was the fire burning before the tent, the tent was burning; and behind it the vast mass of the palace was spouting flame at every window and vomiting fire from an hundred different parts of the roof.

With the raging uproar of flame there came a babel of other noises; yells of defiance, and roars of encouragement; torrents of imprecations, and the dismal yapping of wounded men.

A man came bursting from that torment of noise and flame. He ran past Nera with his desperate eyes staring, and nothing in his hand but the splintered handle of a spear.

Nera recognised with a shock that the man had looked at him and had not seen him.

In a few minutes three or four others came flying in his direction, and they also darted past without a halt, without even the recognition of voice or eye.

When another man came, Nera thrust himself into his path, and, to his surprise and horror, the man ran through him.

Then Nera recognised that he was neither in the world nor out of the world. That he was between worlds—that he was in Faery.

He rushed into the circle of light to the tent. Outside it he saw the body of Ailill stretched on its back, one arm thrown over the face and the other lying along the ground 'with the hand still gripping a broken sword. Within the tent Maeve was lying with her head huddled into her knees, and a dark pool forming about her. Fergus was tumbled a pace beyond, and here and there other bodies lay in every aspect of abandonment and ignominy. Everywhere soldiers were running with red weapons and roaring mouths. He ran into one of these, and that man was solid as a rock.

"Join the work, comrade, join the work," the man shouted with a great laugh.

Nera said to himself: "This is a man of the Shí, and he takes me to be one of his host."

"Alas," he thought, "all my friends are dead, or they are flying on the desolate hills in that bleak, bitter darkness, and I am translated."

But the wild work was finished, and the victorious fairy troop was re-forming into its companies and regiments, and were beginning their march back to the Shí in the enchanted Hill of Cruachan.

Chapter VIII

Nera did not wish to go with them, and yet he could not conceive of anything else to do. He felt far more lost than even a lost dog can feel. Not alone had he lost his comrades, his world and all his habitual contacts had disappeared, and he was more astray and bewildered than any strayed dog could be.

With the passing of his people and his world his sense of identity seemed to have passed or lapsed; so that, if one had asked, he should have found it difficult to tell who he was. If one tumbled into the sea and was there questioned by fishes, what use would there be in the statement that one was, or had been, a man, with a name, and a pedigree, and a memory filled with deeds and emotions which they could not be interested in?

It seemed better that he should go into the fairy dún than that he should remain where he was to wander and stare in the fairy wilderness. Human desolation and silence he knew, but what would fairy desolation, fairy silence be like? How would he feel in fairy darkness? and what might come to him out of the unknown gloom of the Country of the Dead?

He marched, therefore, at the tail of the host, and when they reached a door set in the hillside he also went in, following the men in front of him, and keeping military pace with them.

Each man as he entered sang out cheerily:

"A man on the track here."

And the voice of a guard within replied:

"The heavier is the track."

When it came to Nera's turn, he also cried out:

"A man on the track here," and he received the reply that the others got.

CHAPTER IX

They went into a hill apparently, but, once entered, the hill was as translucent as air. It ceased to be a hill. There was no feeling or evidence of being underground, for when he looked about he saw the conditions and phenomena to which he was accustomed in the world that he had left.

Here was space and trees. Water splashed along in a moody brook, moody only, perhaps, because it was night time; and when he looked up he saw through the darkness a faint far glitter of stars, and he noted a silvery radiance in the sky which might tell of an obscured moon, or might be the first delicate intimation that dawn was on the way.

He had lost count of time, and could not tell if one hour or six had elapsed since he set out on his adventure from the lawn of Cruachan.

The companies, of which he formed a part, marched along a sunken pathway arched over with trees, and this pathway wound around and about like a coiling snake.

Nera could hear the slow bubble and hush of waters coming

from the right hand, but in a minute the same sound came to him from the left.

They tramped across echoes and hollownesses which told of wooden bridges under their feet, and at times they trod up high-graded, precipitate bridges of ringing stone. These sounds, and darkness, and a gleam, these made the world that ringed him in.

There was much gay talk among his companions, but it consisted mostly of allusions to which he had no clue, and the men directly in front turned now and again to stare at him with good-humoured fixity, or with quizzical or calculating eyes.

They came at length to the entry of a great building and marched into a courtyard surrounded on three sides by towering, battlemented walls. The courtyard was lit with innumerable torches, and at one end, on a raised dais, Ethal Anbual, the King of the Shí of Connacht, was sitting with a small group of men and women about him.

When the troops had been ranged in a semicircle about this dais, men came forward from each company carrying heads which they swung by the hair, and they laid these in order before the King, who stared fixedly at each head and demanded its name and quality.

Among the trophies Nera recognised the auburn, wide-browed head of Ailill, and the long-faced, yellow-haired head of Maeve. But he recognised each head as it was put down, and his heart nigh broke with pity for his dead companions, and with fear for himself.

When all the trophies had been ranged, the chief of the company to which he was attached beckoned to Nera and marched with him to the dais.

"What is to be done with this man?" he asked the King.

The King of the Shí looked steadily at him, and Nera had a confused impression of calm eyes and flashing teeth, of a long, silky, yellow beard, and of much sly amusement behind the regard that was bent on him. Several of the people on the dais leaned together whispering and laughing, and the King, bending forward with an elbow on his knee, smiled as though he divined what was being discussed behind him.

"What brought you here, my friend?" said the King.

"I came with the warriors," Nera stammered.

"That I know, but how does it happen that you have been able to leave your world and come blundering into ours?"

"I do not know how it happened," Nera replied. "All I know is that I suddenly found myself invisible to my own people, and as there seemed to be nowhere else for me to go, I came with the people of the Shí."

"It is very vexatious," said the King; "but now that you are here you must stay here, for although you have not become one of us, you have certainly ceased to be one of them. Are you prepared to work in return for your life and your food?"

"I will do anything you tell me to do."

"Very well," said the King.

Chapter X

The thin radiance which he had noticed when he passed through the door of Faery did not flow from a hidden moon. It was the faint first peeping of the dawn away on the low horizon. And, minute by minute, that radiance spread, so that what had been a stain not bigger than a hand was now a lake flooding up the eastern sky.

Nor was it any longer the colour of grey water or unpolished metal. It was the hue of silver of great purity. It was a tender whiteness; a spotless radiance; a deep translucency; it was a snowy immaculate loveliness, in the heart of which there grew a flush not quite to be called rose, for it was tinged with green.

In a little that flush blushed deeply, radiantly, and glowed out into gold, and by these gradations the day was born and the sun began to shine.

The torches paled, for the centre of being had gone from them to where the young mild orb was climbing.

For a moment the face of the King of the Shí and the faces about him paled also; they seemed careworn, preoccupied, and pinched with a chill they had not felt before. The diadems, the carved helmets, the bronze shoulder-pieces and the shields with metal rims and bosses did not shine for that moment. They glinted, furtively, coldly, until the sun came; and then they sparkled again mellowly, friendlily, and the great yellow beard of the King foamed out in gold, and the aura about his brows took on an hundred colours.

Looking at Nera, he said thoughtfully:

"Now that you are here, I suppose you must stay here."

And Nera recognised in the word "must" a compulsion against which he was powerless; and in that moment he bade good-bye to the world he had left, and which he should see no more, or should only see as through a window.

He bade adieu to preoccupations which had been important, and were now remembered with trouble, as though they came to him from the other side of the grave. Enemies against whom he yet had a grudge he forgave. The friends with whom he had sported he blessed. And a bright-eyed girl who had glanced at him and on whom his eyes had stayed he blessed also. For all that was finished and done with, and there was no longer any meaning in such things.

He squared his shoulders, and drew into his lungs the breath of a new life, and he drew into his mind all the implications which were borne on that deep breath.

"There is a house yonder where you can stay," said the King of the Shí; "and there you will do as you are told until you have learned to do without being told."

CHAPTER XI

It was a small dwelling, half hidden among flowering bushes. About the door and in and out of the windows there was the low deep hum of bees. From the sloping roof there came, in delicate monotony, the soft cooing of doves; and in the trees about there was an unceasing song, or chirp, or call, as summer birds went to and from their nests.

Within the house there was a young woman who looked on him uncritically as she received the instructions which his escort gave.

"Take care of him," said the escort, "see that he does not get lost again, for he has been badly lost already."

The young woman smiled.

"I shall see that he does not go astray," said she. "Come into the house, decent man, and rest your tiredness."

Nera went into the house, and she gave him a wooden bowl full of new milk, a slice of wheaten bread and a great piece of honey.

"That will put heart into you," she murmured.

And it did put heart into him, so that in a few minutes, as she moved about her duties, he began to look at her with an absorbed attention, and it seemed to him that having looked at her he could not want to look away again.

But in the middle of that gaze he fell asleep, for he was tired by the loss of his night's rest, and was yet more wearied by reason of the adventures that he had gone through and the mental disturbance to which he had been subjected.

He slept well.

The sun had climbed to the height of his course, and was beginning to descend again when Nera awakened and went out into a world so endlessly new that he could not but marvel and be delighted thereat. He felt full of joy as he walked in the garden among bees and birds and flowers, while the mild sunlight stole into and lived in him.

In the world that he had left summer had departed and all its sweets, and although winter had not come with snow and iron, it had yet ventured so many of its heralds and had blown so chill a breath that the autumn had shivered and her russet cheek had paled.

Now here was summer again, found just as he had lost it,

and it was summer of a loveliness such as he had never experienced.

Here were flowers of a hue, of a sweetness, beyond all that he had seen. The sunlight here was more tranquil and more rich than the light to which he was accustomed, and the breeze was freighted with such balm and spice as he could never weary of savouring.

The woman of the house called to him.

"Now you must work, sweet lad."

She gave him an axe and sent him to the wood which was at a little distance to cut down a tree. He was then to chop the wood into logs, and on the morrow he should carry these in a pannier on his back to the palace. It was only certain trees that he should cut; those which burned well and which gave out a sweet savour while burning.

It was rude work, but it did not exercise him severely, for he was very skilful with an axe. He had practised with that arm, and had been captain of a band of axemen while in the service of the King of Munster, so that once the tree came to the ground he could lop so delicately and cleave so powerfully that the work seemed almost to accomplish itself, and in small time he had amassed logs enough to fill many panniers.

In the morning he began the transport of these to the palace of Ethal Anbual.

Chapter XII

As he was returning from one of these journeys he heard two men talking as they came down a path that ran wildly among the trees.

It was a very slender, very twisting path, along which one could only see for a few yards; and it wound about so crookedly, and it was so deep in leaves, and it was so clumped and grassed and tussocked that no person could be seen or heard coming along it. Nera did not hear any step, but he caught voices, and he was so new to this country that he followed his first impulse, and striding a few paces to the side he crouched behind a tree.

A voice said:

"Will you go on, lazybones?"

And another replied:

"Lazybones yourself. I'll go on or I won't go on just as I please, but will you look out where I'm going?"

"I am looking out," the first voice said, "but you walk so slow that I want to go asleep between each step. Can't you raise a trot out of you, lazybones? Go six inches to the right or you'll rub your nose off against a tree. Now go ahead, and foot it out."

"Ah, it's hard to be dark, it's hard to be dark," said the first voice.

"Ah," said the second voice, "will you hold your prate, for I'm sick of that song. Move twelve inches to the left, my pippin, and go straight on. Wait now until I duck or I'll be scraped off by a branch. Go ahead and stir your stumps."

"Ah, it's hard to be dark, it's hard to be dark," said the first voice.

"Can't you say something besides that?" the other cried.

"I can't, and I won't. I'll say it's hard to be dark, it's hard to be dark until I die, and I'll say it when I'm dead, and I'll say it after I'm dead."

"You'll die now," his companion roared, "if you don't take two steps to the left and one to the right."

Nera peeped, and saw the two who were coming. One was mounted on the shoulders of the other. The man who was on top had no legs, and Nera saw that the man who was walking had no eyes. The blind man acted as legs to the lame man and the latter acted as eyes to the blind man.

Nera followed, for he wondered where they were going, and admired the manner in which they had doubled their abilities and halved their troubles. After a while they turned from the path and went where a smaller track ran among trees. In a little they came to a well, and the blind man halted, leaning against the well, while the lame man stared into it.

"Is it there, my soul?" said the blind man testily.

"It is," his companion replied.

"Very well," said the other, "let us get out of this, for my back is broken, so it is. Ah, it's hard to be dark, it's hard to be dark."

"Will you hold your tongue?" the cripple snarled.

"I won't," the blind man screamed. "I'll say, it's hard to be dark until Doom, and I'll say it afterwards as well."

"Go nine inches to the left," his companion roared, "or you're done for, for there's a rock in the way will split your shin and crack your skull and dinge your stomach, and kill the pair of us."

The blind man trod a careful nine inches.

"Am I to go on now?" said he, "or what am I to do? Can't you mind where I'm going?"

"Amn't I minding it, lazybones. Will you go on ten steps, and then—"

"Ah, it's hard to be dark, it's hard to be dark," cried the blind man, and then they turned among trees and disappeared.

Nera went home in a tranquil, dewy eve.

The sun had been steadily declining. Now, but one red shoulder of the Titan rested on the dreaming slope; and from it there came a beam rosy and gentle as the light we imagine in dream.

Still from the roof-tree came the faint, intermittent moaning of the doves: so low the ear must wait to catch it; and at times so low it seemed but as a surmise in the heart, as though the air itself cooed gently at long and longer intervals. A lazy hum stayed for one long instant in the air as a late bee, gorged with sweets, took the way of content homewards. From the trees near by there came but a sound or two, a chirp of welcome or inquiry, and a swift whirr as wings flew into and folded among the leaves.

And as he stood in the last faint beam, no longer red but brown, he thought of the friends that he had left, so long ago it seemed, and that they all were dead, and he thought how that dear world was lost to him for ever.

He went sadly into the house then, and the sweet-cheeked, honey-haired woman set before him bread and meat and honey, with a bubbling mether of new, sweet milk, and a great horn filled with wine; and in partaking of this food, and in the regard of that quiet-eyed companion, he forgot his friends and comrades, and the disasters that had overtaken them, and the plight in which he was.

CHAPTER XIII

He stayed for a long time talking, for he was loath to leave her for his couch, and she was as unwilling to let him go.

"Tell me, Woman of the House, what is really the life in this world?"

"We wish, and what we wish we get."

"Do you get all that you wish for?"

"Only the simple things. Things to eat and to wear; sunlight and sweet scents. Every person gets what he is able to wish for, but the power of every person to wish is different."

"You, for instance, O honey-haired companion! what do you get?"

"What I can wish for," she answered with a smile.

"Are you not easily satisfied?" said Nera, looking on the neat and pleasant but poor interior.

"Before I came here from the world of mortal men," said she, "I had small peace, and it will take a long time before I grow discontented with this quiet happiness."

"Also," she continued smilingly: "I do not yet know how to wish powerfully and grandly as the King does and as others do, for I am not educated in these things; therefore, I only have what I can wish for, and am contented. I shall get other things when I learn the way to want them."

"I know what I want," cried Nera roguishly.

"If you know that, you will certainly get it," she answered, and her eyes rested on him gently as the cooing of the doves had rested on the rosy air.

"Tell me more of these things," said Nera, "for I could listen to your voice for ever."

"This world is called Tir na n-Og, the Land of the Young. It is within the world you have left, as an apple is within its skin, and all who die in your world come to this one. But within this world there is another called the Land of Wonders, and those who die here, or who can wish to do so, go to the Land of Wonders. Within the Land of Wonders there is yet a world called the Land of Promise, and those who die in the Land of Wonders are born into the Land of Promise, but they cannot die there until they can wish to do so."

"And after the Land of Promise?"

"After the Land of Promise there is your world again."

"All this is very wonderful," said Nera. "Are there any other things that you can tell me?"

"In the world you come from," she continued, "time moves slowly, but in this world it goes yet slower."

"I do not understand that at all," cried Nera.

"Nothing is real here, for everything is wished, so that here a minute is like a day, time moves so slowly with us and we live so quickly. In the Land of Wonders time moves yet more slowly and life goes faster, so in that land a minute is like a thousand years. And in the Land of Promise time ceases entirely and there is only life."

"These are hard sayings," said Nera. "I do not comprehend them."

"I do not understand them well either," she replied; "but that is what we are taught."

"Still," said Nera, "there is something that I do comprehend."

"And what is that?" she inquired.

"That I adore you," said he.

As she made no reply he strode to her and gave her three kisses.

"You must not do that," said she, "for Ethal Anbual has not given permission."

"But since it is my wish," said Nera. "Since it is our wish," he continued tenderly. "Do you not wish it also?" he asked.

She smiled at him, as one surprised and delighted:

"Indeed I did not know that I wished it," said she, and placing her arms about his neck she gave him three gentle kisses.

Chapter XIV

All the next day he was busy cutting and carrying wood.

He had no desire for companions, and did not meet any. He only saw those in the palace to whom he delivered the timber, and as his work needed no explanation he did not enter into talk with them. A few people went by him among the offices; some hurrying servants, some agile and laughing children, but all that he passed with these was the word of blessing, which is the word of greeting.

"God to you," he said.

"God be with the work," they answered.

At times, as he went to and fro, there came from the farther side of the palace a great blowing of bugles. At times a body of armed men marched past him with rhythmic step and fierce, alert faces. Or a cloud of horsemen, with a gallant shining of shields and spears and a great clashing of accoutrement, went galloping by.

Saving for these, his marchings were as solitary as though he moved through a desert, and his true companion was the sunlight that danced among the leaves or the cool shadows that slept behind tree and rock.

He had leisure, so, to consider the things he had been told of, and to make some attempts at wishing.

If his opinion had been sought, Nera would have said that to wish is an ideal occupation for an idle man, and one which called for no particular endowment. But he now discovered that what he had regarded as wishing was merely a lax wandering of the mind; a superficial fancying in which, although his sympathies were engaged, his mind or will was quiescent. He tried to wish,

but found that he did not know how to do it, for when one image
formed in his mind, another succeeded to it before the first had
received one-half its due attention.

He found, also, that he did not know what to wish for. He had
food in abundance, there were sunshine and sweet airs about
him, and no person interfered with him. His health was perfect,
and his strength was equal to any call that could reasonably be
made upon it.

He was a little bewildered.

"Is there nothing I lack?" he cried. And he sat upon a moss-
grown trunk to consider this matter.

He could not consider it cogently, for his mind would run to
the world that he had left, calling up faces, characters, events,
about which it warned him also that he need be no more exercised. Ambitions had been his in that world, but in this one they
did not seem to have any relevancy.

What did it now matter that his comrade Cairbre might take
his place as captain of a troop? And it was likely, moreover, that
his comrade Cairbre was dead, and that the troop was stretched
with him in equal chilly stiffness.

"They are dead," he thought, "or they will shortly die; and I,"
he thought again, in a flash of amazement that was also terror,
"and I can never die, for I am dead now, and I am yet as alive as
I have ever been or ever can be."

The thought terrified and sobered and steadied him.

"I must learn more of this world," he thought, "and find out
what in it is worth attention."

And then he remembered that dove-eyed companion who was
waiting for him where birds were singing, where the bees went
in contentment. And he knew that he lacked nothing which she
could not give, and that he need wish for no more than the joys
of which she was mistress.

Her tranquil eyes; her cool and tender hands; her breast that
could woo him to rest and rest again, and could quit him of that
weariness which had gathered with the years. There he could

forget all the effort and agitation which had been that which he once thought of as life.

He arose joyful, impatient, full of desire and eagerness, and, swinging the axe lustily as he strode, he took his way to that house of dream.

Chapter XV

He was welcomed there, and as he took his dear mistress in his arms he felt that there was nothing more to be wished for, and that his hands were holding all that existence had to offer of tempting or satisfactory.

After they had eaten, he began to ask questions, for he was yet full of curiosity; and he loved, furthermore, to look on her lips as they moved and shaped words. He loved to hear the delicate sweet sound of these words as she uttered them, and to look in her eyes as they widened and narrowed, and as they shaded or emphasised her thought.

He told her of the men he had seen on the previous day, one mounted on the shoulders of the other, one of them being without legs, while the other was without sight, and he begged that she should tell him the meaning of this collaboration, and of that journey.

She informed him that these were men who guarded certain treasures belonging to the King of the Shí, notably the Crown of Bruin, the Mantle of Laery, and the Shirt of Dunlaing. That nobody knew where the treasures were hidden except these two and the King, and that it was a strange accident he should have come on them while they were making their visit of duty.

"But why should the King choose such curious guards for his treasure?" he asked.

"They cannot steal it, for they cannot run away. The one is too blind to see the treasure and so he cannot get it. The other can see the treasure, but as he has no legs he cannot get away with it."

"But," Nera objected, "they might tell a third person, an evil comrade, and he could take the treasure. They," said he, for he lived hopefully, "they could tell me, and I have all the legs and eyes that any one could need."

"No," she replied, "they will not tell any one else. These men covet the treasure and they will tell no one about it. They wish for treasure, and in a way they have it, but they have wished themselves into slavery to get it."

"It seems to me," said Nera, "that one's wish does not always turn out as one wished."

"You must not desire a thing which belongs to another person," she answered, "for then there are two wishes, each acting against the other, and the people who are thus covetous are left in an unsatisfactory middle place which is torment."

"I see that it is of no use to wish at all," cried Nera discontentedly.

"Yes," she replied, "you may desire things which everybody can enjoy with you, and that is true wishing."

"Such things as—?" said Nera scornfully.

"Sunlight and the song of birds, good food and health, a contented mind and a good understanding. These hurt no one, and every one is the better for possessing them, or for living among people who have them."

Nera revolved these thoughts, but it seemed to him that they were not profitable, for he considered that the things worth having were those which other people owned or lacked, and he thought there was small value in possessions which anybody might enjoy who cared to want them.

CHAPTER XVI

But suddenly the young man's face went purple and he smote the table a blow with his fist, so that everything on it went jigging up and down, and his companion leaped in surprise.

"What is it, my lamb, my little calf?" said she, and she ran to him.

"I know what I wish for," cried Nera triumphantly, furiously.

"What is it?" she whispered.

"I want the prize I won; I have been cheated out of my prize," he cried savagely.

"But what prize are you speaking of? Who has dared to cheat you?"

"My gold-hilted sword," he cried. "The blade that Ailill dared me to win, and which I won."

And as he said these words a terrible despair came on him, the light turned grey before his eyes, and he beat his fists together.

"Tell me about your prize," she pleaded.

And she pressed a soft hand over his forehead, and she kissed his eyelids tenderly.

"Tell me all that happened to you," she urged.

So Nera sat again in his chair, and looking backwards in memory and in the world that he had left, he arranged his thoughts and began to tell of his adventures.

His companion listened, wide-eyed, while he told of the wager that Ailill had made, and of the dreadful night through which her beloved had passed.

"And now," he concluded, "I can never get my prize, for I have strayed away from that world. Noble Ailill and Maeve of the Long White Cheek are dead, and all who were with them have been slaughtered."

But at this his lady began to laugh, and her merriment was so infectious that, in his own despite, Nera laughed with her, but he was hurt also.

"What is there in my story to make you happy?" he inquired.

"It is all a mistake," she murmured, wiping the tears of laughter from her eyes.

"What is all a mistake?"

"They are not dead," she replied.

"But I saw the slaughter with these same eyes which are now marvelling at you. I saw Ailill lying outside the tent with a broken sword in his hand, and I looked down on Maeve lying inside the tent, all doubled up, and all in and out of blood."

"Nevertheless—"

"And, after that, I saw men swinging up the heads of my companions for the King of the Shí to look at."

"It was only a game," she cried.

"A game! Alas! that game went against my comrades."

"You will not listen," she cried, beating her hands together. "It was a game, it was not real."

"It was not real!" he murmured, staring at her. "I no longer understand anything, and you are right to laugh at me."

"You will understand," she cried, "if you will only listen."

"Very good," said Nera, "I will listen, but I am perfectly certain that I shall not understand, for I saw their heads swinging by the hair while the King of the Shí stared at them."

"It was not real. It did not happen."

"Whether it happened or whether it did not happen I saw it happening," said Nera stubbornly.

"I shall beat you," she cried, "if you do not listen to me."

"I am listening indeed," he replied, "my ears are waggling," said he.

"The King of the Shí was angry because of a thing Maeve did long ago, when she helped Angus of the Brugh to take a girl out of Faery, out of this very Shí of Connacht."

"I heard of that. So far I am sane."

"And so the King wished to make war on Maeve, and his wish was fulfilled in his world, but it was not fulfilled in her world."

"Very good, and what follows from that?"

"It follows that Maeve is not dead, and that Ailill is not dead, and that all the companions you left alive are just as living as when you left them."

Chapter XVII

"I shall awaken soon," said Nera, "for I surely must be asleep and dreaming."

"You saw a wish being fulfilled," she continued, "and as a wish is formed in the mind, so it must be satisfied in the mind; and as this is the first world of the mind, and as you strayed into it, you have seen something happening which happened in the mind, and did not happen anywhere else."

"My mind is about to slip out through my ears and leave my head empty."

"It is quite plain," she insisted.

"Doubtless it is. But I begin to understand that I shall never again understand anything. Alas! alas!" said he, "I have become a fool, and I may go mad presently and bite people on the leg."

But his lovely companion interrupted him soothingly: "Ailill and Maeve and all your companions are alive, for this time," she said.

"For this time?" said Nera. "I am beginning again to wonder, and I cannot stand too much astonishment, for it makes my head buzz."

"A thing," said she, "can be conceived and exercised in the mind, but when it has been so exercised in the mind that it really becomes real there, it then becomes real in every part of nature and in all the worlds where life is living."

"In good truth . . . !" said Nera.

"It is by this wishing and willing that the worlds are made, and that everything is made."

"I will let these things pass," said Nera, "for I perceive that I am not intelligent. But what did you mean by saying that Maeve and Ailill are safe 'for this time'?"

"This time," said she, "the King of the Shí has rehearsed mentally something which may become real the next time he tries to do it. It was so nearly real this time that you were able to see it happening. It will be so real the next time that it will happen, and the Queen of Connacht will die with many of her people unless they are warned, and can pit their wish against our wish; for we, be sure of it, will all wish together."

"And if they can do that?"

"If they can do that, nothing will happen."

"Can they do it?" he asked.

"There are wise poets and magicians in Cruachan," she replied.

"Where there is a poet there is a wish, and where there is a magician there is a will."

"Tell me this also," said Nera, "when does the King of the Shí mean to attack Cruachan?"

"On next Samhain, for at the Feast of Samhain the doors between this world and that world are opened, and those who desire to do so can pass from the one place to the other."

Nera beat his hands together.

"There is no hope," he cried, "for until next Samhain we cannot get out to give them warning, and it will then be too late."

"Do you greatly desire to do that?" she asked.

"By my hand, I do."

"Then," said she, "you can do it."

"But Samhain is past," said Nera.

"It is not past," she said.

Chapter XVIII

"Dear heart," said Nera, "you must bear with me, and forgive me, for I feel in my bones that I am overflowing with stupidity, and that the only words I shall henceforth utter will be words like 'why' and 'what' and the other ones that are used in front of questions. Tell me what you meant when you said they will not be attacked until next Samhain, and that this Samhain has not yet passed."

"I mean exactly that," she replied. "How long have you been here?"

Nera looked at her.

"I must think, lest I say something foolish—I have been here for three days."

"That is according to our time," she agreed. "But according to the time in your world, how long have you been here?"

"Three days."

"No," she said. "You have been here three minutes, for a minute of your time is a day of ours."

"Then," cried Nera, starting up, "this is still Samhain."

"It is."

"How long," she continued, "did it take you to go from the lawn of Cruachan to the hill where the outlaws were hanged?"

"Five minutes."

"And from there back again (for all the rest was magic) five minutes, and you have been three minutes here. The meal which was being prepared when you went away is not yet on the board; Ailill and Maeve are now looking for your return, and you have been absent from Cruachan exactly thirteen minutes."

Nera leaped again from his seat.

"I shall get my sword," he cried. "Tell me," he whispered urgently, "how shall I leave Faery?"

"Would you indeed leave me?" she pleaded, and the tears welled in her eyes and overflowed upon her cheeks.

But he seized her hands:

"I shall return," he promised her. "I could not now exist without you, but I must get the prize I won, or I shall never know happiness again; and I must warn the poets of Connacht of what may happen next Samhain. Tell me, O my dear heart and my one treasure, how can I leave Faery?"

"You will come back?"

"I will surely return," said he; "I swear by the powers of the elements and by the gods of my people that I will surely return."

"Then," said she, "I will tell you. You have only to go back the way you came. The door in the hill is open, for this is the night of Samhain, and when you pass through the door you will pass into the world you came from."

"But Maeve will not believe what I tell her," he cried lamentably. "She will say I am inventing a tale."

"Take fruits of summer with you," she counselled.

"That is a good idea," he agreed, and he breathed at last easily and calmly.

They went to the door then, and she gathered wild garlic and primrose and golden fern, and she put these into his hand, looking at him closely and sorrowfully as she gave the flowers.

But he was thinking of the way he had come; of the winding road that passed over rocky bridges and little bridges of wood, and that took its course in loops and twists and winding ways, with the sound of water brawling now on the one side and again babbling from the other.

"I must go," said Nera, "for I shall have a long journey before I come to the door in the hill."

"It will take a full quarter of a minute of your time," said she.

They kissed each other tenderly then, and parted.

"You will come back to me?" she called.

"I will surely come back," he called in reply.

Chapter XIX

He set out then, and at the bend of the road he halted to look back at the little house bowered among trees and flowering shrubs.

The late sunlight, half gold, half rose, was drowsing peacefully about it, and in the ear of memory he could hear the call and answer as dove murmured to dove from the roof-tree, and the drone of bees as they passed and repassed the windows.

He saw his delicious mate standing at the end of the little path that ran to the house, and they waved a hand to each other once, twice, and thrice.

Then he stepped aside into the wood bordering the roadway and set across to where the palace lay, and where the road began that went in loops and curls uphill and down; and so to the sunken path which ran under an arch of trees, and thus to the door in the hillside, and the world of men.

It was a long journey, but he beguiled it by thinking of what he was coming from and where he was going to; by thinking of the gold-hilted blade which would leave a King's side to be strapped on his own lean thigh. And he remembered her also, the honey-haired, the delicious; his comely mate, his tender-handed comrade; but when he had half turned to go back to her he remembered the evil which must fall on Connacht, and he remembered again the golden-hilted sword which he had won but had not got; and so he marched again, impatient, bewildered, tormented.

When he came nigh the end of his journey, the day, too, had ended. There was but a fleck of colour here and there on the western sky, and as he went these paled or sank below the horizon, so that when he reached the path arched over with trees all that daylight had gone, and he had to walk carefully lest he should strike against one of the trees which he could no longer see.

"I shall not know if I am in or out of the door," he thought, "this darkness is so profound. But," he also thought, "I must be close to it now, for I do not hear the river which I began to hear when I had marched a few minutes' distance from the door the last time."

He stood to listen, and was satisfied that no river was near him. He could hear nothing and see nothing, for the darkness and the silence were of equal unmitigated depth, and each seemed to be portion of the other.

He went forward again, and after a few stumbling paces a voice spoke, which brought him standing stiff as a tree-trunk.

"Who comes?" said the voice.

He remembered the words that had passed when he entered, and replied in these words.

"A man on the track here," he called.

"The heavier is the track," the voice replied jovially.

In two paces he passed the place whence the voice came from, and knew that he was through the door of Faery, and that he was back in the world of men.

Chapter XX

Now he knew where he was.

He started to run in the direction of the lawn of Cruachan,

and although he stumbled and fell, bruising himself against the rocks, and tearing his hands among the bracken, he yet continued to run, for he was wonderfully excited by the adventures he had passed through, and he wished with all his heart to look on men once more.

Hurrying thus he came to the skirt of the lawn, and outside the circle of lights cast by the torches he stood to compose himself, and to gaze. For it did not seem credible. that what he saw was true, and yet what he did see was so precise that he could not deny the evidence of his eyes.

Everything was as it had been when he went from the lawn to the hill of execution.

The torches were casting long golden flames among the branches of the tree, and the fire in front of the tent was tossing tongues of gold into the air. Ailill, the King, was stretched in the opening of the tent, and was still gazing out upon the darkness as though he were trying to pierce it with a profound meditation; and other people, men and women and servants, were moving peacefully or busily about the tent.

Nera stepped from the shadows, and as he advanced Ailill saw him and called out a welcome and a greeting.

"Well, my dear heart, so you did come back?"

"I have come for my prize," said Nera with sober excitement.

"You shall have it with my love, but you must tell us all that happened, for I perceive that something has happened."

"No, no," cried Maeve, "if there is a story to be told—"

"There is a story indeed," Nera interposed, and he laid into the King's hand wild garlic and primroses and golden fern.

"By my soul . . . !" said the King, staring, astounded, on a vanished summer.

". . . It must not be told during the feast," Maeve continued, "but at the banquet which will follow the feast, we can listen to it while we drink the royal liquors that I have provided."

While she spoke the servers and butlers came into the tent bearing mighty dishes and baskets, and the steam which arose from those dishes lent such a savour to the air that the tongues of every person present darted across their lips, and they moved with one accord towards the benches and tables which were ranged about the great tent.

It was a mighty and a glorious feast, and all that Maeve had said about it beforehand was surpassed, for she had not enumerated one-half of her bounty nor extolled in anything like measure the potency of her mead and wine.

When the feast was ended the banquet began, and when all present had been supplied with the drink they loved best, Ailill called to Nera:

"Come beside us on the dais, my darling, for I am sure that you have strange things to tell."

Nera went on the dais then, and he was given a great four-handed mether filled with ale, and when he had drunk to the health of Maeve and Ailill and to the health of the noble company, the mether was refilled for him, and he drank from it to his own satisfaction.

Then he commenced to tell of his adventures.

As he spoke, silence grew about the tent, and in a little time each person was leaning forward staring at him. The silence was so profound that if a pin had fallen each person present would have heard it, and frowned angrily. They forgot the ale as they listened; they forgot the sweet mead, and the glowing wine that had come from distant countries; and they hung on his words as though they had ceased to be men and women, and had become ears only.

When he had made an end to the tale a great sigh went through the tent, and then each person drank soberly from the methers and goblets which were before them, and they seemed to be sunken in a maze that was one-half astonishment and one-half reverie.

"It is a lovely story," said Maeve, "and I should willingly listen to it again."

"But I also," she continued, smiling on Nera, "am honey-haired, and there are some who think that I am sweet-cheeked and desirable."

Ailill sighed also, and stood up. He unstrapped the gold-hilted blade as he spoke:

"Good my soul," he said, "you have won your prize, and no better man will ever wear this sword than the man I am giving it to."

"Nay," cried Maeve indignantly, "it is I that shall give Nera the sword, for it is I am the Queen of Connacht and the giver of gifts in this country."

She took the sword from her husband, and she gazed so kindly on Nera that he was embarrassed and did not know where he should look. Then she strapped the weapon about his waist. As she bent beside him the scent from her hair and from her white shoulders came to him, but although he was moved and happy thereat, it was not of Maeve he thought while he stared down upon her noble head; he thought of the delicious, smiling comrade who was waiting for him in Tir na n-Og, counting the days and watching for his return from the door of a sun-steeped cottage.

"So," said Ailill thoughtfully, "the King of the Shí of Uaman thinks he can destroy Connacht! We shall be prepared for that person next Samhain."

"I shall march into his Shí, as I marched before," said Maeve fiercely, "and when I quit it this time there will be little left for Ethal Anbual to reign over."

"When did you attack the Shí of Cruachan?" Fergus inquired, "I have never heard of that sacking."

"You shall hear it now," Maeve returned, "for I will tell you the story myself."

She sat in the great seat then, and drank a little goblet of mead, and the Bell-Branch was rung so that the company again went silent.

Chapter XXI

Said Maeve:

In the days that are past and gone, Angus mac an Óg, the son of the Dagda Mór, was resting at the Brugh.

He had the gift of perpetual youth, and was therefore called the mac an Óg—The Son of the Two Young Ones. He had the gift of perpetual beauty, and was so called The Wonder; and he had the gift of magic, and was known by it as The Envious.

When he went abroad there accompanied him a cloud of birds that wheeled and sang about his head, so that when we see a cloud of wheeling and singing birds, all frantic with energy and exultation, we know that the son of the Dagda is passing, and we make obeisance to Youth and Beauty and Magic.

It happened that Angus was staying at his father's palace, the Brugh of Boyne, in the Shí of Ulster, for he had not yet cozened his father out of this palace. There had been a feast that night, with a banquet after the feast, and the time had passed in music and singing, and in the recitation of their verse by poets.

After the banquet, Angus went to bed, but he could not sleep. He lay looking on the darkness of his chamber, wondering why he was wakeful, and finding no reason for it. For he was in good health and spirits, and nothing had occurred to disturb his mind.

"Some one," he thought, "is practicing a magical art against me, and but that I do not wish to get out of bed I would weave magic also and destroy that influence, or I should find out where it comes from."

"And indeed," he thought also, "if I cannot go to sleep it is no great calamity, for I have slept many times and shall sleep many a time again."

While he was thus considering, the room lightened, and he saw a figure standing at a little distance from the bed. The young god raised himself on his elbow and looked intently on the figure.

He knew it was not real, because real things do not happen in this way: he knew it was not a dream, because he was awake; and he knew, therefore, that this must be a vision, or the wraith of a person come to visit him.

But the figure did not speak, nor did Angus.

They but looked at, and recognised each in the other the extreme and goal of all that was lovely in the world.

Angus sunk himself in that gaze, as a fish is immersed in water. He forgot all but the delicious face on which he was gazing. He forgot that this was but a vision; and he could only remember to look and look again, and to so concentrate his sight that he could see not only with his eyes, but with every member of his being, and with all the faculties of his mind.

He was lost in that look and drowned in it, so that when the vision faded he could not withdraw his eyes from that rigid forwardness and contemplation.

But the darkness did at last cloud his mind and enable him to withdraw his faculties and to become master of himself.

He sank back on the bed, full of joy, full of wonder and surmise, with his heart hurried by such happiness that it nigh broke from his bosom; and for a long time he lay in the stillness and darkness reconstructing a beauty such as even he had never contemplated before.

The hours of the long night passed for him in an ecstasy of wonder, in a recollection that was all happiness. But when the pale wraith of day began to move through the room, so that all things looked uncertain and discolored, his mood changed with the change that came to his eyes, and he began to remember that he did not know who had come to him, that he did not know where that lovely being might be, nor could he tell if she who had appeared would ever appear to him again.

For he knew that things which begin in one place can have their sequel in another, and may end far from either; and that the whole story may be unknown to any person except that lonely soul which is fulfilling itself in its own experiences.

Therefore, when he left the bed he left it weariedly, and his bearing was so depressed that all the people of the Shí noticed it, and at last his mother noticed it also.

His mother was Boann,[1] the wife of the Great Good God.

Chapter XXII

She questioned him, but as his replies were evasive or distraught, she gave up a fruitless inquiry and sought elsewhere for a solution of her son's trouble.

It was a trouble indeed. He fell sick of it, and would not talk to nor look at any one, nor would he reply to any person who addressed him.

He might glance for a moment on the questioner as though wondering why an inquisitive person should be in the room with him, and then he would turn his eyes aside and stare, far away in space, at something seen only by himself.

The physicians of the Shí were brought, but against his obstinate silence they could do nothing, for they did not seem to exist for him, and he himself did not seem to exist in the world where they were real.

Among these there was a physician whose name was Fergne.

He was a clever doctor. Not only did he understand the afflictions which the body may endure, he was versed also in those ills which come to the body from the mind; and when he had been with Angus for a little time he knew that, however bad his health might seem, the reason was not physical.

He spoke to Angus, and by dint of much speaking he insisted in time on being listened to.

"You know, Angus, dear heart, no one should lie in bed whose body is as healthy as yours is, and what I think is, that there must be a trouble in your mind which is drawing the energy from your limbs, and which will drain all virtue out of you unless you make a stand against it."

He went then and told Angus's mother.

[1] Boann = The River Boyne.

"The boy is in love. That is all that's wrong with him."

"But he always is in love," cried Boann; "love is his normal condition."

"It is his normal condition to have love given to him," replied Fergne; "but this time some one is withholding love from him, and he is sick from desire and dissatisfaction."

Boann and Fergne then returned to where Angus was:

"Brightness of my heart," said Boann severely, "we know what is wrong with you."

He smiled a scornful disbelief at that.

"You are not sick at all," said his mother; "you are in love."

And then, for those in love are convinced that all other people are foolish, Angus did not smile any longer. He looked admiringly at his mother and admitted that she had told the truth.

Then, for one discovered in love can no longer be silent about it, he told her of the vision which had come to him on the night of the banquet, and how, such was his trance of amazement and delight, he had let it go; and he told that he would die unless he saw the girl again; and he so told and retold these things that his mother had to stop him from any more tellings.

"Darling," she said, "I know all the women of Ireland, but I do not know one who resembles in any way the person you describe."

But Fergne declared that the mac an Óg had given a full description of every woman in the world, and he developed this theme to Angus.

"If your fawn had a hump on her back, or a lame leg. If she were one-eyed or covered with warts. If she were even a lunatic, or out-and-out mad, we should have something to look for.

"But," he continued, to Boann, "it is an endless chase that we are asked to go on; and, as an endless chase is a chase without an end, it is useless to begin it."

They heard then that the Dagda had returned from his visit to the Provincial Shís of Ireland, so Boann and Fergne went to him, and described the condition of his son, and how no one could tell what should be done.

Chapter XXIII

The Dagda Mór considered the extraordinary position.

"Angus does not know who the girl is?" he inquired.

"He does not."

"If he knew," the Dagda continued, "we could pick his brain and take the information from it; but, as nobody knows, why, there is no brain to pick, and I do not see what can be done. The boy has managed to get sick by himself, he must manage to get well by himself."

"There is nothing wiser than that to be said," Fergne agreed. But Boann was not satisfied.

"We must do something," she insisted.

"Make a suggestion," said the Dagda.

Boann then suggested that the Dagda should send visions to Angus of all the beautiful women of the Shís of Ireland; and, if that failed, of all the beautiful women of Ireland itself.

"It is a lengthy and cumbersome arrangement," quoth the Dagda.

"Can you suggest a better one?" she asked.

But he could not do so; and it was arranged that the experiment should be tried.

"I must be in the room passing the visions before him," said the Dagda, "so that when he recognises his beloved we shall know which of them it is, for the boy has become feather-brained, and might forget which woman of the sequence was the one he sought, and it would all have to be done again."

"And I," said Boann, "will be present also, for I should like to know which woman of the women of Ireland could make anybody sick for lack of her."

"I," Fergne cried gleefully, "will attend those visions with you, for there is nothing I like better than looking at pretty women, and this time I may see my fill of them."

The Dagda was considering:

"In what order and precedence should these ladies be presented?" he inquired.

"Queens first," replied Boann, "and then Princesses who are rulers of territories, and next Princesses of birth, and then Princesses of beauty, and after them—"

"I do not like that way. We should arouse the rage and jealousy of all the women of the Shí, for not one of them would be satisfied with the precedence allotted to her, except the very first one of all. Make another suggestion."

"Let them go in order of age," she advised.

"They are all twenty years of age," the Dagda mused, "and whoever denied that of any one of them would make a mortal enemy of that one. Make another suggestion."

"I can't," sighed Boann.

"Have you a suggestion?" he demanded of Fergne.

"I have, indeed."

"Then let us hear it," cried the Dagda.

"This is my suggestion," said Fergne: "Let the women be marshalled in the visions according to fatness and thinness; the fat beauties pacing before Angus according to their varying fatnesses, and the slender heroines moving before him in a diminishing scale."

"And when we come to the ones that are too thin to be seen?" the Dagda queried.

"These doves need not be shown at all," Fergne replied.

"There will yet be a question," the Dagda continued, "as to whether this one is as fat as this one, or whether this one is as slim as that?"

"Then let those dainty ones be marshalled according to color; the golden-haired, winsome enchantresses marching before Angus according as their hair is the colour of old gold or new; the proud dark-haired fawns moving in the like descending gradations; the brown-haired doves following in graded beautiful battalions; and the ardent red-haired sorceresses keeping their own brisk companies."

"It is a good advice," said the Dagda, "and that is the way I shall do it."

<h2 style="text-align:center">CHAPTER XXIV</h2>

This scheme was explained to Angus, and he agreed that it should be tried. But he was so anxious to see the girl again that he would have tested any scheme which promised to revive that loveliness.

He was ashamed, too, that he, the Master of Magic, could have been taken at unawares, and should have been so stupefied by any occurrence that he could neglect the very primaries and school-texts of his art; and he knew that the lady who was concerned would not easily forgive that carelessness.

He settled himself, therefore, to observe the visions.

His mother sat at one side of the couch; Fergne sat at the other, and at the head of the couch, between it and the wall, his father sat.

"When you see the lovely one you want, cry Hola," said the Dagda.

Angus Óg nodded comprehension.

"I," said Fergne, "shall look very particularly at that one."

By the power of the Dagda the sunlight which was pouring into the room faded and disappeared, and for a moment they sat in darkness.

Then the darkness glowed to a light that was like molten gold, with, seen far through it, a haze of purple, and while they stared through the golden radiance and at the purple haze, a figure moved out of the haze and stood in the golden light, and it seemed indeed as if the light flowed from her, so beautiful and proud was she, and it seemed also that if she retired the world would go black for lack of her.

"That is Fand, daughter to Bove, the King of the Shí of the Men of Femen," said Boann.

"Whether this be the right one or the wrong one," said Fergne, "what I counsel is, that Angus should take this one quickly, for, by my hand, there can be nothing more beautiful than she is under the eye of day."

But Angus made no remark and the vision faded.

"This one," Boann commended, "is Ailne of the White Shoulder, a Princess from the Shí of Leinster."

"She is lovely as a rose," said Fergne, "she is healthy as a trout, and sweet flavoured as an autumn nut. If Angus is not satisfied with this fawn it is because nothing will satisfy him."

"And this one," said Boann, "is ruler over the Shí of Meath."

"She is a joy for ever," Fergne cried. "She cannot be beaten, and she is the very girl that Angus craves for."

"Do you let this dove pass?" he cried reproachfully as the next vision came. "Will you blink at the Pearl of the World?"

But Angus did let her go.

"Now," Fergne said, "you will cry Hola: now you will surely say, this is the Queen."

And after that, in despair, Fergne ceased to importune him.

CHAPTER XXV

"I perceive," said the physician, "that you have begun with the plump women, and I perceive also that of created beings a well-rounded woman overtops all others, for she can set the heart at ease and fill the mind with fancy."

"There is," he said later, "much to be said of slender women; they have a grace of movement that is infinitely satisfying; they curve and flow."

"How agile the thin maidens are!" he murmured thoughtfully. "How deep is the appeal of their willowy youth!"

"But," he said again, "golden-haired is the one colour for women: only with gold are they adequately crowned."

"And yet," he murmured, "how winsome brown hair can be! What a shy sparkle lies in the braided tress, and how tenderly it finds the heart!"

"Noble," he asserted, "noble is the darkness piled above the dawn: majestic are the black-haired heroines; full of frolic and loveliness are they of the fragrant locks."

"To the red-haired queens I give the palm," he cried; "they warm the world; they are the true Honey of Delight."

The visions came and went, and Angus stared in a fever of hope and despair on each.

Ladies of all ages were there, from the wild young fawn of fifteen years to the massive and magnificent dame of forty.

There were ladies of royal fatness who moved vehemently upon the vision as a great ship, with all sail spread, bears mightily down the sea.

There were others, plump as corn-fed pigeons, active as hares, raising the wind as they passed and lifting the soul to journey with them.

And others again, vehement and bewitching, moving like fierce swans upon the water.

Eyes looked upon Angus that were proud and radiant. Eyes that were meek as doves or soft as the glance of a doe. Sparkling and forward-looking eyes stared from the vision as an eagle stares hardily on the sun. Eyes that were languishing and appealing. Side-sliding eyes. Eyes that tantalised. Eyes that shone with mischief, or stared with stubborn pride. Eyes that promised and appealed and dared and cajoled; and eyes that were contented or indifferent or curious.

They came and went, and as each came, Boann named her name and Fergne murmured a benediction.

"Here," he would say, "is a dove to satisfy even the mac an Óg."

Or:

"This is the Cluster of Nuts. This is the True Blossom of the Branches."

Or:

"To this one I give the palm, for she is surely the Berry of the Mountain."

Or again he would say:

"Now cry Hola, for here is the Star of the Bright Dawn: here is the Loveliness that Broods above the Day."

But Angus took no heed of these admonishments, except that at times he gave a groan, and, at times again, he sighed as though his heart had come and gone upon a bubble of air.

For a year and a day the visions continued, and at the end of that time the women of all the Shís of Ireland had been shown to Angus, and all the women of Ireland had been discovered to him as well.

The wives and daughters of Princes, the winsome consorts of ruling Chieftains, and the dear companions of Champions and Dragons of the Gael were brought before him; but among them he did not discover her for whom he sought; so that when the visions were ended he closed his eyes and lay back upon the bed, and he was delivered to a silence and despair twice as great as that in which he had been beforetime plunged.

CHAPTER XXVI

"I can do no more," said the Dagda.

"Nor could any one," Fergne interposed.

"There is not a woman in the two worlds of Ireland whom I have not brought before our son, and if among them all he cannot content himself it is because he cannot be contented."

"Now," said Fergne, "we are listening to the truth."

"Still," Boann insisted, "the child is sick."

"Make a suggestion," said the Dagda.

But she could not make a suggestion.

Also at that time she became ill at ease, and was agitated by movements and jerks, and half-sittings up and half-sittings down, so that even the Dagda noticed it.

"Dove of Time and Heart of the Heart of the World," said the Dagda, "tell me what it is that moves you and agitates you, so that you can neither sit nor stand nor stay easy?"

"I have seen too many women," Boann replied, "and I must go to some place where I can get the sight of them out of my eyes."

"Surely—" Fergne began in a tone of astonishment and expostulation.

"I wish," said Boann, "to go among my men-servants, and to watch them as they move with agility and circumspection about their work. I wish to look at our soldiers as they perform martial evolutions and leap and run. I wish to see short hair on heads and long hair on chins. I wish to see bald people—"

"Here," stammered Fergne, "is a wish indeed!"

"I wish to look into the eyes of oxen that do not squint or languish or peep. I wish to see legs," said she; "so I shall look steadily on horses and hens, on goats and sheep and warriors."

"In the matter of legs," said Fergne eagerly, "I can assure you—"

"I wish to look," she continued, "on hard and angular and uncomfortable things, for my mind is clouded and there is a bad taste in my mouth from the sight of those endless females."

"There is nothing," cried Fergne, "there is nothing more tonic to the soul or more lifting to the imagination—"

"I can quite understand," said Boann, "why Angus would not lay a finger or an eye on any one of them, for women are hideous and hairy and ridiculous."

"This is not wisdom," said Fergne; "this is not sound common sense."

"And," she continued, "when they are not long and bony and unpleasant they are short and stumpy and squashy, and I must go away now until I can forget that there are any of them living, and until I can discover if there are truly men moving in the world, for I have come to doubt all good things."

Boann left them then, in a condition of agitation and wrath, but Fergne thought that he would shortly have two patients under his hand, and that of the two it was the mother who was the most rankly ill.

CHAPTER XXVII

"Now," said the Dagda, "I don't know what to do, for I have shown Angus all the women of the worlds, and, unless it was a dream my son had instead of a vision, there is a woman somewhere whom we have not seen."

"That," Fergne commented, "is a ripe statement of the case. There must be some one who has hidden a notable pearl, or there is a dove that is modestly concealing itself among the branches."

"Have you a suggestion to make?" said the Dagda.

"I have."

"Then make it."

"Not hard to do," said Fergne, "and here it is. One of your vassal kings is famous for his knowledge of visions and apparitions and sorceries."

"Which of them is that?"

"It is Bove the Red, King over the Shí of the Men of Femen, and if you set him on the work he will discover the charmer that we lack."

"Let a message be sent to that Shí," the Dagda commanded, "to say that we will ourselves follow the messenger and that we shall expect a reply to our question."

"It may be," Fergne continued, "that Bove will have to call up those visions again, so I will go to him myself, for I should not like to miss the sight."

He set out then, and, when a reasonable time had elapsed, the Dagda followed with Angus, and they came to the Shí that Bove reigned over in Munster.

They were brought with all observance to the palace, and were given a feast which lasted for three days, and after the feast a banquet was given in their honour.

Chapter XXVIII

During the banquet a mood of depression came upon the Dagda, and, although Bove had every entertainment for him that was possible, the depression of the god deepened so that he could not listen to the people about him with calmness.

"Good my soul," said Bove in despair, "this banquet is in your honour."

"I cannot help that," the Dagda replied. "My mind is troubled and perplexed, and I feel a great inclination to weep."

"Weep then," Fergne counselled, "for where there is a surplus of salt in the blood weeping conveys away a quantity of that surplus. And," he continued, "it is because women weep easier than men that they are, on the whole, healthier than men."

"I feel," said the Dagda, "that the Heart of the Heart of the World was right, and that we have looked on too many women in these visions, and I think that something female and depressing comes on the mind when it has been too extensively occupied with that sex."

Fergne stared at the Lord of the Underworld.

"You do not say that!" he gasped.

"My wife said it."

"I," Fergne asserted, "have never felt better in my life than I feel now; and, by my hand, if I could see those lovely visions again, I should feel even better than I do now. For there is nothing more tonic to the mind and more uplifting to the understanding than the vision of doves that abound in health and beauty."

"Let it be so," said the Dagda in a tone of resignation.

Bove wished to keep the Dagda in discussion, for by thus holding his mind he might withdraw it from the abyss of dejection into which it threatened to plunge.

"But," he cried to Fergne, "do you truly consider that salt is bad for the system?"

"As everything in excess is, as everything retained too long is, for we must get rid of all that we have or suffer from the retention. And whether it be salt or treasure that we amass we keep them at our peril, for, being kept, they rot and will breed a plague in either the body or the soul."

"But about this salt," Bove insisted, "what do you recommend us to do?"

"Let us do in this, and in all other cases, exactly what the ladies do. Let us weep," said Fergne.

"Let us weep," Bove echoed dismally.

"Let every man weep once a day," Fergne continued, "and in the morning for preference: he will thus cleanse his mind, and he will wash his eyes also."

"I should not know how to weep now," said Bove regretfully. "I have long forgotten how it is done."

"It is for such emergencies that physicians are required," said Fergne, "and I shall tell you how to weep."

"Let us have that prescription," cried the Dagda.

"In the morning," Fergne commanded, "procure for yourself an onion; hold this close to your face and cut it with a blunt weapon, and in that way you will weep."

"And then I shall become as healthy as a woman," said Bove.

"Nearly so, but not quite," Fergne amended, "for the health of a woman truly depends on the amount of affection that she receives from a man. All women in love are healthy."

"I shall certainly search for an onion and an affectionate man," Bove commented.

But at that point the Dagda commenced to laugh.

At a sign from Bove a mether of wine was brought, and it was in extent like a well-sized field, and in depth it resembled a mountain pool, and the scent that came from it was like the fragrance of a clover meadow when the sun shines after rain.

The Dagda bent over this wine, and he gurgled into it so happily that the liquor foamed and creamed against the sides, and a thousand bubbles danced over the brim.

"Indeed, my good heart," said he, "you have made me weep, and my tears are salty."

"Do not taste them," commanded Fergne. "Do not re-imbibe that which you are counselled to reject."

"So far," said Bove, who wished to keep the Dagda occupied, "so far we have received excellent advice, and we may have weeping matches at fairs and tournaments; twelve men to weep against twelve women, and the winner to be presented with an onion, But I am in need of further advice."

"You are laughing at me," said Fergne, "and, as he who laughs will weep, you shall fulfil my prescription. I do not mind your laughter, however, and I am always ready to give advice to those who desire it."

"Nay," replied Bove, "this time it is the advice of our master that I seek."

"Tell me your perplexity, my love," said the Dagda.

Chapter XXIX

Said Bove:

Once there was a man in my service named Friuc. He had a wonderful art in the fattening of swine, but he was wonderful in everything that had to do with swine.

No person could make a pig go where he wanted it to go so willingly as Friuc could.

Everybody who knows anything knows that a pig would rather run a mile in the direction chosen by himself than sidle an inch along the track counselled by another: for pigs have unlimited confidence in themselves, but they have no faith in other creatures, nor have they any trust in the gods.

But Friuc could do whatever he pleased with a pig. They used to rub against his leg like pet dogs, and they always wanted to go to sleep with their heads in his lap. But, if they loved Friuc, Friuc loved them.

He might be impatient with a member of his family—he was

never impatient with a pig. He might exclaim angrily against a horse that trod on his foot, but he would have let a pig eat him. However, although a pig will eat anything, there was not a pork in Munster that would lay a tooth on Friuc otherwise than in affection.

On account of his mastery over, and his understanding of pigs, Friuc was appointed my Chief Swineherd.

It happened that the King of one of the Western Shís, Ochall Oichni by name, had a noted swineherd, one Rucht, and, unless it was Friuc, this Rucht of Connacht had no equal in swine tending. He was a wonder. These two were the champion pig tenders of the Shí. There were some who said that Friuc was the better man of the two, but as many held this to be inexact and claimed that it was Rucht who took the branch. But these famous swineherds were great friends, and they used to meet frequently to discuss curious points about pigs.

Whenever there was a great fall of mast in Munster Friuc would send news of it to Connacht, and Rucht would come, playing on a pipe, leading his charges behind him to fatten in the good Munster beechwoods.

Friuc did this because he liked Rucht, but more he did it because he could not bear to think that any pig was going without his share of what was good for him.

On the other hand, when mast was plentiful in Connacht (which was not so often) Rucht would invite Friuc and his droves to the western forests, and they would go there galloping and would eat Connacht mast and grunt with delight and gratitude.

But the baser sort strove to arouse ill-feeling between the friends; for there are people who cannot bear to see friendship anywhere; people whose hearts are set in ill-humour and violence and war, and these people succeeded at last in raising bitterness between the swineherds.

Chapter XXX

There had been a great fall of mast in Munster.

Within the memory of man there had not been such a provision of the succulent nuts. Under the beech trees the ground was a foot thick in mast; and in places, deep in the forest, where growth was thick or the sun had ingress, the ground was covered to a depth of three feet with mast. And in yet other nooks and crannies of the loopy wood, where there had been a driftage caused by the wind, there were depressions of great profundity, and in these there was a choke and overflow of mast.

The swine of Munster, every pig of the Munster pigs, as well as those of the King, were led into, or let into, the forest by Friuc; and while they were there the sound that arose from among the trees became so deafening that all Munster thrilled to it, and no other sound was heard in the kingdom.

When one listened from a distance it seemed as if a violent sea and a storm of thunder were hammering against a circular rocky shore and echoing back and forth in mighty peals and clashings.

People who lived nigh the forest went mad from the exuberance of that uproar, and, under the delusion that they were swine, they bolted into the forest and pigged it among the pigs.

Those who lived farther away deserted their dwellings and sought hospitality afar.

And those who resided at yet greater distances put plugs of hay into their ears and were enabled to exist in an uproar which they came to look upon as silence.

By day and night that noise, which was composed of squeals and screams; of grunts and gasps; of loud, noisy whistles and deep thrilling gurglings, continued; so that at last the only contented creatures in Munster were the pigs, and Friuc.

He moved tranquilly among his friends, looking at this one's muzzle and at that one's hoof; binding the torn ear of this innocent, and examining that bonneen which was still at milk and thriving on it.

He was happy, and he sent a messenger to Rucht to tell of the good fortune, and to invite him with his droves to the fête.

Rucht came, playing a rustic sweet air upon a pipe, and the swine of Connacht moved behind him in mighty concentrations.

Line after line, along a line that ran out of sight on either side, they came, and on the tails of the first line the noses of the second line rested.

And, behind them, farther than a crow's eye can peer, the pigs of Connacht galloped and pranced; sneezing because of the dust they were raising; yawning after their beloved master, and at intervals making each one the kind of noise with which he was individually gifted.

They marched into the Beech Forests of Munster and disappeared there. But if they vanished from the eye the ear lost nothing of them.

CHAPTER XXXI

Before the Connacht swine arrived there had been a brain-destroying uproar; but now there was a noise for which no description may be found.

Plugs of hay were no longer of any use.

The ear-drums of people blew up inside their heads and exploded violently into the eye or the nose of the neighbour.

While those whose ears were tough took to their heels and ran:

Pell-mell, hodge-podge, helter-skelter—

Charging into choked roads and unchoking these by sheer impetus, and not a stop did a man of them make until they came into Leinster of the Learned Men.

From there some surged sideways and westward to Connacht, while others fled to the north and the grim keeps of Ulster.

It was a marvellous time, a wild time, a time of madness. There were people who shouted:

"Death to the swineherds!"

And others who roared:

"Destruction to the pigs!"

Woe followed them, so that when a man went into a house and saw a piece of pork hanging from a rafter, he would go backwards out of the house with a buzz, and would not stop running until his wind gave out.

Or if a man saw a head of cabbage growing in a field it would remind him irresistibly of a slice of bacon, and he would leap on the cabbage with both feet until the last trace of anything but destruction vanished from the murdered plant.

So far for that.

Friuc and Rucht were where they liked to be—they were among pigs.

The noise of pigs was not a noise to them. It was a suitability, a thing worth listening to.

Nor did it silence them; for they were aware of the infinite gradation of sounds that is in all sound, and into these intervals of quietude, that were less noisy than the crash of Doom and only a little noisier than a hurricane, they injected such remarks as they wished to exchange, and felicitated each other on the happiness about them.

Thus the first day passed, and at night Friuc and Rucht lay down to sleep on the back of six large swine who were lying all in and out, and who had eaten so solidly that they could not wag a hoof, a bristle, or an ear.

Good sleep was with the comrades, and they rested till the dawn.

CHAPTER XXXII

It was the pigs they were lying on that awakened them, and although the language of swine is not comprehended by everybody, Friuc and Rucht understood it well.

This is what the pigs said:

"Darlings of all Darlings, and Pets of the Pigs of the World, get off our backs, for our food is digested, and there is more of it to be eaten."

They then, with precaution, rolled their masters to the ground, and they became jaws and enjoyment and a new portion of the contemporary noise.

Now it is a curious thing that women awaken in the morning uncomely but gay, while men arise to the new day as though they were being reborn into unhappiness; for at the dawn a man is ill-tempered, and a great discoverer of insult.

Friuc and Rucht, being males, were thus constituted. They arose with quietly bad tempers, and each did his best to look at a place where the other was not.

Also, they had no breakfast, for they had forgotten to bring any; and that lack assisted their uncheerfulness to become morose.

Rucht, as the visitor, considered that Friuc, as the host, should have provided him with food; and Friuc thought that the man who had come on a journey should have had the common prudence to bring food with him.

But the Connacht man did not quite see his way to open a subject which must exacerbate his host, and a Munster man is too polite to refer to a personal grievance until he has transformed it into something else.

"They say in Connacht," Rucht commenced, "that you are a better swineherd than I am."

"And they tell me here in Munster," Friuc replied, "that it is you are the better."

"They are trying to make trouble between us," said Rucht with a sigh. "But they can't do it."

"That is true," Friuc agreed dolefully. "They are trying to make us fall out and we won't please them. But," he continued after a moment's pause, and in a deep and thoughtful voice, "But all the same—"

"All the same, what?"

"Nothing; I was thinking."

"I don't like these 'all-the-sames,'" commented Rucht.

"No one said you did," Friuc retorted.

"What are you driving at?" Rucht demanded hotly.

"I am driving at the thing the Connacht man hit when he aimed at the bird—nothing at all."

"All the same!" Rucht quoted morosely.

"Well, if you want to know what I was thinking, I'll tell you. I was thinking that the people who say I am the best swineherd are right, even if they are Connacht men."

"I was thinking the same thing," said Rucht, "but I was thinking it the other way round."

"I'll prove that I'm right," said Friuc.

"Prove it," his companion roared.

"Your pigs are here," Friuc continued, "and they can stay here, but not one inch of fat will one Connacht pig add to his Connacht ribs for all he eats; and the dear knows that a Connacht pig can eat nearly as much as a Connacht man."

And that happened, for Friuc put a spell on the foreign pigs.

The more they ate the thinner they got.

It was as though they were eating hunger, while the swine of Munster throve exceedingly.

Each of the Munster pigs had at first three chins to his jaw, but after a time they got six chins apiece. In another while they had chins all the way down to their hooves. Their stomachs fattened and descended until they rested on the ground so that they had to go to sleep standing up.

Their eyes were so bolstered in fat that they could only look straight in front of them, and their tails disappeared in the overlapping rotundity of their hams.

Chapter XXXIII

But in the matter of the Connacht pig—
The more he ate the leaner he got.

He had been jowled like a Leinster bard, and chinned like a king's baby; but his chins tumbled off him two at a time, and his swagging jowl ran up into his ear.

He became gaunt as a winter wolf and spiny as a hedgehog.

His skull stuck out, lean as a hatchet and pointed as a spear.

His legs grew as lanky as a young foal's, and his upper anatomy was all chest and no stomach like a coursing hound.

His tail poked outwards and downwards like a piece of wet string pasted on a bone.

There was no curl in his tail.

Thus he was, and thus they all were.

As they grew skinny they became afflicted with a rage of eating which was terrifying, and with an agility to baffle the eye that watched them.

You could see what they did, but not how they did it, for they moved too fast.

They leaped into a place where mast was, scooped it clean in an hundred swift gobbles, and bounded thence to another place, with the bound of a red deer and the savagery of a bear.

Their hunger was such that they screamed from the rage of it, and the air whistled through their long lean snouts like the whistle of a wintry gale through a hole.

There were no people left in Munster but the deaf men, and they recovered their hearing; that is, they had hearing thrust violently upon them, and they cursed the gift as they fled.

The people far away in Leinster took to plugging their ears with wads of hay when they wanted to go asleep, but not a wink did they get.

The crows, who for a long time tried to compete with the pigs, caved in, and gave up, and emigrated.

There wasn't a bird left in a tree, nor a beast left in a cave.

The worms of Munster went far underground, and maybe they perished there.

And the fish in the streams and rivers battered their noses to bits and broke their fins trying to swim up-stream against time.

They came floating back again with their bellies turned up, and not a wag left in a fin; dead they were.

It began to rain, too, for the noise brought the rain down.

But the Connacht pigs did not stop. They gave a squeal, a leap, a whistle, and a gobble, and they did that, all day long and all night long, as long as the mast lasted.

The mast could not outlast that ravage.

They cleaned the forests of mast in a day and a half.

They ate the leaves that had fallen.

They chewed the bark off the trees; at first as high as they could reach, but afterwards as high as they could jump; and they could jump like cats.

They rooted up the grass and ate it.

They ate clay.

They cleared the forests of all the droppings of all the pigs.

They picked up stones in their mouths, and mumbled at them until they got the toothache.

And they overturned Munster hogs that were too fat to right themselves, and ate the hooves off these while they lay helpless.

They would have eaten the young ones, only that Friuc stopped them, for he couldn't stand it.

"Be off with your pigs," he commanded. "Take them out of my forests and out of my sight, and don't let a hoof of theirs or of yours step in this land again."

"I'll go," Rucht replied, "but I know what you did and how you did it.

"I can do it myself," said he.

"You can crow here," he shouted, "but come to Connacht and crow if you dare.

"I'll do as much to your pigs as you did to mine, You-This-And-That of Munster!" he roared.

"Emigrate from here," cried Friuc; "get out of Munster," he cried.

"I will," Rucht replied, "I'll fly the land where a man doesn't get his breakfast, and the pigs eat wind."

"Come on with you," he called then to his swine.

They ran howling, weeping, squealing to him, and he set himself at their head and started running like a hare.

Chapter XXXIV

He did not stop running until he got to Connacht, but the track of land that stretches from the Beech Woods of Munster to the Swine Pens of Connacht was a desert for years after their passing, for the Connacht pigs ate that land to the butt, and ruined it.

Friuc then took up Rucht's challenge and followed him with his swine.

But in Connacht the tables were turned on him, and the Munster swine became so lean that you could only see them by looking at them very steadily, and for a long time, and sideways at that; and, even then, it was only a streak you saw.

That was how enmity began between the swineherds. The pigs of both were ruined, so that I told Friuc I did not want him any longer as a swineherd, and Ochall Oichni said the same thing to Rucht.

But the swineherds were unrepentant.

They did not want employment.

They had more than enough to do chasing each other, for that became their employment, and they went at it day and night.

Wherever they met they fought, and although each stretched the other at the door of death, either of them was able to push the other through.

They began to change shapes then, thinking that in another form they might have a better chance; but they were always equal. One bit and the other tore, and the tear was as bad as the bite. They harried each other out of this shape and into that. They fought as birds, and in that shape they were known as Talon and Wing. Then they fought as sea-beasts and were called Shark and Whale. Then they became spectres called Shadow and Woe, and after that they were dragons. And in all these shapes they fought savagely.

Each of them half-killed and three-quarter killed his rival; but neither could absolutely get the victory over the other, and they cannot rest until they find out which of them is the better man.

They have been like that for seven years.

"What are they now?" the Dagda inquired.

"They are bulls, and they are both in Connacht in strong well-separated pens. They are in the Shí of Eithal Anbual, and they have been quiet for a long time."

"And what was the advice you wanted?" Fergne asked.

"I wanted to know how these enemies might be made friends again."

"They fell out over pigs, let them fall in over pigs. Feed them on bacon," said Fergne.

"They are not really enemies," said the Dagda. "They only wish to know which is the better man. It is not a question of hate, but of fact, that is between them, and when they have settled this they will be able to be friends again. But as they have taken up the burden of proof they must carry it through, and no one can help them."

Bove was contented with this statement, not because he was assisted by it, but because he noticed that the Dagda had forgotten his depression; and it was to make his master merry that he had told the tale.

Musicians and dancers and jugglers were then called in, and the gaiety of the Dagda was such that he gave rich presents to these entertainers, and, when the company separated for the night, each went to his bed in high good humour, but the Dagda went to sleep in the merriest humour of them all.

Chapter XXXV

On the day following the banquet the Dagda asked an account from Bove of the work he had ordered him to do.

"That girl," said he, "who has been destroying my son Angus; what have you discovered about her?"

"I have found the girl," said Bove.

"Was I a good counsellor?" Fergne cried joyfully.

"Who is she?" the Dagda inquired.

"She is Caer, the daughter of Ethal Anbual, King of the Shí of Uaman in the kingdom of Connacht; and she is in her father's Shí at the Lake of the Dragon's Mouth, hard by the place known as the Harp of Cliach."

"Now," said Fergne, "Angus can go to that place and take his treasure."

"I have no power," cried the mac an Óg peevishly. "I am consumed by desire, and cannot control my will."

"But let us be certain," the physician continued, "that you have found the right girl, for if we make a mistake now we might give the matter up in despair. Call her up in a vision," he suggested eagerly.

So that was done.

The Dagda made first a darkness, and then a golden radiance, and then they looked through the purple haze which was beyond the radiance.

They saw a sandy strip, and sunshine, and a rolling sea: and upon that strand a band of girls were romping. Among them there was one taller than the rest, and, although the others were beautiful, this one was so lovely that she could scarcely be looked at. She dazzled the eye as the sun does, and she filled the mind with delight and wonder, so that the person who looked at her forgot to think, and could remember nothing beyond that beauty.

"Do you cry Hola to that?" gasped Fergne. "If you do not say Hola to her I shall say it myself."

"She is my love beyond the loves of the worlds," said Angus, "she is the crown of the soul and the fulfilment of desire."

"She is," cried Fergne. "I swear by my hand that she is all that has been said, and all that has not been said, and it is to her I give the palm."

The vision then faded, and Angus sat with Bove and Fergne on his either hand, and they were all stupefied with wonder.

Chapter XXXVI

"Why has Ethal Anbual concealed his daughter from me?" the Dagda asked.

"He conceives that you have no right to demand her," Bove replied.

"And it is true that I have no such right," said the Dagda, "and, therefore, there is no more to be said on this matter, and we may all go home."

"But the boy!" said Fergne, "the boy will fade away."

"Have you a suggestion to make?" said the Dagda.

"I have one," Bove interposed.

"Make it," said the Dagda.

"It would be very wrong of us to do a thing that was wrong," said Bove, "and, therefore, we shall not do it."

"We certainly shall not," Fergne agreed.

"But there are other people, and it is right for those people to do what is wrong."

"How so?" said Fergne, scandalised.

"Wrongdoing is their base of existence," said Bove.

"What people are those?" the Dagda inquired.

"Mortals," Bove replied.

"Indeed," cried Fergne, "I do not often hear truth and wisdom spoken, but this time I hear it with my two ears."

"Give power for a day to mortals," Bove counselled. "They will get the girl for us, and there will be an end to all this anxiety."

"Who is the mortal King of Connacht?" the Dagda asked.

"There is not really a King," Bove replied; "there is a Queen and her consort."

"And this Queen?"

"She is Maeve, daughter of the High King of Ireland: she is the noblest of the queens of the world, and she is the most beautiful woman under the sun."

"I shall certainly look closely on that Queen," said Fergne.

"We shall visit Maeve of Connacht about the Feast of Samhain," said the Dagda, "for at that time the doors are opened between this world and that one, and whoever dares . . . Will this Queen dare to enter Faery?"

Bove replied to that with conviction:

"There is nothing that Maeve of Connacht would not dare, for she is not alone beautiful, she is greatly courageous."

"I shall seek her assistance," the Dagda announced.

"Now, Angus, my heart," cried Fergne jovially, "you may begin to get well, for although that fawn is not yet in your arms, she is condemned to them and cannot escape."

"I do feel better," said Angus; "I begin indeed to feel well."

"But," Fergne concluded, "the person I wish to see, and the person whom I must see, is this courageous and lovely Queen, for I feel assured that she is the Silk of the Flock and the Early Fragrance of the Hawthorn. How does this fawn look?" he asked. "Is she dark and slender and of a middle stature?"

"She is tall and well-rounded," Bove replied. "She is long-faced and pale, and her hair shines like gold."

"It is thus she should be," Fergne agreed, "and it is in that fashion I shall think of her."

CHAPTER XXXVII

The Feast of Samhain was at hand, and when it wanted but three days to the Feast, the Dagda, with Angus and Bove and Fergne, set out for Connacht, and a company of sixty chariots went with them. They reached Connacht at noon of the day before the Feast, and a messenger was sent from them to the palace demanding an interview of Ethal Anbual.

But the King of the Shí of Connacht refused to grant it.

"I know what the Dagda wants," he said; "I will not consent to give my daughter to Angus Óg."

When the messenger returned evening was advanced, and the hour was almost at hand when the doors are down between the two realms, so that the Dagda and his company mounted their chariots and drove in the direction of the door in the hillside. When they reached it the door was open, and they passed through it and rode into the world of men.

From the hillside to the palace at Cruachan Ai was but a short journey, and in five minutes the guards at Cruachan reported that a company was advancing on the palace. In another minute preparations had been made to receive them, and in one minute more they were at the fortifications.

They were ushered into the palace with ceremony and respect, for neither the guards, the chamberlains, nor the servants had ever before seen a host so beautifully apparelled, or with such comely dignity of bearing, for they were plumed and crested with fire, and they were radiant as the sun itself.

Maeve was seated on her throne in the great reception hall, but when the Dagda appeared so great was his majesty and so noble his regard that she rose to receive him, and seated him on a throne beside her own, so that the Dagda sat on her right hand, Ailill, her husband, on her left, and the other people of the Shí were given honourable places.

"Will you tell your name and qualities yourself," asked Maeve, "or shall we send for your heralds to recite them?"

"I am the Dagda Mór," said her guest. "I am the High King of the people of Dana, and Lord Supreme of the Kingdoms of the Dead."

"And I am Maeve of Cruachan, daughter of the High King of Ireland, and Ruler of the Realm of Connacht."

The people of the Dagda and Maeve's people were introduced to each other in seemly order, and then, for Maeve was a famous housekeeper, a feast was brought in, and for the space of three hours it was enjoyed by all who were present and was praised.

Chapter XXXVIII

"I think," said Fergne, who had been looking at Maeve as one in a trance, "I certainly think that this Queen is more worthy to be called Hola to than even the daughter of Ethal Anbual is."

"This Queen is married," Bove remarked.

"Would you limit the joy of life?" cried Fergne reproachfully. "Would you put a stay to happiness?"

He stroked the beard that flowed down to his middle like a river of silver silk, and became lost in that contemplation.

The Dagda then set before Maeve the whole of the story that has been told, and, after she had spoken with her counsellors, and been advised by them that she should have nothing to do with the matter, Maeve decided that she would give the assistance required.

"For," said she, "I have never yet paid a visit to Faery, and as I am the ruler of Connacht I should like to see the ruler of the Shí of my own country."

One of her counsellors interposed:

"There has always been peace between the Shí and Cruachan; but after this there may be ill-feeling and bicker, and who knows if the High King of the Shí will protect us from the vengeance of the Tribes of Dana."

"I will answer for that," replied the Dagda. "No harm shall come to Connacht from the people of the Shí, although much may happen in Connacht in consequence, for no action can cease until it has worked out all its possibilities."

"If you guarantee me against the Shí," said Maeve, "I will be my own guarantor for all that may happen in Connacht or in Ireland."

That was settled, and, as the evening was advanced and the darkness great, it was decided that they should set out at once while the doors of Faery were open, and in half an hour Maeve, at the head of a thousand chariots, was dashing to the hill of Cruachan.

CHAPTER XXXIX

She sacked the Shí of Uaman, and took away booty and treasure, and she took Ethal Anbual and all his chief people prisoner, and she brought away from the Shí two young bulls, one of which was known as The Whitehorn and the other was called The Brown Bull.

"These bulls," said Ethal Anbual, as he stared fiercely on Maeve, "will avenge me."

"They will do what they can," Maeve replied, "and in order that you may have a fair chance of being revenged, I shall keep the bulls."

"That is sound sense and queenliness," said Fergne.

"And," said Bove, "our famous Swineherds are off on their travels again."

"Are those the two you told me of?" the Dagda inquired.

"They are the identical two," Bove answered. "There go Friuc and Rucht."

"There is many a man of Ireland and of Connacht will come to my realm because of these bulls," Ethal Anbual repeated.

"Is that true?" Maeve inquired.

"It is not a lie indeed," the Dagda replied.

"We must all come sometime to the Country of the Dead," said Maeve, "and whether we come on account of these bulls or on some other account does not greatly matter, and, therefore, I shall take the bulls."

"And now about your daughter!" said the Dagda.

"My daughter is no concern of yours," replied Ethal Anbual. "It is true that I am your vassal, and in all proper ways I render obedience and service, but my daughter does not come within your rights."

"That is verity," the Dagda agreed. "I do not properly see what we can do."

"I do not wish to see my daughter married to the mac an Óg," Ethal Anbual continued, "for there is a feud between Angus and myself, and therefore I shall not give her up to him."

"There is nothing left us but to go home," said the Dagda.

"But we cannot go home until we have performed what we set out to do," Bove insisted.

"Have you a suggestion to make?" cried the Dagda.

"I have indeed."

"Then make it," said the Dagda.

"It is," said Bove, "that if this thing is to be done by mortals, we should let mortals do it."

"Now . . ." cried Fergne.

But Maeve broke in tempestuously:

"I came to get this girl, and I shall not go away until I have got her."

"I think also," she continued, turning fiercely on Ethal Anbual, "that it is an impertinence for any chit to refuse the embraces of a proper man like Angus."

"The girl does not wish for these embraces," he replied stubbornly.

"Let her wish or not wish, she must be given to me, for by my hand, I shall not leave without her, and the booty I have already seized is nothing to the plunder I shall presently take unless that girl is given to me."

"That is the way to talk," cried Fergne. "It is thus deeds are done, even by a dove."

"The girl does not desire to go," said Ethal Anbual. "I cannot force her. She is a Mistress of Arts."

"How do you know that she does not wish to go with Angus?" asked the Dagda.

"She told me that herself," he replied triumphantly.

"That settles it," said the Dagda mournfully. "If she does not wish to go she cannot be forced."

"Of course she wishes to go," cried Maeve.

"But she told her father . . ."

"What a girl tells her father is seldom of any importance and is never true."

"She is cold-headed as a spring morning," cried Fergne. "She is warm-blooded as a summer noon. Now we are listening to wisdom indeed."

Maeve leaned to Ailill.

"That companion of the Dagda pleases me very much, and although he is old he is robust."

She turned again to Ethal Anbual.

"If you wished to conceal your daughter, why did you send her wraith and vision to Angus the mac an Óg?"

"By my word," cried Ethal Anbual, "I did not send that vision, and, by my hand, I would not let the son of the Dagda see anything I possess, for he is envious, and a thief."

"If you did not send the vision," said Bove, "who sent it?"

"I know nothing of that."

"The girl sent it herself," said Maeve, "and she sent it because she wanted Angus to see her, and to desire her, and to come after her."

"Yes?" said Bove.

"And the reason she wanted the mac an Óg to desire her was because she desired the mac an Óg."

"This Queen gets the palm," cried Fergne. "I cry Hola to this Queen, for she is the Pulse of the Heart, and the very Tongue Tip of Wisdom."

"That nobleman," said Maeve to Ailill, "is not only pleasant and courteous and robust; he is also intelligent."

"Where is this girl?" she demanded of Ethal Anbual.

"She is at the Lake of the Dragon's Mouth," he replied sullenly.

"Go there," Maeve counselled to Angus Óg. "You will find that she is waiting for you, and you will find that she is impatient."

"And now," she said, turning to Ethal Anbual, "I shall return the booty I took from you; that is, the Crown of Bruin, the Mantle of Laery and the Shirt of Dunlaing, for I did not come to sack the Shí, but to give help to the Dagda, and to bring two lovers together."

"You will also return The Whitehorn and The Brown Bull," said Ethal Anbual.

"I shall not give them back," she cried. "You have threatened me about those bulls, and against a threat I will maintain my defiance and my power.

"And now," said she, "I will go back to my own country."

The Dagda then gave her three kisses, and it was thus Maeve of Cruachan went into and out of Faery on that occasion.

CHAPTER XL

"That is the story of the sacking of the Shí of Cruachan," she said to Fergus.

She turned to Nera.

"But next Samhain I shall go there again, and I shall not leave what will be worth any king's reigning over."

"Tell me," said Fergus, "what happened to those bulls you took from the Shí?"

"The Whitehorn is here in Connacht. It is the master of my husband's herds, but The Brown Bull would not stay with us; it took itself away to Cuailgne in Ulster, and it is just as well that it did go off, for Connacht is not wide enough to hold two such bulls. No person could sleep for their roarings at and challengings to each other, and if they meet, one or both of them will be dead before they can be separated. Therefore, I do not greatly mourn for the loss of The Brown Bull. But as it is," said she, "there is not a bull in the whole of Connacht that dares to give one bellow out of him for dread and terror of The Whitehorn."

"And the threat of Ethal Anbual as to the disasters to be worked in Ireland by reason of those bulls?"

"That," said Maeve, "will be as it will be. But you do not drink!" she cried to Nera.

"I must crave your leave to depart before the door in the hillside closes," said Nera, "for I made a bargain and a compact with my comrade that I would surely return to her."

"If you must return, you must return," Maeve replied, "and we will ourselves go with you a little distance, and will send with you our greetings and affection to that lovely lady you told us of."

"When you come next Samhain," said Nera, "you will not sack her house."

"We shall spare that house for your sake and for hers," the Queen answered.

Nera set out then with Maeve and a royal company, and when they reached the hillside he bade them farewell, and they bade him farewell with a blessing.

Then Maeve returned to Cruachan Ai with her people, and Nera went on into the Shí, and 'tis said that he will not come out of the Shí till Doom.

from Etched in Moonlight

HUNGER

I

On some people misery comes unrelentingly. It comes with such a continuous rage that one might say destruction had been sworn against them and that they were doomed beyond appeal, or hope.

That seemed to her to be the case as she sat, when her visitor had departed, looking on life as it had moved about her; and she saw that life had closed on her, had crushed her, and that there was nothing to be said about it, and no one to be blamed.

She was ten years married, and she had three children. One of them had fallen when he was a baby, and had hurt his back so badly that the dispensary doctor instructed her not to let him walk for a few years.

She loved all her children, but this child she loved greatly; for she had to do more for him than for the others. Indeed she had to do everything for him, and she did not grudge doing it. He was the eldest and was always with her. The other youngsters wore with her as screamings, as demands, to be attended to and forgotten, but he was with her as a companion eye, a consciousness to whom she could talk and who would reply to her, and who would not, could not, by any means get into mischief.

349

Her husband was a house-painter, and when work was brisk he got good wages: he could earn thirty-five shillings a week when he was working.

But his work was constant only in the summer months: through the bad weather there was no call for him, for no one wanted house-painting done in the winter; and so the money which he earned in the fine months had to be stretched and made to cover the dead months.

Nor were these fine months to be entirely depended upon: here and there in a week days would be missed, and with that his Society dues had to be paid, for he would pay these though he starved for it.

II

Wages which have to be stretched so lengthily give but the slenderest sum towards a weekly budget. It was she who had to stretch them, and the·doing of it occupied all the time she could spare for thinking.

She made ends meet where nothing was but ends, and they met just over the starvation line.

She had not known for years what it was like not to be hungry for one day; but life is largely custom; and neither she nor her husband nor the children made much complaint about a condition which was normal for them all, and into which the children had been born.

They could scarcely die of hunger for they were native to it. They were hunger. There was no other hunger but them: and they only made a noise about food when they saw food.

If she could have got work how gladly she would have taken it! How gladly she would have done it! Sweated work! Any work! so it brought in if it was no more than a few coppers in the day. But the children were there, three of them, and all were young and one was a cripple.

Her own people, and those of her husband, lived, existed, far

away in the country. They could not take the children off her
hands. She could not give a neighbor anything to look after them
while she went out working. She was held to them as fast as if
she were chained to them; and, for to think in such cases is only
to be worried, there was no use in thinking about it. She had
already all the work she could deal with, and she wanted no
more.

She remembered a tale that she had laughed at, when she was
young, about a woman who had been circumstanced as she was
now. This woman used to put her two children into a box, for
she had to go out every day to work in order that she might feed
them; and she kept them in the box so that they might not injure
themselves during her absence.

It was a good idea, but the children came out of the box
hunchbacks, and so stunted in their growth that it might be said
they never grew thereafter. It might have been better for the
children, and easier for them, if they had died; anyhow, their
mother died, and the poor little oddities went to the workhouse;
and must all their lives have got all the jeers which their appearance sanctioned.

There was nothing to be done; even her husband had long ago
given up thinking of how this could be arranged; and although
she still, and continually, thought about it, she knew that nothing
could be done.

III

Her husband was a jolly man; he used to make up lists of the
gigantic feeds they would have when the ship came home (what
ship he did not say, nor was it understood that he expected one),
and he or she or the children would remind each other of foods
which had been left out of his catalogue; for no food of which
they knew the name could justly be omitted from their future.

He was a robust man, and could have eaten a lot had he got
it. Indeed he had often tempted his wife to commit an act of

madness and have one wild blow-out; for which, as she pointed out to him, they would have to pay by whole days of whole starvation, instead of the whole days of semi-hunger to which they were accustomed.

This was the only subject on which they came nigh to quarrelling, and he brought it forward with fortnightly regularity.

Sometimes she went cold at the thought that on some pay-day he might go in for a wild orgy of eating, and perhaps spend half a crown. Less than that sum could not nearly fill him; and the double of it would hardly fill him the way he needed to be filled; for he wanted to be filled as tightly as a drum, and with such a weight and abundance of victual that he could scarcely be lifted by a crane.

But he was an honourable man, and she knew that he would not do this unless she and the children were with him and could share and go mad with him. He was very fond of them, and if she could have fed him on her own flesh she would have sacrificed a slice or two, for she was very fond of him.

IV

The mild weather had come, and he got a cut in his hand, which festered and seemed stubbornly incurable. The reason was that the gaunt man was not fed well enough to send clean blood down to doctor his cut hand. In the end he did get over it; but for three weeks he had been unable to work, for who will give employment to a man whose hand looks like a poultice or a small football?

The loss of these three weeks almost finished her.

The distinguishing mark of her family had been thinness, it was now bonyness.

To what a food-getting fervour was she compelled! She put the world of rubbish that was about her through a sieve; and winnowed nourishment for her family where a rat would have unearthed disappointment.

She could not beg; but she did send her two children into the street, and sometimes one of these got a copper from a passing stranger. Then, like the call of a famished crow who warns his brothers that he has discovered booty, that youngster gave out a loyal squeal for his companion; and they trotted home with their penny. The sun shone on the day they got a penny; on the days when they got nothing the sun might bubble the tar and split the bricks, but it did not shine.

Her man returned to his work, and if she could hold on they would be able to regain the poverty of a few months previously, but which now beamed to her as distant, unattainable affluence.

She could hold on, and she did; so that they tided feebly across the evil day; and came nigh at last to the longed-for scarcity which yet was not absolute starvation; and whereby they could live in the condition of health to which they were accustomed, and which they recognised and spoke of as good health.

They could not absolutely come to this for at least a year. Provision had still to be made for the lean months to come; the winter months; and more than three weeks' wages which should have been skimmed in this precaution had been unprofitable, had not existed. The difference had to be made up by a double skimming of the present wage; which must also pay the present necessities, and recoup the baker and grocer for the few weeks' credit these shop people had given her.

In all, their lot for a long time was not to be envied, except by a beast in captivity: and envied only by him because he lusts for freedom and the chance of it as we lust for security and the destruction of chance.

V

The winter came—the winter will come tho' the lark protest and the worm cries out its woe—and she entered on that period with misgiving, with resolution, and with a facing of everything that might come.

What bravery she had! What a noble, unwearying courage; when in so little a time, and at so small a pain, she might have died!

But such an idea did not come to her head. She looked on the world, and she saw that it was composed of a man and three children; while they lasted she could last, and when they were done it would be time enough to think of personal matters and her relation to things.

Before the summer had quite ended, e'er autumn had tinted a leaf, the war broke out; and with its coming there came inse curity. Not to her, not to them. They had no standard to measure security by. It came to the people who desire things done, and who pay to have doors varnished or window-frames painted. These people drew silently but resolutely from expense; while he and she and the children sunk deeper into their spending as one wallows into a bog.

The prices of things began to increase with a cumulative rapidity, and the quality of things began to deteriorate with equal speed. Bread and the eater of it came to a grey complexion. Meat was no more. The vegetables emigrated with the birds. The potato got a rise in the world and recognised no more its oldest friends. Nothing was left but the rain; and the rain came loyally.

They, those others, could retrench and draw in a little their horns; but from what could she retreat? What could she avoid? What could she eliminate, who had come to the bare bone and shank of life? The necessity for the loaf comes daily, recurs pitilessly from digestion to digestion, and with the inexorable promptitude of the moon the rent collector wanes and waxes.

They managed.

She and he managed.

Work still was, although it was spaced and intervalled like a storm-blown hedge. Here was a week and there another one, and from it they gleaned their constricted existence.

They did not complain; for those who are down do not complain. Nor did they know they were down. Or, knowing it, they did not admit their downness. For to front so final a fact is to face with naked hands a lion; and to admit is to give in. Is to be washed away. To be lost and drowned. To be anonymous; unhelpable; alive no more; but débris, or a straw which the wind takes and sails, or tears, or drifts, or rots, to powder and forgetfulness.

A bone in a world of bones! And they gnawed these bones until it seemed that nothing moved in the world except their teeth.

VI

The winter came, and his work stopped as it always did in that season.

He got jobs cleaning windows. He got jobs at the docks hoisting things which not Hercules nor the devil himself could lift. But which he could lift, or which his teeth and the teeth of his children detached from the ground as from foundations and rivettings.

He got a job as a coalman; and as a night-watchman sitting in the angle of a black street before a bucket of stinking coal, which had been a fire until the rain put it out. To-day he had a job; but to-morrow and for a week he had none.

With what had been saved, skimmed, strained from the summer wages; with what came from the jobs; with the pennies that the children unearthed from strangers as though they dug in those loath souls for coin, they lived through the winter, and did not feel that they had passed through an experience worthy of record, or that their endurance might have been rewarded with medals and a pension.

They were living, as we all manage, amazingly, to live: and if others had an easier time that was their chance. But this was their life, and there were those who were even worse off than they were.

For they paid the rent! And, when that was done, what a deed had been accomplished! How notable an enemy circumvented!

VII

The spring came; but it brought no leaves to their tree. The summer came; but it did not come to them; nor warn them of harvest and a sickle in the yield.

There was no building done that summer; the price of material had gone up and the price of wages. The contractors did not care for that prospect, and the client, remembering taxes and the war, decided to wait.

And her husband had no work!

Almost he had even given up looking for work. He would go out of the house and come into the house and go out of the house again; and he and she would look at each other in a dumb questioning.

It was strange how he had arranged with himself not to look at the children. How he had even arranged that their whimperings should seem to be inaudible, and their very presences invisible! And they, having raked his coming as with search-lights, and discovering that he brought nothing, looked at him no more.

They looked at her. They projected themselves to her, about her, upon her, into her. . . .

A wolf-mother, thus badgered and possessed, would have escaped from her young by mercifully or unmercifully slaughtering them. But she still could preserve her soul, her tenderness. Yet, if a whole infinity of tenderness seemed to be preserved for the children, a major, a yet more marvellous, tenderness was reserved for her man—it was without words, without action. It was without anything whatever. It was itself alone. Unproven, unquestioned, unending. To be perceived, received, only by the soul, and from the soul, or not to be received or perceived at all.

Sometimes she would say—not that she had anything to say, but to ease her husband's heart with a comradely word—

"Any chance to-day, do you think?"

And he would reply:

"Chance!"

And he would sit down to brood upon that lapsing word.

They were not angry; they had not the blood to be angry with; for to be wrathful you must be well fed or you must be drunk.

The youngest child died of an ill which, whatever it was at the top, was hunger at the bottom; and she grew terrified. She heard that there was work to be had in the Munition Factories in Scotland, and by some means she gathered together the fare and sent her husband across the sea.

"Write, if you can," said she, "the minute you get a place."

"Yes," he replied.

"And send us what you can spare," she said. "Send something this week if you can."

"Yes," he said.

And he went away.

And she went into the streets to beg.

VIII

She left the boy behind in his chair, and brought the other little one with her.

She was frightened, for one can be arrested for begging. And she was afraid not to beg, for one can die of hunger.

How well she knew those streets! and yet she did not know them in this aspect! These were atrocious streets!

She got a penny here and a penny there, and she bought bread. Sometimes even she bought a twist of tea. She could manage until the end of the week; until her man sent the money.

She had thoughts of singing at the corners of streets, as she had so often seen done by the toneless, ashen-faced women, who creak rusty music at the passer, and fix him with their eyes. But she was ashamed; and no song that she could remember seemed suitable; and she only could remember bits of songs; and she knew that her voice would not work for her, but that it would creak and mourn like a rusty hinge.

Her earnings were small, for she could not get in touch with people. That too is a trade and must be learned. They recognised her at a distance as a beggar, and she could only whisper to the back of a head or a cold shoulder.

Sometimes when she went towards a person that person instantly crossed the road and walked for a while hastily.

Sometimes people fixed upon her a prohibitive eye and she drew back from them humbled, her heart panting and her eyes hot at the idea that they took her for a beggar.

At times a man, without glancing at her, stuck a hand in his pocket and gave her a penny without halting in his stride.

One day she got twopence; one day she got sixpence; one day she got nothing.

But she could hold out to the end of the week.

IX

The end of the week came, but it brought no letter.

"It will come to-morrow," she said.

"He is in a strange country," she thought in panic. "He must have missed the post, God help him!"

But on the next day there was no letter; nor any letter on the day after; and on the day that succeeded to it there was no letter.

"He . . . !" she said.

But she could not speculate on him. She knew him too well, and she knew that this was not he; he could no more leave them in the lurch than he could jump across Ireland in one jump.

"He has not got work," she said.

And she saw him strayed and stranded; without a hand; without a voice; bewildered and lost among strangers; going up streets and down streets; and twisting himself into a maze, a dizziness of loneliness and hunger and despair.

Or, she said:

"The submarines had blown up the ship that was coming with the money."

The week went by; another came, and still she did not hear from him. She was not able to pay the rent.

She looked at the children; and then she looked away from them distantly to her strayed husband; and then she looked inwardly on herself, and there was nothing to see.

She was down.

No littlest hope could find a chink to peer through. And while she sat, staring at nothing, in an immobile maze of attention, her mind—she had no longer a heart, it had died of starvation—her mind would give a leap and be still; and would leap again, as though an unknown, wordless action were seeking to be free; seeking to do something; seeking to disprove stagnation, and powerlessness, and death; and a little burning centre of violence hung in her head like a star.

She followed people with her eyes, sometimes a little way with her feet, saying to herself:

"The pockets of that man are full of money; he would rattle if he fell."

Or:

"That man had his breakfast this morning; he is full of food to the chin; he is round and tight and solid, and he weighs a ton."

She said:

"If I had all the money of all the people in this street I should have a lot of money."

She said:

"If I owned all the houses in this street I should have a lot of money."

The rent collector told her imperatively that she must leave at the end of the week, and the children called to her for bread, clamorously, unceasingly, like little dogs that yap and whine and cannot be made to stop.

X

Relief kitchens had been started in various parts of the city, but she only heard of them by chance; and she went to one. She told a lady in attendance her miserable tale, and was given the address of a gentleman who might assist her. He could give her a ticket which would enable her to get food; and he might be able to set her in the way of earning what would pay the rent.

This lady thought her husband had deserted her; and she said so, without condemnation, as one states a thing which has been known to happen; and the poor woman agreed without agreeing, for she did not believe it.

But she did not argue about the matter, for now that she accepted food, she accepted anything that came with it, whether it was opinions or advice. She was an acceptor, and if she claimed to possess even an opinion it might jeopardise her chance of getting anything.

She set out for the house of the gentleman who could give her the ticket which would get her food to bring home to the children.

He lived at some distance, and when she got to his house the servant told her he had gone to his office; at his office she was informed that he had gone out. She called three times at the office, and on the third time she was told that he had come in, but had gone home.

She trudged to his house again; and would have been weary, but that her mind had lapsed far, far, from her trudging feet; and when the mind is away the body matters nothing.

Where was her mind? At times it was nowhere. It was gone from her body and from material things. It might be said to have utterly quitted that tenement, and to be somehow, somewhere, refuged from every fear, haven from every torment and eased of every memory that could deject it. She was life and a will; or, if these are but one, she was the will to be, obscure, diligent, indefatigable.

And then, again, as at the opening of a door, her mind, laden with recollections of time and space, of deeds and things and

thwartings, was back in the known and incredible room, looking
at the children, listening to them, consoling them; telling them
that in a little while she should be home again, and that she
would bring them food.

They had not eaten anything for—how long was it? Was it a
year? Had they ever eaten? And one of them was sick!

She must get back. She had been away too long. But she must
go forward before she could go back.

She must get the ticket which was food and hope and a new
beginning, or a respite. Then she should be able to look about
her. The children would go to sleep; and she could plan and
contrive and pull together those separated and dwindling ends.

She came to the gentleman's house. He was in, and she told
him her story, and how her case was desperate.

He also believed that her husband had deserted her; and he
promised to write by that night's post to find out the truth about
the man, and to see that he was punished for his desertion.

He had no tickets with him; he had used them all, for the
hungry people in Dublin were numerous; work was slack everywhere, and those who had never before applied for assistance
were now obliged to do so by dreadful necessity. He gave her
some money, and promised to call at her room on the following
day to investigate her case.

She went homewards urgently, and near home she bought
bread and tea.

When she got in the crippled boy turned dull, dumb eyes upon
her; and she laughed at him excitedly, exultantly; for she had
food; lots of it, two loaves of it.

But the other child did not turn to her, and would not turn
to her again, for he was dead of hunger.

XI

She could not afford to go mad, for she still had a boy, and he
depended on her with an utter helpless dependence.

She fed him and fed herself; running from him in the chair to that other in its cot, with the dumb agony of an animal who must do two things at once, and cannot resolve which thing to do.

She could not think; she could hardly feel. She was dulled and distressed and wild. She was weakened by misery and tormented by duties; and life and the world seemed a place of busynesses, and futilities, and unending, unregulated, demands upon her.

A neighbour, hearing that persistent trotting over her head, came up to the room to remonstrate, and remained to shed for her the tears which she could not weep herself. She, too, was in straits, and had nothing more to give than those tears; and the banal iterations which are comfort because they are kindness.

Into this place the gentleman called on the following day to investigate, and was introduced to a room swept almost as clean of furniture as a dog kennel is; to the staring, wise-eyed child who lived in a chair; and to the quiet morsel of death that lay in a cot by the wall.

He was horrified, but he was used to sights of misery; and he knew that when things have ceased to move they must be set moving again; and that all he could do was to remove some of the impediments which he found in the path of life, so that it might flow on before it had time to become stagnant and rotten.

He took from the dry-eyed, tongue-tied woman all the immediate worry of death. He paid the rent, and left something to go on with as well; and he promised to get her work either in his house or at his office, but he would get her work to do somehow.

XII

He came daily; and each day, in reply to her timid question as to her husband, he had nothing to say except that enquiries were being made.

On the fifth day he had news, and he would have preferred any duty, however painful, to the duty of telling her his news.

But he told it, sitting on the one chair; with his hand over his eyes, and nothing of his face visible except the mouth which shaped and spoke the sentences.

The munition people in Scotland reported that a man of the name he was enquiring for had applied for work, and had been taken on a fortnight after his application. The morning after he began work he was found dead in a laneway. He had no lodgings in the city; and at the post-mortem examination it was found that he had died of hunger and exposure.

She listened to that tale; looking from the gentleman who told it to her little son who listened to it. She moistened her lips with her tongue; but she could not speak, she could only stammer and smile.

The gentleman also sat looking at the boy.

"We must set this young man up," said he heavily. "I shall send a doctor to look him over to-day."

And he went away all hot and cold; beating his hands together as he walked; and feeling upon his shoulders all the weariness and misery of the world.

ETCHED IN MOONLIGHT

TO

MARY AND CORNELIUS J. SULLIVAN

I

He waved his pipe at me angrily:

"Words," he said. "We are doped with words, and we go to sleep on them and snore about them. So with dream. We issue tomes about it, and we might as well issue writs for all the information we give."

I halted him there, for I respect science and love investigation.

"Scientists don't claim to give answers to the riddles of existence," I expostulated, "their business is to gather and classify whatever facts are available, and when a sufficient number of these have been collected there is usually found among them an extra thing which makes examination possible."

"Hum!" said he.

"The difficulty lies in getting all the facts, but when these are given much more is given; for if a question can be fully stated the answer is conveyed in the question."

"That's it," said he, "they don't know enough, but there is a wide pretence—"

"More a prophecy than a pretence. They really state that this or that thing is knowable. It is only that you live hurriedly, and you think everything else should be geared up to your number."

"And they are so geared, or they would not be visible and audible and tangible to me. But a ghost is geared differently to me; and I think that when I am asleep and dreaming I am geared differently to the person who is talking to you here."

"Possibly."

"Certainly. Look at the time it has taken you and me to chatter our mutual nonsense. In an instant of that time I could have had a dream; and, in its infinitesimal duration, all the adventures and excitements of twenty or forty years could take place in ample and leisurely sequence. Someone has measured dream, and has recorded that elaborate and complicated dreams covering years of time can take place while you would be saying knife."

"It was du Prell," I said.

"Whoever it was, I've seen a person awake and talking, but sleepy; noted that person halt for the beat of a word in his sentence, and continue with the statement that he has had a horrible dream. It must have taken place in the blink of an eye. There is no doubt that while we are asleep a power is waking in us which is more amazing than any function we know of in waking life. It is lightning activity, lightning order, lightning intelligence; and that is not to be considered as rhetoric, but as sober statement. The proposition being, that in sleep the mind does actually move at the speed of lightning."

He went on more soberly:

"Last night I had a dream, and in it twenty good years were lived through with all their days and nights in the proper places; and a whole chain of sequential incidents working from the most definite beginning to the most adequate end—and perhaps it all took place between the beginning and the ending of a yawn."

"Well, let us have the dream," said I; "for it is clear that you are spoiling to tell it."

He devoted himself anew for a few moments to his pipe and to his thoughts, and, having arranged that both of these were in working order, he recommenced:

"After all this you will naturally expect that something dramatic or astonishing should follow; but it is not surprise, not even interest that is the centre of my thought about this dream. The chief person in the dream was myself; that is certain. The feeling of identity was complete during the dream; but my self in the dream was as unlike my self sitting here as you and I are unlike each other. I had a different physique in the dream; for, while I am now rather dumpish and fair and moonfaced, I was, last night, long and lean as a rake, with a black thatch sprouting over a hatchet head. I was different mentally; my character was not the one I now recognise myself by; and I was capable of being intrigued by events and speculations in which the person sitting before you would not take the slightest interest."

He paused for a few seconds as though reviewing his memories; but, on a movement from me, he continued again, with many pauses, and with much snorings on his pipe, as tho' he were drawing both encouragement and dubiety from it.

"Of course I am romantically minded. We all are; the cat and the dog are. All life, and all that is in it, is romantic, for we and they and it are growing into a future that is all mystery out of a past not less mysterious; and the fear or hope that reaches to us from these extremes are facets of the romance which is life or consciousness, or whatever else we please to name it.

"But," he said energetically, "I do not pine to rescue a distressed dragon from a savage maiden; nor do I dream of myself dispensing life and death and immortality with a spoon. Life is Romance; I am living and I am Romance; and that adventure is as much as I have the ability to embark on.

"Well, last night, in a dream, I was a person natively capable of such embarkations; and altho' I did not rescue anything from anybody, I am sure I should have done it as one to the manner born. And that character fitted me there, then, as a cat fits into its skin.

"In the dream I was unmistakable I, but I was not this I, either physically, mentally, or temperamentally.

"And the time was different. I don't know what date it was, but it was not to-day. I don't know what place it was, but it was not this place. I was acting in a convention foreign to the one we act in, and I was acting from an historical or ancestral convention which has no parallel in these times. I don't remember what language I was speaking. I don't remember the names of the people I was in contact with; nor do I recollect addressing anybody by name. I was too familiar with them to require such explanatory symbols. You and I have been chattering these years— do we ever call one another by a name? There is no need to do so; and there was no need to do so with the people of my dream."

He halted, regarding me.

"Do you believe in reincarnation?" he said.

"Do not push casual mountains on my head," I replied, "but get on with the dream."

"Well," said he, "I dreamed a dream and here is the dream."

II

My mind was full of disquietude, impatience, anger; and as the horse stretched and eased under me I dwelt on my own thought. I did not pursue it, for I was not actively thoughtful. I hatched it. I sat on a thought and kept it warm and alive without feeling any desire to make it grow.

"She shall end it to-day," I thought in summary.

And then:

I'll end it to-day.

And thereon I ceased thinking, for when the will has been

invoked a true, the truest, act of being has been accomplished, and the mind, which never questions the will, may go on holiday. As against willing all thought is a form of laziness, and my thought, having in that realm neither business nor interest, went lazily to the nearest simple occurrence that could employ it, and I became only a person on a horse; listening to the horse; looking at it; feeling it with my limbs and feeling myself by its aid.

There was great pleasure in the way my legs gripped around that warm barrel: in the way my hands held the beast's head up; in the way my waist and loins swayed and curved with the swaying and curving of the animal. I touched her with my toe and tapped her neck; and on the moment she tossed her head, shaking a cascade of mane about my hands; gathered her body into a bunch of muscles, and unloosed them again in a great gallop; while from behind the hooves of my servant's beast began to smack and pelt.

In some reaches the surrounding country flowed into and over the track; and everywhere in its length the grass threw a sprinkle of green. There were holes here and there; but more generally there were hollows which had been holes, and which had in time accumulated driftage of one kind or another, so that they had a fullish appearance without having anything of a level look; but on the whole I knew of worse roads, and this one was kept in tolerable repair.

Not far from this place we left the road and struck along a sunken path all grown over at the top with shadowing trees; and so to another and much better-kept road, and on this one I shook out the reins and we went galloping.

It was not unknown to me, this place. Indeed it was so well known that I had no need to look to one side or the other, for everything that was to be seen had been seen by me many hundreds of times; and, if we except grass and trees and grazing cattle, there was nothing to be seen.

Here and there rude dwellings came to view. Low shanties

patched together with mud and rock, and all browned and baked by the sun and the rain; and as I rode, these small habitations became more numerous, and from them dogs and children swarmed, snarling and yelping and squeaking.

Again these fell behind, and on another turn a great park came to the view; and across it a building showed gaunt and massive, with turrets at the corners and in front, and the black silhouettes of men were moving in those airy tops.

III

My horse pulled up, all spread-eagled and snorting, before a flight of stone steps, before which and on which armed men were clustered and packing, and I went up those steps as one having right of entry. At the top I stood for an instant to look back on the rolling grass through which I had galloped a minute before.

The evening was approaching. Ragged clouds, yet shot with sunlight, were piling in the sky, and there was a surmised but scarcely perceptible greyness in the air. Over the grass silence was coming, almost physically, so that the armed rattle and tramp and the chatter of voices about me had a detached sound, as though these were but momentary interruptions of the great silence that was on its way. That quietude, premonition of silence, brings with it a chill to the heart; as tho' an unseen presence whispered something, unintelligible but understood; conveying a warning that the night comes, that silence comes, that an end comes to all movement of mind and limb.

For when I parted from my horse I parted from my mood; and was again a discontented person, filled with an impatience that seethed within me as water bubbles in a boiling pot.

"She," I thought, "shall choose to-day whether she likes to or not."

And, having expressed itself, my will set in that determination as a rock is set in a stream.

A person came to my beckoning finger, and replied to my enquiry—

"Your honour is expected. Will your honour be pleased to follow me?"

She was sitting in the midst of a company and on my approach gave me her hand to kiss. I saluted it half kneeling, and raking her eyes with a savage stare, which she returned with quiet constancy to which I was accustomed and which always set me wild, so that the wish I had to beat her was only laid by the other— and overflowing—desire I had to kiss her.

I rose to my feet, stepped some paces back, and the conversation I had interrupted recommenced.

I was intensely aware of her and of myself; but saving for us the place was empty for me. I could feel my chin sinking to my breast; feel my eyes strained upwards in my bent face; feel my body projecting itself against the lips I stared at; and I knew that she was not unaware of me.

As she spoke, her eyes strayed continually to me, carelessly, irresistibly, and swung over or under me and would not look at me. She could do that while she was talking, but while she was listening she could only half do it; for when her tongue was stilled I caught her mind or her body and held her and drew her; so that, would she or would she not, she had to look at me. And I delighted in that savage impression of myself upon her; following her nerves with the cunning of one who could see within her; and guiding her, holding her, all the time to me, to me, to me. . . . And then she looked, and I was baffled anew; for her eye was as light, as calm, as inexpressive as the bright twinkle of a raindrop that hangs and shivers on a twig.

But the game was broken by a tap on my shoulder, and, at the moment, her voice stumbled on the word she was uttering, her eyes leaped into mine and looked there, and then she was talking again and merry and gracious.

It is a little difficult to explain these things, for I can give no name to the people I am speaking of; nor can I say how I was known to them; but I knew their names and qualities well and they knew mine; so, at the tap on my shoulder, I, knowing whom I should see, turned my eyes to that direction, and saw, for our brows were level, a great golden head, great blue eyes and, just under the rim of vision, a great pair of shoulders.

Everything about him was great in bulk and in quality, and with the exception of our mistress, I had never met one so founded in strength and security as he was.

We turned amicably and went from the room together; out of the great building and across the field; and as our feet moved rhythmically in the grass we smiled at each other, for indeed I loved him as my own soul and he loved me no less.

As we paced in long slow strides the darkness had already begun to be visible, for the second half of twilight was about us. Away in the direction towards which we trod an ashen sky kept a few dull embers, where, beyond sight, down on the rim of the horizon, the sun had set.

There was silence except for the innumerable rustling bred of grass and quiet trees and a wind too delicate to be heard and scarcely to be felt; for, though the skies were brisk, there was but little ground wind. Naught moved in the trees but the high tender branches that swayed lazily and all alone; leading their aery existence so far from my turbulence of passion that I chid them for their carelessness of one, who, in the very cleft of anxiety, could find an instant to remember them in.

At a time, even while we strode forward, we turned again and retraced our steps; and my mind took one shade more of moodiness. It was he had turned and not I. It was he always who did the thing that I was about to do one moment before I could do it; and he did it unthinkingly, assuredly; with no idea that rebellion might be about him; or, that, being there, it could become manifest.

We re-entered and sat to meat with a great company, and she spoke to us equally and frankly and spoke to others with the gracious ease which was never for a moment apart from her.

But I, brooding on her, intent on her as with internal ears and eyes and fingers, felt in her an unwonted excitement, touched something in her which was not usual. When she looked at me that feeling was intensified; for her bright, brief glance, masked as it was and careless as it seemed, held converse with me, as though in some realm of the spirit we were in unguarded communion.

We were close together then; nearer to each other than we should be again; so close that I could feel with a pang by what a distance we might be separated; and could feel with doubled woe that she grieved for that which she could not comfort.

We left the table.

Little by little the company separated into small companies, and in a while the great room was boisterous with conversation. They had withdrawn and were talking earnestly together; and I was roving about the room, sitting for a breath with this company and that; listening to my neighbors with an ear that was hearkening elsewhere; and replying to them in terms that might or might not have been relevant to the subject I chanced on.

But in all my movements I managed to be in a position from which I could watch those two; so close in converse, so grave in their conduct of it; so alive to all that was happening about them; and yet sunk spheres below the noise and gaiety of our companions.

Her eye looked into mine, calling to me; and at the signal I left my sentence at its middle and went towards them.

Crossing the room I had a curious perception of their eyes as they watched me advancing; and, for the first time, I observed the gulf which goes about all people and which isolates each irreparably from his fellows. A sense of unreality came upon me, and, as I looked on them, I looked on mystery; and they, staring at me, saw the unknown walking to them on legs. At a stroke we had become strangers, and all the apprehension of strangers looked through our eyes.

She arose when I came within a few paces of them.

"Let us go out," said she.

And we went out quietly.

IV

Again I was in the open. I breathed deeply of the chill air as though drawing on a fount of life; as though striving to draw strength and sustenance and will into my mind.

But the time had come to put an end to what I thought of evasively as "all this"; for I was loath to submit plainly to myself what "all this" noted. I took my will in my hand, as it were, and became the will to do, I scarcely knew what; for to one unused to the discipline and use of will there is but one approach to it, and it is through anger. The first experience of willing is brutal; and it is as though a weapon of offence, a spear or club, were in one's hand; and as I walked I began to tingle and stir with useless rage.

For they were quiet, and against my latent impetuosity they opposed that massive barrier from which I lapsed back helplessly.

Excitement I understood and loved; the quicker it mounted, the higher it surged, the higher went I. Always above it, master of it. Almost I was excitement incarnate; ready for anything that might befall, if only it were heady and masterless. But the quietude of those left me like one in a void, where no wing could find a grip and where I scarce knew how to breathe.

It was now early night.

The day was finished and all that remembered the sun had gone. The wind which had stirred faintly in tall branches had lapsed to rest. No breath moved in the world, and the clouds that had hurried before were quiet now, or were journeying in other regions of the air. Clouds there were in plenty; huge, pilings of light and shade; for a great moon, burnished and thin, and so translucent that a narrowing of the eyes might almost let one peer through it, was standing far to the left; and in the spaces between the clouds there was a sharp scarce glitter of stars.

There was more than light enough to walk by; for that great disc of the heavens poured a radiance about us that was almost as bright as day.

Now as I walked the rage that had begun to stir within ceased again, and there crept into me so dull a lassitude that had death stalked to us in the field I should not have stepped from his way.

I surrendered everything on the moment; and, for the mind must justify conduct, I justified myself in the thought that nothing was worth this trouble; and that nothing was so desirable but it could be matched elsewhere, or done without.

It is true that the mind thinks only what desire dictates; and that when desire flags thought will become ignoble. My will had flagged, for I had held it too many hours as in a vice; and I was fatigued with that most terrible of exercises.

The silence of those indomitable people weighed upon me; and the silence of the night, and the chill of that large, white moon burdened me also. Therefore, when they came to talk to me, I listened peacefully; if one may term that state of surrender peace. I listened in a cowardly quietness; replying more by a movement of the hands than by words; and when words were indispensable making brief use of them.

It was she who spoke, and her tone was gentle and anxious and official:

"We have arranged to marry," said she.

To that I made no reply.

I took the information on the surface of my mind as one receives an arrow on a shield, and I did not permit it to enter further. There, in neutral ground, the sentence lay; and there I could look on it with the aloof curiosity of one who examines an alien thing.

"They were going to get married!" Well . . . But what had it to do with me? Everyone got married sometime, and they were going to get married. This was a matter in which I had no part, for they were not going to get married to me: they were going to marry each other; it was all no business of mine.

So a weary brain thinks weary thoughts; and so I thought; separating myself languidly from the business of those who were making me a partner in their affairs. All I desired was that the explanations should cease, and that I might heave myself into a saddle and jog quietly to my own place.

But I knew, almost with sickness, that I could not go until this sentence had been explained and re-explained. They would inevitably consider that I could not grasp its swollen import until they had spoken under it and over it; and explained that there was a necessity for it; and detailed me that also.

I could foresee a dreary hour that would drone and drone with an unending amplification of duty and interest and love, and a whole metaphysic to bind these together.

Love! They would come to that at last. But when they dared the word they would not leave it while they had a tooth to put into it.

They would tell me around it and about; and the telling would excite them to a fury of retelling. I should have its history, and all the din and crackle of all the words that could be remembered on that subject or germane to it.

I found it happen so.

I was initiated into the secrets of their duty to their people and to themselves. I learned the intricacy of the interests wherein all parties were involved; until it was impossible to tell where duty ended and interest began. And, in the inevitable sequel, I was the confidant of their love. And I listened to that endless tale with the drowsy acquiescence of one moonstruck and gaping . . . drowsily nodding; murmuring my yes and yes drowsily. . . .

They were good to me. They were sisterly and brotherly to me. By no hairsbreadth of reticence was I excluded from their thoughts, their expectations, their present felicity, and their hopes of joy to come. For two people going alone may have verbal and bodily restraint but the company of a third will set them rabid. It is as though that unnecessary presence were a challenge, or a query, which they must dispose of or die. Therefore, and because of me, they had to take each other's hand. They had to fondle paw within paw; and gaze searchingly on each other and on me; with, for me, a beam of trust and brotherliness and inclusion which my mood found sottish.

They were in love.

They whispered it to each other. They said it loudly to me. And more loudly yet they urged it, as though they would proclaim it to the moon. . . . And about their hands was a vile activity; a lust of catching; a fever of relinquishing; for they could neither hold nor withhold their hands from each other.

"Do they expect me to clasp their hands together, and hold them so that they shall not unloose again? Do they wish me to draw their heads together, so that they may kiss by compulsion? Am I to be the page of love and pull these arms about each other?"

We walked on, heedless of time; and I heedless of all but those voices that came to me with an unending, unheard, explanation; the voices of those who cared naught for me; who cared only that I was there, an edge to their voluptuousness.

V

But when one walks one arrives somewhere. If the environment had not changed we might have gone on for ever. This walk and talk had grown into us like a monstrous habit from which we could not break away, and until a change came to the eye our minds could not swerve from the world they were building nor our feet from the grasses we walked on.

A change did occur, mercifully; the little variety which might deturn that level of moonbred, lovesick continuity or inertia; for we think largely through the eyes, or our thoughts flow easily to the direction in which our gaze is set.

The great park, waving with separated trees, came abruptly to an end.

At this step it was yet a sward. But ten paces beyond it was a rubble of bush and rock, unkempt as a beggarman's beard. Everywhere there were bits of walls with crumbling ledges up which the earth was gradually mounting and which the grass had already conquered.

Under the beam of that great flat moon the place seemed wildly beautiful; with every mound a glory of silver and peace, and every hollow a pit of blackness and mystery. A little beyond, perfect, although in the hub and centre of ruin, a vast edifice reared against the sky, and it shone white as snow in the moonlight except where a projecting battlement threw an ebon shade.

"The old castle," said she, "I have not walked this way in ten years."

And saying so, she walked to it.

I had never been that way, and I looked on that massive pile of silence almost with expectation, as tho' a door might open and something emerge, or a voice roar rustily at us from the moonclad top.

It was old, and it was built as they built of old and build no more; for the walls were fifteen feet thick, and time might have sat before it through half-eternity marvelling by what arts such a solidity could possibly be reduced.

We paced about it, wondering at it, and at the silence which came to and from it; and marvelling that men had with such patience consummated so vast a labour; for the lives of generations had passed e'er this was ended and secure.

There was but one door, and we came on this in our silent walk. It was swung to, but was yet open just a little; barely a foot of opening; a dense black slit in the moonlight.

"I must slip in," said she.

He smiled at her, catching again her hand. And into his ear, but with her eyes fixed on mine, she said:

"I want to whisper something in the ear of silence and desolation."

She slipped within; and, when in, she pulled at his hand. With a look at me half laughing, half apologetic, he squeezed after her; and I was alone staring at the bossed and plated door.

There was silence without and within, but I found that my eyes were fixed on that silence within; and from it, as I expected, almost as I willed, there came, as though bred from the silence, a sound. It was ten times more discreet than a whisper, and was to be heard only by an ear that knew it would come.

A sudden panic leaped within my heart and rolled into my ears like a beaten drum; and that rage of fear was my memory, sprung suddenly from nowhere, of the hands that had gripped and released each other; of the eyes that had flashed upon eye and lip; of the bodies that had swung tenderly sideways and fell languidly away again.

And at that my mind emptied itself of thought, and I saw nothing, heard nothing, was nothing. Only in my head there came again a sudden great throb as though a muffled bell had thudded inside it. My hands went out without any direction from me; they gripped on the door; and, with the strength of ten men, I pulled on it.

It fell to with a crash which might have been heard about the earth; and yet which let through one infinitesimal fraction of sound; a beginning of sound only; so tiny, it could scarcely be heard, so tense that the uproar of doom could not have covered that sound from my ear.

It began and it never finished, for it never continued. Its beginning was caught and prevented; but within my ear it continued and completed itself, as a scream which I should never cease to hear; while still with hanging jaw and fixed eyes I stared at the closed door.

I walked away.

I turned from the place and went slowly in the direction we had come.

I was a walking statue; a bodily movement only; for the man within had temporarily ceased to be. Within I was a silence brooding on silence and darkness. No smallest thought, no stir towards thinking crept in my mind; but yet I was not quite as a dead man walking, for something was happening . . . I was listening. I was listening for them to speak in my heart. . . .

And then I began to run; a steady pelt of running, as though I could run away from them, mewed in that stony den, and yet liable to shriek on me from the centre of my being.

Again the change to the eye brought change to the mind; and when I sighted the great building all glimmering with lights I came to my breathless self.

I went to the stables; found my man; and in five minutes was in the saddle, and, with him behind, went plunging through the darkness to my own place.

How often during that ride did I clench my hand to pull on the rein and go back to release them. Every minute, every second, I was going to do it. But every minute, every second, my hand refrained from pulling on the horse, and my heels gave her notice to go yet faster.

For I was not quite a man. I was an inertia . . . or I was the horse. I was something that ran; and my whole being was an unexpressed wish to run and never stop. I did not even wish to come to my place; for, arrive there, I must halt and dismount, and fumble and totter among obstacles of doors and people. . . .

That halt had to come; and I dismounted in a mood that merged rapidly from impatience to anger, and from that to almost blind fury. In a little while my dispositions were made, and I was on the road again on a fresh beast, a bag of money and valuables strapped on the nag, and behind me two servants coming on at a gallop.

I was running away from the country. I was running away

from those two mewed in the prison to which nobody knew they had gone. But more urgently even than that I was running away from myself.

VI

There comes an interval which my recollection would figure as ten or twelve years. During this time I did not return to my own country, and, so far as was possible, I did not even think of it.

For it was in my nature to forget easily; or, by an effort of the will, to prevent myself remembering whatever I considered inconvenient or distressing. I could put trouble to one side as with a gesture, and this trouble I put away and did not again admit into mind.

But a trouble that is buried is not disposed of. Be the will ever so willing, the mind ever so obedient, a memory cannot be destroyed until it has reached its due time and evolved in its proper phases.

A memory may die in the mind as peacefully as an old man dies in his bed; and it will rest there tranquilly, and moulder into true forgetfulness, as the other débris moulders into dust. But a memory cannot be buried alive; for in this state of arrested being, where it can neither grow old nor die, it takes on a perpetual unused youth, and lies at the base of one's nature as an unheard protest; calling to the nerves instead of to the brain, and strumming on these with an obstinate patience and an unending fertility of resource.

It has been banished from the surface to the depths; and in the deep of being, just beyond the borders of thought, it lies, ready as at the lifting of a finger to leap across these borders, as new and more poignant than at its creation.

Upon those having the gift of mental dismissal a revenge is taken. They grow inevitably irritable; and are subject to gusts of rage so unrelated to a present event that their contemporaries must look upon them as irresponsible.

A buried thought like a buried body will rot; and it will spread a pestilence through the moral being that is its grave or its gaoler.

It was so with me.

From being one frank and impetuous and careless, I became moody, choleric, suspicious; and so temperamentally unstable that as I could not depend on myself so no one else could depend on me either.

All things that were commenced by me had to be finished by another; for in the very gust and flooding of success I would throw myself aside from it; or bear myself so outrageously that my companions would prefer failure and my absence to a success which had me within a league of the prize.

Everything, even a memory, must be faced at last. No man can rest until he has conquered or surrendered to his enemy; for, be success attained or failure, a legitimate bourne is reached wherein the mind may acquiesce and be one with the result.

So, one day, I unburied my dead; looking upon it with a curiosity and fear which were the equal of each other; and having once looked I could not forbear to look again; until I became a patient, timid devotee of my own evil.

A treacherous story in truth; and if repentance could have retrieved my crime how quickly it had been erased. But the fact of repentance comes home only to the person in fault. It has no value for the victim; for a man may outrun the laws of man, but the law of his self he can neither distance nor dodge.

Half the value of an act is its reaction, for the one pays and completes the other. My act was vanity and here came shame to make of it a total; and there, in the mixture of the two, was I, fully expressed and condemned. Vanity had sentenced me to shame; and shame would take up the tale again with vanity, and would lead me to the further justice of which I had need. For that which we do outwardly we do inwardly. We condemn or reward ourselves in every action; and the punishment we receive is due to us in a sense deeper than that indicated in the word retribution.

I thought of those two; and I thought of them shyly as one who no longer had the right even to remember them. For they had counted on my nature, as they judged it; on my honour as they knew it; and on my friendship as they thought to have proved it. But into these aspects of me they had been sucked as into a bog. I had given way under their feet and they had sunk into and died in me.

Was it a wonder that I fled across the fields fearful lest they might scream to me from my soul? Alas, it was there they had been betrayed, and there were buried; wherever else their bones might whiten.

And now I began to brood on them deeply and perpetually, until nothing in the world was so important as they were, and they became me almost in my entirety.

I reconstructed them and myself, and the happy days which had preceded that most wicked of hours; and I knew that, whatever other enmity or suspicion had been in the world, there had been naught but friendship between us and the frankest and freest trust. I had reason to trust them, and had given them occasion to believe that in my keeping their honour and their all was safe; and to that trust I had given the lie at the moment of its reposal.

Indeed I was stupefied to think that I had committed this baseness; for on behalf of these two I would have counted on my own loyalty with as little calculation as they had.

There was indeed something to be said for me if that enquiry were rigorously pursued. But it was a poor thing and only to be advanced in my favour for it could not be urged.

She had halted between us for a long time; not balancing our values or possibilities; but humanly unwilling to judge, and womanly unable to wound. That delicate adjustment could not have continued indefinitely; but it would have continued longer had I not forced the issue, or stated the position; and once that a case is truly stated nothing remains but the judgment which is already apparent in the statement.

It was I had failed in the trial. I whose nerves gave way. I who became impatient and would gamble on the chance; and the gambler is always an incomplete man. In all real things the gambler must lose, for he is staking on chance that which can only be won by the knowledge which is concreted merit; and in all memorable deeds the personality must win, and chance have not even the ghost of a chance.

They had bettered me; and, although they were dead and I alive, they were beyond me and topped me as a lion tops a dog.

So, pride having proved to me that I was treacherous, shame came to teach me the great lesson of life; for in humility the mind is released from fleshy fogs and vapours; and in that state only can it be directed to its single natural work, the elucidation of character.

Ideas which enter the mind only have no motive force—they are alive, but have not yet energy. They exist but as subjects of conversation, as intellectual gossip, but before a thought can become an act it must sink deeper than the mind and into the imagination where abides the true energy of all thinking creatures. It is not the mind but the imagination that sets the will to work; and both mind and will obey it instantly, as a horse winces instantly to the touch of a spur.

So these two, having got into my imagination, could not be let out again, until it was satisfied that all which could be done was done, and a moral as well as a logical end arrived at.

I took to horse, therefore, and set out for home.

VII

Apart from my adventure with those people my memory is blurred. My dealings and encounters with them are distinct as though they happened to-day; but the portions of the narrative interspacing that adventure have already more than half faded from memory. Yet it seems to me that my journey back was a long one, and that ships had to be taken as well as horses ere I had returned and could recognise landmarks and faces.

In many of these recognitions the passage of time was marked for me as tho' it had been written.

Here was a dwelling which had not before been here: and in this place, where a house had been, there was a roofless ruin.

Here a man tended his sheep. When I passed the last time he had not been old; but his beard had whitened as though in one night of snow.

I passed youths and girls who knew me and stood aside; but they had changed from the children I might have remembered into lusty and lengthy and unknown people.

The word that I was coming must have far preceded me, for these people recognised me with curiosity but without astonishment; and in my own house I was clearly expected and welcomed with all the preparedness a master might hope for.

I had not hoped for any welcome, and would have preferred to come back as anonymously as a bird does who returns to its last year's hedge; for, although I did not wish to escape anything that might be in keeping for me, I did desire to inform myself of the circumstances by which I should be surrounded, and the dangers that I might have to front.

There was no hint of danger or disquietude among my people. Their welcome was as free, their service as easy and accustomed as though I had returned from a visit to the next town. And the marvel of this almost stupefied me; while the impossibility of demanding direct information from those unsuspicious people plunged me in dismay.

I thought to myself—"The bodies have never been found, and, by some extraordinary chance, suspicion has not turned upon me for their disappearance."

At the thought a weight was lifted from my soul; but only for a moment; for I had not come back in search of security, but in order that whatever debt was due by me should be paid.

But I had to know how things were, and, after eating, the man of whom I enquired, replied that my return was known at the Castle (as I shall call it) and that a visit from its chatelains was expected on the next day to welcome me home.

With this news my alarm vanished and an almost excessive joy took its place. My mind lightened, and poured into my body, as from a fountain, well-being and energy.

For how long? Was it more than ten minutes? ten seconds? The mind that can hold joy must be strong indeed. I could no more contain it than I could round the sea in my palm; and, almost as it had swirled into me, it swept out, leaving behind only that to which I had a right and which was my own.

Nothing happens without mental acquiescence, and that which had emptied my mind of joy and my body of buoyancy was the memory that I should see them on the morrow, and, with that memory, egotism pushed up its head and I thought—"They will not meet the unfledged youngster they parted from!"

That was all. But it was sufficient to ride me as I would ride a horse, and to pull me round to its direction, and to the vanity I imagined to have left behind.

I chid myself for a fool. I looked back with a lightning eye on the wasted years; the useless misery; the unnecessary toil and sordid excitement through which I had passed; and at a stroke my mind became filled with a tumult and admixture of emotions which no one word would synthesise, nor could I describe them in many words.

In undisciplined minds a conflict of thought will provoke anger or sleep; but in almost any mind a conflict of emotion will breed rage; and, for the mind is lazy, a thought will seek for an emotion to rest on, and will lie in it as in a bed. So nobility rots in dream, and action grows stagnant in imagining itself. Behind life is laziness, and from it, in direct descent or ascent, is desire and lust and anger, which master words describe up to a point the world and its working.

Thus, having torn myself out of anger as from a pit, I hurried back to it, and I found that I was thinking of my coming visitors with a dislike which was as near to hatred as I could arrive at.

They were alive, and I had paid for their death! I had wasted myself and my years grieving for them; repenting for them;

idealising them in a dull torment and agitation of nerve and brain!

For nothing! And nothing became symbolised by them. They stood for it: they were Nothing; and, with that, vanity was in possession again, for I stood for something as against their nothing; and all the coil of pride and shame and payment had to recommence.

VIII

They came, and for a time resentment was covered by curiosity; and while we talked together I found myself glancing at one and the other with the curiosity of him who peeps at a camel or a criminal.

There was a difference in them, but it was not essential; it was only the change which comes with the passage of time.

All that I remembered was here, but more pronounced. What had been quietude had deepened to tranquillity. All that sense of certainty and command was more certain and commanding, for ease and power and good humour was as unconsidered and native a part of them as their limbs.

He had been great in bulk, he was now huge. He had filled out, and filled in, and he strode and towered like a mountain.

Her I remembered as one remembers a day of April beauty and promise, various with that uncertainty which troubles and delights. Now summer was on her with its gorgeous endowment.

She was a rest to the eye. She was a benediction to the senses. She calmed desire. For to look on her was to desire no more, and yet to be satisfied. Her beauty was so human, her humanity so beautiful, that she could embrace the thought that would embrace her; and return it absolved, purified, virgin again to the lust that sent it out.

There are beings in this world who are secured against every machination of evil. They live as by divine right, as under divine protection; and when malice looks in their faces it is abashed and must retreat without harming them. All the actions of these are harmonious and harmless and assured; and in no circumstances can they be put in the wrong, nor turned from their purpose. Their trust is boundless, and, as they cannot be harmed, so it cannot be betrayed. They are given their heaven on earth as others are here given their hell; and what they get they must have deserved; and they must indeed be close to divinity.

Of such were these, and I hated them with a powerlessness which was a rage of humility; and I mourned for myself as the hare may mourn who is caught in a trap and knows that it will kill him.

I did not hate them, for they could not be hated. My egotism envied them. My shame, and, from it, my resentment, was too recent to be laid, though the eyes of a dove looked into mine and the friendliest hand was on my shoulder. Something obstinate within my soul, something over which I had no charge, stiffened against them; and if one part of my nature yearned for surrender and peace the other part held it back, and so easily that there was never a question as to where obedience must go.

I was easy with them and as careless as I had ever been; and the fact that I had not harmed them put out of my mind the truth that I had tried to do so. Not by a look, an intonation, did they show a memory of that years'-old episode; and what they could forget I could forget as quickly; or could replace by the recollection that in a distant time they had set me adrift in a world of torment.

This did not express itself even in my mind. It lay there like a bulk of unthought thought; which, as it was expressed in its entirety and not in its parts, had to be understood by the nerves where the intelligence lacked width and grasp; and there was I again in the trough of the sea and twisting to any wind.

In a little time I had reaccustomed myself to the new order of things. The immediate past of wandering and strife grew less to be remembered, and my new way of life became sequential and expected.

I knew, and there is contentment in that kind of knowledge, exactly what I should do on the morrow; and I might have ventured a prediction as to how I should be employed in the month to come. For life gathered about me in a web of unhasty occupation and untiring leisure; so that the thing to be done and the doing of it flowed sweetly to each other; and all was accomplished without force, and almost without volition.

Many times my horse took that well-remembered road, and it became as natural to me to turn in that direction as to turn to the rooms of my own house. For I found there much I desired, even unconsciously: friendship, companionship, and, more than all, gaiety; for their young lusty brood began to knit themselves about my life and knot themselves into it.

To go from a sedate, unruffled house into a home that seethes with energy and innocence, and all the animation of budding life, is a notable thing for one who has come to the middle term; and though he had before suffered children with a benevolent impatience he grows to be thankful if they will notice him with even an approach to interest.

It is a blessed thing that whoever wishes to be welcomed benevolently by a child will be so welcomed; for the order of young years is to respond, and they do that without reservation. Children and animals, however we can hurt, we cannot hate; for they are without reserve; and that lack is the one entirely lovable quality in the world.

In the meantime events moved with me, for they, having settled their own lives, charged themselves with the arrangement of mine; and, by a delicate, untiring management, I found myself growing more friendly or more accustomed to a lady of her kin; whom at last, they expected me to marry; who certainly expected to marry me; and whom I should wed when the time came with neither reluctance nor impatience. But this lady I do not remember even slightly. She is a shade; a fading smile, and exists for me as a dream within the dream.

It was settled, and whether I or they or she arranged it I no longer know. It may have been just propinquity, or that sense of endlessness, that inertia of speech, which causes one to continue talking when there is no more to be said; so that, and inevitably, one asks a girl to marry one, there being nothing left to be said; and she, terrified lest silence should fall upon her, agrees to do so, and marvels thereat until she is endlessly wed.

So I asked and she replied; and those who take charge of such arrangements took charge of this; and settled all about time and place, and removed every impediment to our union.

IX

It was the night before my wedding, and I was filled with that desolation of the traveller who must set forth on the morrow, and does not quite know where he is going, nor why he should go there. I had, as was now my custom, taken horse and gone to the castle. The girl I should marry was there, and those two who walked like gods on the earth and who stirred like worms in my mind.

We talked and ate, but beyond that I can only remember the atmosphere of smiles and kindliness to which I was accustomed.

My recollection begins towards nightfall. I had kissed that girl's hands and she went away to her bed; and I was preparing to perform the same duty to my hostess, when she postponed it.

"It is a lovely night," she said, "and," looking at her husband, meaningly, as I thought, "after to-morrow we three shall not be the companions we have been. We shall not meet so often nor so carelessly."

To my glance of enquiry she continued, smilingly:

"A husband belongs to his wife. Your leisure will henceforth have so many claims on it that we may see little of you. When we see you again we may, like drunken men, see you double."

My glance was humorous but questioning.

"Let us take a last walk," she suggested.

"Yes," her husband assented. "One more walk of comrades; one more comfortable talk, and then let to-morrow work what changes it may."

It was a lovely night, with a sky swept bare of all but the moon.

High in the air, bare and bright and round, she rode in beauty.

And, but for her, we might have seen how lonely was the blue serene that swung about her.

Naught stayed in that immense for eye or ear. Naught stirred or crept. All slept but sheer, clear space and silence. And they, with the wonder of the wide, high heaven, were wonderful.

Afar, apart, in lovely alternating jet and silver, the sparse trees dreamed. They seemed as turned upon themselves. As elves they brooded; green in green; whisht and inhuman and serene.

All moved within.

All was withdrawn.

All was infolded and in solitude.

The sky, the grass, the very earth rejected knowing; and we hied with the moon as though she and we were atune to naught beside.

Against that blank withdrawal we struggled as the uneasy dead may, who would regain a realm in which they can find no footing. Silence came on us as at a command; and we were separated and segregated, each from the other, and from all things, as by a gulf.

I looked to the faces on either side of me. They were thin and bright and utterly unknown to me. They seemed wild and questing; stern-poised eagle profiles that were alien in every way to the friendly faces I had known.

And I! I could not see my own face, but I could feel it as a blanch of apprehension.

Why should fear thus flood my being? For thero was nothing within me but fear. I was a blank that swirled with terror; and was stilled as suddenly to a calmness scarcely less terrifying. I strove to engage my thoughts in common things, and, with that purpose, I scanned on every side so that my mind might follow my eye and be interested in its chances.

But in the moonlight there is no variety. Variety is colour, and there was about me but an universal shimmer and blanch, wherein all shape was suppressed, and nothing was but an endless monotony and reduplication of formless form.

So we went; and in the quietude we paced through and the quietness we brought with us we scarce seemed living beings.

We were spectres going in a spectral world. Although we walked we did not seem to move; for to that petrified universe our movement brought no change; and each step was but an eddy in changeless space.

I looked at them; at those faces cut by the moon to a sternness of stone; and I knew in a flash that I was not going between friends but between guards; and that their intention towards me was pitiless.

My will was free. I could have turned and walked backwards, and they would not have hindered me in any way. But they might have smiled as they turned, and that smile would be deadly as an arrow in the heart.

To dare be a coward how courageous one must be! I thought with envy of those whose resolution is so firm that they can fly from danger while there is yet a chance. But to be a coward and to be afraid to save oneself! Into what a degradation must one have fallen for that!

I clenched my hands, and at the contact of my nails I went cold to the bone.

X

At a certain moment each of those silver-pale faces seemed to look forward more straitly, more distantly; and I, withdrawing my eyes from the grey-toned vegetation at my feet, looked forward also.

We had reached the extreme of the park. Beyond was a rugged, moon-dozed tumble of earth and bush and rock; and beyond again was the vast silver-shining keep, to which, in years long gone, we three had walked; and from which, and in what agony, I once had fled.

In the miracle we call memory I recovered that night, and was afflicted again with the recollection of clasping and unclasping hands, of swaying bodies, and of meeting and flying eyes.

But the same hands made now no mutual movement. Those eyes regarded nothing but distance; and those bodies but walked and did no more. It was my hands that twitched and let go; my eyes that stared and flinched away; my body that went forward while its intuition and intention was to go back.

In truth I did halt for a heart's beat; and when I moved again, I was a pace in advance, for they had stayed on the instant and could not move again so quickly as my mood drove.

I looked at them no more. I looked at nothing. My eyes, although wide, were blind to all outward things, and what they were seeking within me it would be hard to tell.

Was I thinking, or feeling or seeing internally? For I was not unoccupied. Somewhere, in unknown regions of my being, there were busynesses and hurryings and a whole category of happenings, as out of my own control as were the moods of those who went with me.

All thought is a seeing. No idea is real if it be not visualised. To see is to know; to know is to see clearly, and other knowledge than that is mechanical. But as we cannot see beyond a stated range of vision so we cannot speak beyond a definite range of thought. Fear has never uttered itself; nor has joy; nor any emotion that has quickened beyond normality. These stir in a mood too remote for expression by words that are fashioned to tell the common experiences of sense and its action.

How should I tell that which was happening to me as I trod forward, my face as impassive as theirs, my brow as calm? The reaction to extreme events is in the spine or the pit of the stomach, but the action is elsewhere, and is in an organ uncharted yet by man.

I trod with them, free to all appearance as a man can be, and yet bound by fetters which had been forged through long years by myself for myself.

We halted, and I looked again on the bossed and monumental door which stood in my memory almost as a living thing. It was as it had been formerly. A black gape, little more than a foot wide, yawned from the top to the bottom. I noticed the rough herbage sprouting grossly among pebbles at its foot, and the overhanging jut of harsh stone that crowned or frowned from its top. And then I looked at them.

His gaze was bent on me, massive as the stone itself.

"Go in," he said.

I looked at her, and although her lips said nothing her eyes, gleaming whitely in the moonlight, commanded as sternly as her husband's voice.

"Go in," he said harshly, "as we went in, and get out, if you can, as we got out."

He reached a monstrous hand to my shoulder, but, at my motion to put it aside, he let it fall; and instead his hand took hold of the great knob. I cast one look at the vast, white moon; at the steady blue spaces about it; at the tumbled sparkle that was the world; and, without a word, I squeezed through the narrow aperture.

I turned and looked back. I had one glimpse of a black form set in a dull radiance. Then the door closed on me with a clang that echoed and echoed and echoed in my ears long after its cause had ceased.

XI

It was dark where I was.

It was a darkness such as I had never experienced. The blackness about me was solid as ebony. It was impenetrable to thought itself.

It flooded my brain so that the blindness within me was as

desperate as that without. I could not keep my eyes open; for, being open, they saw the darkness. I dared not close them; for, being closed, I became that darkness myself. . . .

And at every moment, from the right hand and the left, from before me and from behind me, I imagined things. Darknesses that could move, silences that could touch. . . .

I dared not realise my speculations, and yet, in lightning hints, my mind leaped at and fled from thoughts that were inexpressible except as shivers. My flesh twitched and crept, and I shrank from nothing, as though it could extend a claw; as though it could clutch me with an iron fist. . . .

I was standing yet, long after they had gone, beside the door; fearing to move from it; afraid to stir; and looking about me, as it were, with my ears.

I had no anger against them. I was too occupied for any emotion but those, or that, which was present. I ceased even to think about them; or such seconds of thought as chanced through my agony were humble. They were not forgiving or regretful; they were merely humble, as the thoughts of an overdriven sheep might be towards its driver.

They were gone; and with them everything had gone. I was surrounded by nothingness. I was drowned in it. I was lost and solitary as some grey rock far out in sea. Nay, for the sun shines on it, the wind blows, and a gannet halts there and flaps his wing. There was loneliness nowhere but where I was. There was not such a silence even in the tomb as the silence in which I was centred; for, while the terror of darkness did not diminish, the horror of silence began to grow. And it grew as some monstrous thing may that reproduces itself, on itself, tirelessly, timelessly, endlessly.

Nature abhors a vacuum, and so does the mind, for the mind is nature. It will contrive sound when silence oppresses it, and will people any desolation with its own creatures. Alas for man! With what pain he can create how meagre a joy! With what readiness he can make real a misery!

And my ears had two duties to perform! They must look for me as well as listen, and when the mind is occupied in two endeavours something of craziness comes, even in trivial things.

I began to hear, and at no time could I tell what I heard. I began to see, and no words will impart what I saw. I closed both eyes and ears with my fingers, and was aware in a while that my under-jaw was hanging; that my mouth was open; and that I was listening and looking through that.

At the knowledge my will awakened, and I placed calmness forcibly on myself as tho' I were casing my soul in mail. I strode firmly to my right hand, and after a few steps I came against a wall. I strode in the opposite direction, and in double the paces I came against a wall. I walked backwards, and in twenty steps I came against a wall; and following this my groping fingers tapped suddenly in space.

There was an aperture. . . .

My hair rose on my head stiff and prickling. I did not dare to enter that void in the void. I should more willingly have leaped into a furnace. I went from it on tip-toe, striving to make no sound lest that hole should hear me, and tread behind. . . .

It would come noiselessly. And yet it would be heard! It would roll gently, overwhelmingly, like some new and unimaginable thunder—

"No . . . !" I said in panic to my soul, as I trod cautiously from that behind.

"Great God!" I thought, as I stood somewhere, for now I had lost all direction, and was nowhere. "Great God, what shall I do?"

I lowered myself secretly to the ground, groping with a blind hand to make sure that nothing was there.

"I will try to sleep," I said in my mind.

Nay, I said it to my mind; striving to command that which I

had never learned to control. I huddled my knees up and curved my chin forward like a sleeping dog. I covered my face with my hands, and was still as the stone on which I lay.

"I will try to sleep," I said. "I will think of God," I said.

And it seemed to me that God was the blankness behind, which might advance. And that nothing was so awful as the thought of Him—unimaginable and real! withheld, and imminent, and threatening, and terrific! My knees were listening for Him to the front of me: my back was hearkening from behind; and my brain was engaged elsewhere in matters which I could not cognise.

"If I were to speak aloud!" I thought.

And some part of my mind dared me to do so; wheedled at me to utter one clapping shout: but I knew that at the sound of a voice, of even my own voice, I should die as at a stroke.

XII

How long did that last? Was it an hour, a year, a lifetime?

Time ceases when emotion begins, and its mechanical spacings are then of no more account. Where is time when we sleep? Where is it when we are angry? There is no time, there is but consciousness and its experiences.

I stayed where I had lain myself, and whether my eyes were open or closed I no longer knew. The miseries of this place had abated. No, that does not express it, for this was no longer a place. This place had disappeared, or it had been merged in the new dimension which I call Nowhere.

It is immeasurably great; it is unimaginably small: for as there is no time so there is no space: there is only being, and its modes: and in that region my misery continued itself far from the knowledge of this brain and beyond the let or hindrance of this body.

And yet somewhere, somehow, I knew something that I can

only think of as nothing. An awful, a deadly business was proceeding, with me as the subject. It can only be expressed negatively. Thus I may phrase it, I had gone in the spirit into that aperture from which I had fled. I was in contact with the unmanifest, and that, in its own sphere, is as competent and enduring as are its extensions with which we are familiar. But of that I cannot speak; for as it was out of range of these senses so it was out of range of this mind whose sole preoccupation is these senses.

I had been in terror, but in what was I now? How little to me was the human absence of light, the normal absence of sound that had frightened me.

I was nowhere, and it was real. I was nothing and I was enduring. I would have returned to my blank, dumb prison as one flies to a paradise, but I could not, for something had happened to me. I was translated; and until that experience was fulfilled I could not regain myself nor evade in any way my happenings.

Therefore, I do not know how long I remained crouched in that stony den. Nor how I lay; nor aught that happened to me. But at a point I did return to normal consciousness, and that as swiftly as though one had taken me by the shoulders and clicked me to another direction.

All that monstrous Something-Nothing ceased; and I was listening with these ears, and staring through known darkness with these eyes that see you.

There were footsteps outside the door, and in an instant the door grinced and screeched and swung.

XIII

It was those two. But I did not move from where I lay, and when I did so it was because he lifted me. Those giant arms could lift me as one plucks up a cat; and in a moment I was walking, and the arm that was yet around my waist was pressing me lovingly to his side.

"We were only playing with you," he said.

And she at my other side cooed, as she fondled my hand.

"It was only a game."

I looked wordlessly from one to the other and laughed gently. It was strange that I did not wish to speak. It was strange still that I would not speak; and to everything that they said I returned my gentle laugh. That, it seemed to me, must be sufficient communion even for them; and who in the world could wish to speak when he might laugh?

We walked on, slowly at first, and then hastily, and sentences came from one to the other across me; sometimes explanations, at times assertions and assents.

"It took us ten minutes to get out," he said, "and we thought—"

"For you are so much cleverer than we are," she interposed.

"That you would have been home almost as quickly as we were."

"It took us ten long minutes to imagine that although the door was closed it might not be fastened," he went on, "but when I pulled on it it opened at once.

"I was glad to see the moonlight," he continued in a tone of reverie.

"Glad!" she exclaimed.

"Those ten minutes were unpleasant," he assented.

"They were wicked," she exclaimed energetically. "They—" she paused and took my arm again: "They are forgotten and forgiven. Our thoughts of each other now can be all frankness and trust."

I must have been imprisoned for some hours, for when I went in there had been a bright moon in a bare sky, where now there was no moon and the heavens were deeply shadowed. Our faces were visible to each other as dull shapes, and the spaces about us were bathed in that diaphanous darkness through which one looks without seeing, and against which things loom rather than show.

A wonderful feeling of well-being flowed through me, warming and bracing me. A feeling of astonishing rest for myself, and of endless affection for my companions.

And with it all there was a sense, confused and yet strong, that I knew something which they did not know. That I had a secret which would astonish them when they discovered it.

I knew they should discover it, for I would reveal it to them myself, as soon as I became aware of what it really was. And my mind was filled with joy at the thought of how I would surprise them, and of how they should be surprised.

That strange knowledge lay like a warmth at my heart. It lit the dull night for me, so that through the gloom and mirk I walked as on air and in radiance. All that I had gone through vanished from my memory. It was as though it had never been. Nothing was any more but this new-found rest and contentment.

Happiness! I had found it at last; and it was more worth finding than anything I had yet experienced.

But the end of our walk was nigh. At a distance was the gleam of lights, and black silhouettes about them. We increased our pace, I willingly enough, for I wished to tell them a secret; and in a short time we came to the great steps and mounted them. Men were there with torches, and we walked gaily from darkness into light.

Reaching the top, on the wide platform before the door, she turned to me with a smile, and she stopped dead. I saw the smile frozen on her face. I saw her face blanch to the whiteness of snow, and her eyes widen and fix and stare. She clasped her bosom with both hands and stood so, staring.

Then something, a self of me, detached itself from me, and stood forward and looked also.

I saw myself. My mouth was twisted sidewards in a jolly grin. My eyes were turned inwards in a comical squint, and my chin was all a sop of my own saliva.

I looked at myself so for a mortal moment, and I awakened.

On Prose and Verse

I have done my best to make this little work worthy of accompanying your name. But, if it were twice as good as it is now, it would yet not be half good enough for that.

J.S.

ON PROSE

AN HITHERTO UNPUBLISHED PREFACE WRITTEN FOR THE FRENCH TRANSLATION OF THE CHARWOMAN'S DAUGHTER

When his first booklet of verse is printed, the young writer has discovered that he is an artist. He may then find out that writing is an art. But this is, and usually for a long time, unlikely. The limbs and, in especial, the mind of a young man will compel him to think mainly on their concerns, and a matter that does not implicate agility and desire may seem too slow to merit real attention. He will make many discoveries, and one of the earliest will be that in the matter of mental and physical energy he is superhumanly endowed; so highly vitalized indeed that he is prepared to affront any mass or magnitude that can be presented to him: and he will inevitably arrive at the opinion that poetry

NOTE: If a reader should wish to compare the English and French versions of this essay it should be noted that I have largely re-written the original matter for this English publication.

alone cannot absorb the torrent that he actually is. He will turn
hopefully to prose.

A young writer who reviews the work of the masters in prose
cannot but see how easily it could be bettered; and, if he has any
piety, he will laud the Providence that reserved this glorious task
for one worthy of it. It is at this most powerful-seeming moment
of his life that he comes also to realize how meagre are the opportunities allotted to us for a really energetic treatment of life.
Our elders, our books of reference, our own intelligence, everything assures the writer that he must seek the material of his art
in the human flux that is about him, and that, having assembled
some quantity of this stuff, he must breathe into it the breath of
life.

But, when he looks closely at current events and at the daily
beings that are about him, he discovers little of interest in them,
and nothing of excitement. He cannot but notice that, relatively
to himself, life and thought and art are undervitalized, or are
stagnant. He is willing to remould the sorry scheme of things,
but if the task of fabricating a universe is to devolve on him, he
must be permitted to invent one wherein excitement will be
the major reality. Thus, by an urgent and consequently trust-
worthy instinct, he is led to perceive that in a Universe-with-a-
Lack there are only two subjects really worth writing about,
namely, murder and philosophy.

Having essayed it, the young writer apprehends with some
exasperation that it is much easier to commit a murder than it
is to write one; or even that it is easier to eat a breakfast, or
to fall into and out of love, than it is to break these subjects into
fragments of one word each, and thus to recreate them. His first
prose-work is, consequently, a philosophical novel, and it should
be violent enough to be catalogued as a murder.

That the volume to which these lines serve as an introduction
is neither violent nor philosophical, is due solely to chance. This
writer had written and published his first book of verse. He had

gone daily to stare in the bookseller's window that displayed hundreds of ordinary novels and only one copy of his work.— Even so, that one copy had to be sought for diligently, for it was placed in a back bottom corner and was flanked and overhung and eclipsed by the brilliant covers of everybody else's imbecilities. He was gloomily proud of its modesty, which was far greater than his own, and was as gloomily angry with the person who had so ignorantly dressed his window.—

I began to see reviews of my poems and was amazed to find that the writers of these were benevolent, were encouraging, and were, some, even enthusiastic. I noted with a pain that I shall carry to the grave a remark of George Russell's in an otherwise admirable review "of course we are not comparing Mr Stephens to Shakespeare." That uncourageous second-thought clouded my day. And I was exalted and terrified by the statement of another reviewer, a statement composed apparently more in sorrow than in anger, that "Mr Stephens used his God-given talents to glorify all that is detestable and subversive." The judicious will understand that this writer was in the condition of gloom and grandeur that was proper to his years, and that his next book ought to have been murderous and philosophical.

Of course there were some things that I did not know everything about. I knew, for instance, nothing about murder, and less than that about philosophy, and I did not know how to write prose.

Nobody did know how to write prose. Nobody does now. Nobody ever will.

If one were to assert that poetry is closer to speech than prose is we should, rightly, dislike and evade that malicious person, but we should be relieved that the statement had at last been made.

Poetry is created in the whole phrase; is even, when the gods are benevolent, created in the entire verse. But prose must be invented from comma to comma.

Everything that is in his nature helps the person who can

write poetry to write it. Everything that can be conceived combines to prevent the writing of prose. And, though the soul is not tensed to that extreme in prose as it is in verse, yet is the mind especially tensed.

And the ear must be unflaggingly active and watchful, and inquisitive. It must serve even as an eye, surveying whole swathes and pastures of sense and action and passion, which poetry needs only to indicate, but which prose must wholly fabricate and complete to the last possible verb and noun and adjective. For the matter of poesy comes eagerly to its statement, but that which prose can serve is loath and reluctant; is without any spring or readiness; is void of good-will or good-humour, and of all else that is good.

In verse, even before the work is begun, the ear is marvellously, is prophetically, attuned to an unknown key and its permissive harmonies; but prose is chromatic and accidental, and the ear dealing with it must cover strange and continuously-changing intervals, and must seek harmonic values in unexpected places and at great and greatly-varying distances from its tonic—and the key changes after every full-stop . . .

In fact a writer of English might be forgiven, and might be somewhat petted and praised, if he should declare with rage, with resignation, that it is not possible to write prose at all.

A possible French reader may wonder what all the pother is about. He may say that Monsieur Jourdain spoke prose, and that every Frenchman writes it: and this may not be untrue. Indeed Frenchmen will boast, and with what glee, and with what an air of super-superiority, that their prose is better than their verse!

There is a curious disagreeing and, yet, complementary quality that holds apart and holds together England and France, and English and French literatures. In war and peace, in literature, science and in social progress, the work of these great nations has been diverse but complementary. The modern world is their joint operation, and, in the making of it, each has contributed qualities that the other lacked but could accept. Rome plus Greece conquered the world. England and France have done much the same thing. An exceedingly disinherited mind could almost conceive that these are two races but one nation—two methods used by one mind. They extend into, they interpenetrate and complete each other in a way that no other two nations do, and their endless mutual curiosities, borrowings, and comprehensions spring from a spiritual identity that should be precious to both of them.

This concurrence and departure runs even into the two languages. When a cultivated Englishman refers to foreign literature he usually means French prose. A cultivated Frenchman is as generally thinking about England when he condescends to think about poetry.

Now it is held that one valid Frenchman can write a sound book of prose, but that it takes forty Frenchmen, aided by their families, to write one notable poem. And the converse is, that an honest Englishman may produce one book of decent lyrics, but that it required forty-eight of them to give a literary value to the Bible. And, as Shakespeare says, "there's the rub." For, to the person who can write verse, the idea that he cannot write prose is degrading and repulsive and to be disproven.

I, knowing nothing of possible difficulties, was prepared to vanquish prose with one hand tied behind my back and one eye blindfolded. My trouble, and it was lightly borne, was that I did not know what to write about, and was, so, prepared to excogitate the murders and philosophies before referred to, when I chanced on a certain book.

I had picked up, idly enough, *The House of Pomegranates* by Oscar Wilde. After reading about twenty pages I closed the book (and, in parenthesis be it said, I have not since re-opened it)—I closed the book because an illuminating idea came to me, not from its pages, but from, as it were, between the lines. This thought was—

The art of prose-writing does not really need a murder to carry it.

And further—

Writing can be quite good, and yet have no violence whatever in it. It can be powerful on a very minimum of action. It can be wise on a very minimum of thought. It can exist by writing alone . . .

And, again—

By some means which I do not understand, it is obvious that good writing is not a way of saying, it is a way of doing—or, even, it is a way of being . . .

And, finally—

Verse is a manifesting of the angel in man, but prose is an unburying of the god . . .

I sat forthwith in my one room, which contained my one new table, my one new wife, our one brand-new baby, and our one large female mouse. This mouse we cherished exceedingly, and it appreciated us cordially in return. It was a motherly, a diligently-companionable mouse, and it would do anything whatever for a friend.

(May the possible reader forgive me and, for I shall not have this opportunity again, permit me here to disembarrass my memory of that excellent mouse.) She, later on, scandalized our young ménage by producing, entirely from herself, or without the visible collaboration of any other creature, battalions of small new mice regularly every few months.

Our home scampered and squeaked. It sat upon forty of its hind legs and washed twenty of its faces with forty of its front paws. It chased twenty of its own tails, and was itself chased and bitten by nineteen agile pursuers. The roof fell on to our bed at night, and the floor climbed into our laps at breakfast. Our babe knew a mouse long before she knew a cat, and should thus have become perfected in kindness.

Four mice, with their tails curled around each other's hind legs, and their front paws wrapped about each other's necks, and their four furry heads squeezed at impossible and adorable adjustments into each other's furry bellies, were asleep in the bottom of a cup. Three, with ears and eyes fixed in an unblinking attention, their noses wriggling in a mathematical ecstasy, were listening closely, intelligently, critically, to the ticking of a watch. One, continuously changeable, sat up on its hind legs on a piece of coal and roared:

> *I'm the King of the Castle,*
> *Who dares wrastle?*

The mother of them all sat on the table, teaching a devoted semi-circle the three best things to do I when you saw a cat, II when a cat saw you, III how to turn on one foot (*a*) in a quarter of your own length, (*b*) at a moderate pace, (*c*) at full speed.

At times, her band of scholars would emit one simultaneous squeak, and, erupting from her lecture, would scoot to their fellows at play . . .

And then, for she would lecture, she lectured to me—

She knew, for she could see that I only had to shave once a week, that I was younger than she was, and that I had not much sense; and she taught me unweariedly I what to do when I saw a cat, II what to do when a cat saw me, III how to turn on one foot (*a*) in a quarter of my own length, (*b*) at a moderate pace, (*c*) at full speed.

No scholar at a Sorbonne has ever listened nor ever will listen with such affection and enthusiasm to his lecture as, shivering with hope, shivering with terror, I hung on her counsel . . . "Good mice, like you and I," she admonished me, "must . . ."

But the alliances, and interalliances of this band resulted at last in so-congested a population of mice that we were forced to emigrate them. At dead of night, with six mice in each of my pockets and three in my hat, I used to steal from the house and let my mice escape, under the swinging lintels of neighbouring houses, into the neighbouring houses. I put two or three into each house, so that they should not be lonely. (But I have shuddered to think of the rats, the cats, the terriers, and the housemaids these poor innocents must have fronted and fallen to.)

I began to write then—much in the manner of the above large, unpardonable parenthesis—not with the idea of saying anything, for I had nothing whatever to say, but with the idea of doing a something which I conceived that Wilde had tried, and perhaps failed to do. I looked at my new wife, and had immediately a model for the Mary of this book. I looked within myself, and found as immediately my Charwoman. Indeed, I discovered that a patient examination of myself could produce the model of anything whatever, from a cake of soap to an hippogriff. And since then, each time that I have sat before virgin paper, and whether the medium was to be in prose or verse, I have tried to do precisely as I tried then.

A sentence from the Vedas explains that nothing stands between man and Knowledge except words; and it is true that between the artist and his own most intimate comprehensions there is a screen of words which have wide general significances, but no precise meanings. It is variously stated that the quest of art is Truth, Beauty, Reality, Romance, the Good, the Bad, Creation, or the various converses and extensions and particles of these. The values of these words fluctuate so violently—their meanings are at every moment so great and so small, as to render them purely personal to the user and practically meaningless to the neighbour; to say nothing of the fact that mere usage had at once deflowered and defaced them, demoded them.

Nor does it greatly help to say that the task of an artist is Self-Realization. 'Tis a limiting term. Man, and the artist in especial, is a Protean creature. Which self shall he realize, whose self is innumerable, and is closed only by Being itself? The content that is to be realized under this heading must be, in the narrowest sense, psychological, and, in the scantiest degree, realistic.

The realization of a self by the artist is a secondary act; is, as it were, a simple by-product of the work done. His prime aim is to identify himself, first, with the matter under description, ultimately with everything that is; and to express from the worm to God with such propriety that others are aided to recollect, as he does, and to approve or disapprove as knowledge bids them. For speech has to do with informations, but if writing does not exhibit a knowledge, some knowledge, it is merely a business like any other, and of only that singularity.

Lack of knowledge is, in general, more apparent than real. At every moment, man knows more than his personal, his communal, experience would seem to warrant—for his whole experience is communal—, and he can be helped, or even forced, to recollect all that was or is or shall be almost without limit. The fact that neither Shakespeare nor his readers have wittingly participated in the violences, the exaltations, the profound comprehensions and divinations in which both are interested, is no bar to the perfect expression and the perfect understanding with which these are met.

A work of art will rarely fail by reason of its author's intellectual poverty—it can fail when the identity between subject and object has broken: It fails when the artist cannot will to be his matter, and, so, cannot will his matter to be. It will fail, too, when comprehension ceases to be sympathetic. In writing, at least, you must love your enemy, or love's labour is lost. To identify the object; to fuse self and not-self, is the privilege, and is the first and the last duty of an artist.

This duty of universal self-identification is the same for the prose writer as for the poet. The distinction between them lies in the various tensions which these arts are competent to handle.

So, in a certain fever of discovery, and all among my mice, I poised a pen, and tried to be whatever my mind should at that instant chance on, and this book is the result. But my real desire in writing this forward is to congratulate myself on having a translator who is securely at home in two literatures, in two languages. Thanks to him, my book goes voyaging with this in its favour, that the translation accurately conveys whatever the original intended. If the book should not please French readers, the fault will not lie at Mr Chevalley's door.

LA POÉSIE PURE

One can scarcely utter the words "pure poetry" nowadays without making a genuflexion towards France and towards the Abbé Brémond, for it is in France that this ghost has been conjured, and it is perhaps only in France that the question is as yet of a special interest. The subject has been touched upon by many great English poets, but it has not been rigorously explored by any of them. In the main, the testimony of these writers, and of all antiquity, coincides with the findings of Monsieur Brémond, and, as they evaded the difficulty of a definition by using the unknown term "inspiration," so the Abbé Brémond evades the same difficulty by using the term "mysticism."

It is not only that we cannot say what poetry is—we cannot say what anything is. We can treat with the modes of motion, but not with motion. We can utilize the mechanics of things, but not things. In fact, reality (poetry) is incapable of expression or exposure, or definition.

This incapacity is not because Reality is unknown to us. On the contrary, for there is nothing better known. There is nothing else known. And, intellectually, no man can say the thing that he knows, but only the thing that he thinks. The limit of transmissible knowledge is as the East says, Name and Form. And these we endlessly translate and define. The sum of untransmissible knowledge is—I am—and its variants, thou art, he, she and it is—And when, by a chance, something of this quality of actual Being is caught into thought, we recognize it with delight and cry: this is poetry.

We cannot say what poetry is, but we may adventure a speculation as to what it is not; and, by a negative definition, approach to something that has the appearance of the impossibly positive statement.

Poetry is not action, nor passion, nor thought. It contains all of these, carelessly as it were; but, in a true instance, when these qualities have been eliminated, there remains yet a quality, and that residue is poetry. Nor is it correct to say that a "residue" remains—an excess remains, and that excess is poetry.

If we dare to speak in a more positive fashion, we shall say that poetry is a superior energy, and that this special energy cannot be held or manifested in any other than the poetic form. Poetry is a magical act, and it truly strikes the competent reader or listener as an act of magic, and as nothing else. No emotional utterance, however poignant; no intellectual content, however pregnant, can achieve poetry. Poetry achieves itself, and it uses emotion or intellect as vehicles to carry it, and as fairly inconsiderable vehicles at that.

Also, poetry will not permit the matter it uses to remain in its own or prime form. It will intellectualize the emotion that carries it; it will emotionalize any intellectual matter that is submitted to it, turning these into Pure Thought, into, that is, Poesy. This is the only terrestrial work that it will do, and it compasses these singular changes by virtue of its own excessive speed working on the natural polarities of these qualities. The true work of poetry is not to teach anything, nor to explain anything—it is to intensify life.

Once you have made it your own, once it has become habitual to you, you may weary of the finest tune that any musician has created; but the line of poetry that you have spiritually received shall never stale, shall never tarnish; and the magic that justly commended it to you shall be as undiminished at your last use of it as at your first.

For the purpose of this question, I shall, temerariously, consider that the title of poet which has been given to me has been properly earned; and I will try to describe, as clearly as I can manage, what I remember of the process of making a poem.

I always knew when I had a poem, and in, perhaps, much the

same way that a hen knows that it has an egg. The hen, very likely, does not know if its egg will turn out to be a white or a brown egg. Nor did I ever know anything at all about my poem beyond that I had one. Of that, however, I was always quite certain.

So far as I can establish it, nothing in the nature of thinking had part in the birth or even the maturing of a poem. There was a feeling of intense, living activity; and this feeling, if it was not joy, certainly neighboured it.

This feeling would last for perhaps three days, during which time there would be occasional, recurring moments of close, of absorbed attention. Speaking normally, this steady attention was not directed to anything in especial, or perhaps even to anything at all. It has just a joyous collectedness, and it was even tremendously stimulating—more so, indeed, than any other stimulus which I have received from life or pleasure, or excitement.

There came next a sort of rhythmic movement in the mind, to which the body could sway, and this movement was still unconnected with words or thought. A line of words came thereafter, appearing, as it seemed, from nowhere; and around and about that line the rhythm I speak of disported itself, swinging on it and around it as an acrobat swings on a trapeze; this rhythm was shaping the line certainly, but it was as yet making no effort to add another line to it.

The poem was born and that one line was, as it were, the egg from which it would organically evolve.

In a short poem, in a lyric certainly, the entire technique and rhythmic scheme is implicit in the first line. The tempo of the poem; the entire succeeding sound-value or tone-effect, the emotional and intellectual colouring are all latent in that one line; and it unfolds to completion as simply and organically, as thoughtlessly, as a seed grows to a shoot, a sapling and a tree.

That line is the creative act made manifest. The rest of the poem lies *in the will to continue it*, or in the will to continue in the state from which it sprang.

The same thoughtless absorption of attention is the instrument by which the poem is completed; and the ability to hold that absorbed interest is the ability to make a poem. One does not think, one *looks* to see what will happen next—it happens—and then, one looks again.

It may be said that if one is absorbed one must be absorbed in something—and to that I would reply that one must be absorbed in joy (it may be that Joy and Will are identical terms); and this joy is so complete in itself that it can only be thought of as nothing.

All of the poems arrived at in this way may not be good ones. It was my almost invariable experience that ere I could deliver myself of my real poem, I had to write two others. That is, I had three poems in hand at the end of my labour; and (if the word "good" can be properly applied to my work) I was in possession of two poor poems and one good one. The two bad poems were perhaps actually necessary in order to take the edge off energy, and to assist that process of absorption (already spoken of) to become continuous, instead of intermittent.

Occasionally a poem would come in one sole jet; in absolute completion, that is; but often it arrived a sketchy, disconnected ghost of what it should have been. The building and repairing of it was still undertaken by that same process of looking at it without thinking about it. (I think that the condition known in the East as Yoga and that which we call Poesy are identical.)

Let it not be considered that I am here criticizing or degrading thought. Thought has its own wonderful realms. But an artistic failure is rarely traceable to an incapacity for thinking. Such a failure is always attributable to a failure of the will; and the will has failed when delight is not focussed upon itself, and focussed afterwards upon a subject-matter. For this reason, the (so-called) realistic artist must fail, for it is impossible to be delighted with that pseudo-real, that limited cognition, which is his matter.

The will must refuse to be joyous if the matter it regards is not illimitable. Happiness and limitlessness are one rare mode of the mind; they are the same thing; and it is this illimitable quality which we recognize and recollect when the poet achieves it.

For the poet is not singular nor unique: if he has memories, they are shared by us; and if he has poesy, so have we all. Unless delight is behind the writer of even a sad tale, his very sadness will be untrue; for it is the function of the artist to transform all that is sad, all that is ugly, all that is "real" into the one quality which reconciles the diversities that trouble us; into Pure Poetry.

POEMS

from Insurrections

WHAT TOMAS AN BUILE SAID IN A PUB

I saw God. Do you doubt it?
  Do you dare to doubt it?
I saw the Almighty Man. His hand
Was resting on a mountain, and
He looked upon the World and all about it:
I saw Him plainer than you see me now,
  You mustn't doubt it.

He was not satisfied;
  His look was all dissatisfied.
His beard swung on a wind far out of sight
Behind the world's curve, and there was light
Most fearful from His forehead, and He sighed,
"That star went always wrong, and from the start
  I was dissatisfied."

He lifted up His hand—
  I say He heaved a dreadful hand
Over the spinning Earth. Then I said, "Stay,
You must not strike it, God; I'm in the way;
And I will never move from where I stand."

He said, "Dear child, I feared that you were dead,"
And stayed His hand.

TO THE FOUR COURTS, PLEASE

The driver rubbed at his nettly chin
With a huge, loose forefinger, crooked and black.
And his wobbly, violet lips sucked in,
And puffed out again and hung down slack:
One fang shone through his lop-sided smile,
In his little pouched eyes flickered years of guile.

And the horse, poor beast, it was ribbed and forked,
And its ears hung down, and its eyes were old,
And its knees were knuckly, and as we talked
It swung the stiff neck that could scarcely hold
Its big, skinny head up—then I stepped in,
And the driver climbed to his seat with a grin.

God help the horse and the driver too,
And the people and beasts who have never a friend,
For the driver easily might have been you,
And the horse be me by a different end.
And nobody knows how their days will cease
And the poor, when they're old, have little of peace.

FOSSILS

And then she saw me creeping,
Saw and stood
Transfixed upon the fringes of the wood,
And straight went leaping.

Headlong down the pitch
Of the curved hill,
Over the ditch
And through the skirt of bushes by the rill
She pelted screaming,
Swerved from the water sideways with a twist
Just as I clutched and missed.

Flashed white beneath my hand and doubled back,
Swift as a twisting hare upon her track,
Hot for the hill again,
But all in vain.

Her hair swung far behind,
Straight as a stream balanced upon the wind,
O, it was black, dipped
In the dregs of midnight with a spark
Caught from a star that smouldered in the dark.

It I gripped,
Drew for a moment tight,
Jerked with a victor's cry
Down in the grasses high
Her to the hot, brown earth and threatened—daft
And then she laughed.

THE SHELL

And then I pressed the shell
Close to my ear
And listened well,
And straightway like a bell
Came low and clear
The slow, sad murmur of far distant seas,

Whipped by an icy breeze
Upon a shore
Wind-swept and desolate.
It was a sunless strand that never bore
The footprint of a man,
Nor felt the weight
Since time began
Of any human quality or stir
Save what the dreary winds and waves incur.
And in the hush of waters was the sound
Of pebbles rolling round,
For ever rolling with a hollow sound.
And bubbling sea-weeds as the waters go
Swish to and fro
Their long, cold tentacles of slimy grey.
There was no day,
Nor ever came a night
Setting the stars alight
To wonder at the moon:
Was twilight only and the frightened croon,
Smitten to whimpers, of the dreary wind
And waves that journeyed blind—
And then I loosed my ear—O, it was sweet
To hear a cart go jolting down the street.

A STREET

Two narrow files of houses scowl,
Blackened with grime, on either side
Of the road, and through them prowl
Strange men and women, shifty-eyed
And slinking, and a drink-shop throws
Its flare of yellow light adown
The cracked pavement. The gutter flows

A turbid, evil stream. A clown,
Drink-sodden, lurches by and sings
Obscenely. A woman trails behind
With old, bad eyes; her clothing clings
Rain-soaked about her. No daring wind,
Light-hearted, from a garden blows
Its sweetness here from any rose.

SEUMAS BEG

A man was sitting underneath a tree
Outside the village, and he asked me what
Name was upon this place, and said that he
Was never here before. He told a lot
Of stories to me too. His nose was flat.
I asked him how it happened, and he said
The first mate of the *Mary Ann* done that
With a marling-spike one day, but he was dead,
And jolly good job too; and he'd have gone
A long way to have killed him, and he had
A gold ring in one ear; the other one
"Was bit off by a crocodile, bedad."
That's what he said. He taught me how to chew.
He was a real nice man. He liked me too.

OULD SNARLY-GOB

There was a little fire in the grate
   A fistful of red coal
   Might warm a soul,
But scarce could heat a body that had weight—
   Not mine, at any rate.

A glum old man was sitting by the fire,
  With wrinkled brow,
  Warming himself somehow,
And mumbling low, this melancholy sire,
  A singular desire.

If I were young again, said he, if I
  Were only young again,
  I'd laugh at pain:
I'd jeer at people groaning, and I'd try
  To pinch them ere they'd die.

The young folk laugh and jump about and play,
  And I am old,
  And grey, and cold;
If I were only young again, and they
  Were old, and cold, and grey,

I'd pull them from the fire, I'd jeer and shout.
  I'd say for fun,
  Get up and run
And warm yourself, you lazy, doddering lout,
  Get up and run about.

from The Hill of Vision

EVERYTHING THAT I CAN SPY

Everything that I can spy
Through the circle of my eye,
Everything that I can see
Has been woven out of me.
I have sown the stars; I threw
Clouds of morn and noon and eve
In the deeps and steeps of blue;
And each thing that I perceive,
Sun and sea and mountain high,
Are made and moulded by my eye
Closing it, I do but find
Darkness, and a little wind.

IN THE POPPY FIELD

Mad Patsy said, he said to me,
That every morning he could see
An angel walking on the sky;
Across the sunny skies of morn
He threw great handfuls far and nigh

Of poppy seed among the corn;
And then, he said, the angels run
To see the poppies in the sun.

'A poppy is a devil weed,'
I said to him—he disagreed:
He said the devil had no hand
In spreading flowers tall and fair
Through corn and rye and meadow land,
And gurth and barrow everywhere:
The devil has not any flower,
But only money in his power.

And then he stretched out in the sun
And rolled upon his back for fun:
He kicked his legs and roared for joy
Because the sun was shining down,
He said he was a little boy
And wouldn't work for any clown:
He ran and laughed behind a bee,
And danced for very ecstasy.

DANNY MURPHY

He was as old as old could be,
His little eye could scarcely see,
His mouth was sunken in between
His nose and chin, and he was lean
And twisted up and withered quite,
So that he could not walk aright.

His pipe was always going out,
And then he'd have to search about
In all his pockets, and he'd mow

—O, deary me! and, musha now!
And then he'd light his pipe, and then
He'd let it go clean out again.

He could not dance or jump or run,
Or ever have a bit of fun
Like me and Susan, when we shout
And jump and throw ourselves about:
But when he laughed then you could see
He was as young as young could be.

NORA CRIONA

I have looked him round and looked him through,
Know everything that he will do
In such a case, and such a case,
And when a frown comes on his face
I dream of it, and when a smile
I trace its sources in a while.

He cannot do a thing but I
Peep to find the reason why,
For I love him, and I seek,
Every evening in the week,
To peep behind his frowning eye
With little query, little pry,
And make him if a woman can
Happier than any man.

Yesterday he gripped her tight
And cut her throat—and serve her right!

BESSIE BOBTAIL

As down the street she wambled slow,
She had not got a place to go:
She had not got a place to fall
And rest herself—no place at all.
She stumped along and wagged her pate
And said a thing was desperate.

Her face was screwed and wrinkled tight
Just like a nut—and, left and right,
On either side she wagged her head
And said a thing, and what she said
Was desperate as any word
That ever yet a person heard.

I walked behind her for a while
And watched the people nudge and smile:
But ever as she went she said,
As left and right she swung her head,
—*"O God He knows," and "God He knows*
And, surely God Almighty knows."

WHY TOMÁS CAM WAS GRUMPY

If I were rich what would I do?
I'd leave the horse just ready to shoe,
I'd leave the pail beside the cow,
I'd leave the furrow beneath the plough,
I'd leave the ducks tho' they should quack,
"Our eggs will be stolen before you're back";
I'd buy a diamond brooch, a ring,
A chain of gold that I would fling

Around her neck. . . . Ah, what an itch,
If I were rich!

What would I do if I were wise?
I would not debate about the skies,
Nor would I try a book to write,
Or find the wrong in the tangled right,
I would not debate with learned men
Of how, and what, and why, and when;
I'd train my tongue to a linnet's song,
I'd learn the words that couldn't go wrong—
And then I'd say . . . And win the prize,
If I were wise!

But I'm not that nor t'other, I bow
My back to the work that's waiting now.
I'll shoe the horse that's standing ready,
I'll milk the cow if she'll be steady,
I'll follow the plough that turns the loam,
I'll watch the ducks don't lay from home.

—And I'll curse, and curse, and curse again
Till the devil joins in with his big amen,
And none but he and I will wot
When the heart within me starts to rot,
To fester and churn its ugly brew—
. . . Where's my spade? I've work to do.

THE GIRL I LEFT BEHIND ME

She watched the blaze,
And so I said the thing I'd come to say,
Pondered for days.

Her lips moved slow,
And the wide eye she flashed on me
Was sudden as a blow.

She turned again,
Her hands clasping her knees and did not speak:
She did not deign.

And I, poor gnome!
A chided cur crawls to a hole to hide:
. . . I toddled home.

MAC DHOUL

I saw them all,
I could have laughed out loud
To see them at their capers;
That serious, solemn-footed, weighty crowd
Of angels, or say resurrected drapers:
Each with a thin flame swinging round his head,
With lilting wings and eyes of holy dread,
And curving ears strained for the great foot-fall
And not a thought of sin—!
I don't know how I kept the laughter in.

For I was there,
Unknown, unguessed at, snug
In a rose tree's branchy spurt,
With two weeks' whisker blackening lug to lug,
With tattered breeks and only half a shirt.
Swollen fit to burst with laughter at the sight
Of those dull angels drooping left and right
Along the towering throne, each in a scare

To hear His foot advance
Huge from the cloud behind, all in a trance.

And suddenly,
As silent as a ghost,
I jumped out from the bush,
Went scooting through the glaring, nerveless host
All petrified, all gaping in a hush:
Came to the throne and, nimble as a rat,
Hopped up it, squatted close, and there I sat,
Squirming with laughter till I had to cry,
To see Him standing there
Frozen with all His angels in a stare!
He raised His hand,
His hand! 'twas like a sky!
Gripped me in half a finger,
Flipped me round and sent me spinning high
Through screaming planets: faith, I didn't linger
To scratch myself, and then adown I sped
Scraping old moons and twisting heels and head,
A chuckle in the void, till . . . here I stand
As naked as a brick,
I'll sing the Peeler and the Goat in half a tick.

from Songs from the Clay

THE RIVALS

I heard a bird at dawn
   Singing sweetly on a tree,
That the dew was on the lawn,
   And the wind was on the lea;
But I didn't listen to him,
   For he didn't sing to me.

I didn't listen to him,
   For he didn't sing to me
That the dew was on the lawn
   And the wind was on the lea;
I was singing at the time
   Just as prettily as he.

I was singing all the time
   Just as prettily as he,
About the dew upon the lawn
   And the wind upon the lea;
So I didn't listen to him
   As he sang upon a tree.

THE DAISIES

In the scented bud of the morning-O,
  When the windy grass went rippling far,
I saw my dear one walking slow,
  In the field where the daisies are.

We did not laugh and we did not speak
  As we wandered happily to and fro;
I kissed my dear on either cheek,
  In the bud of the morning-O.

A lark sang up from the breezy land,
  A lark sang down from a cloud afar,
And she and I went hand in hand
  In the field where the daisies are.

TO BE CONTINUED

I smiled at the angry maid,
  And said that I did not care
Whether she went or stayed.

And she, going down the glade,
  Thought, "Now he will fall to prayer."
I smiled at the angry maid.

Indeed I was sore afraid;
  But I said it was her affair
Whether she went or stayed.

About her a nimbus rayed
  Where the sun made love to her hair.
I smiled at the angry maid.

And while, like a fool, I played,
   I had not a smile to spare
Whether she went or stayed.

She in her youth arrayed!
   I stolid and scant of hair!
I smiled at the angry maid
   Whether she went or stayed.

DEIRDRE

Do not let any woman read this verse;
It is for men; and after them their sons
And their sons' sons.

The time comes when our hearts sink utterly;
When we remember Deirdre and her tale,
And that her lips are dust.

Once she did tread the earth: men took her hand;
They looked into her eyes and said their say,
And she replied to them.

More than a thousand years it is since she
Was beautiful: she trod the waving grass;
She saw the clouds.

A thousand years! The grass is still the same,
The clouds as lovely as they were that time
When Deirdre was alive.

But there has never been a woman born
Who was so beautiful, not one so beautiful
Of all the women born.

Let all men go apart and mourn together;
No man can ever love her; not a man
Can ever be her lover.

No man can bend before her: no man say—
What could one say to her? There are no words
That one could say to her!

Now she is but a story that is told
Beside the fire! No man can ever be
The friend of that poor queen.

THE SATYR

There came a satyr creeping through the wood,
  His hair fell on his breast; his legs were slim:
His eyes were laughing wickedly; he stood
  And peeped about on every side of him.

He peeped about; he minced upon the ground,
  He put a thin hand up to hide a grin:
He doubled up and laughed without a sound;
  The very bodiment of happy sin.

The bodiment of sin: timid and wild
  And limber as a goat: his pointed feet
Were not at peace an instant: like a child
  He danced and glanced; and like a goat was fleet.

He danced, he peeped; but at a sound I made,
  A crackling twig, he turned and suddenly
In three great jumps he bounded to the shade,
  And disappeared among the greenery.

THE GOAT PATHS

The crooked paths go every way
　　Upon the hill—they wind about
　　Through the heather in and out
Of the quiet sunniness.
And there the goats, day after day,
　　Stray in sunny quietness,
Cropping here and cropping there,
　　As they pause and turn and pass,
Now a bit of heather spray,
　　Now a mouthful of the grass.

In the deeper sunniness,
　　In the place where nothing stirs,
Quietly in quietness,
　　In the quiet of the furze,
For a time they come and lie
Staring on the roving sky.

If you approach they run away,
　　They leap and stare, away they **bound**,
　　With a sudden angry sound,
To the sunny quietude;
　　Crouching down where nothing stirs
　　In the silence of the furze,
Crouching down again to brood
In the sunny solitude.

If I were as wise as they
　　I would stray apart and brood,
I would beat a hidden way
Through the quiet heather spray
　　To a sunny solitude;

And should you come I'd run away,
  I would make an angry sound,
  I would stare and turn and bound
To the deeper quietude,
  To the place where nothing stirs
  In the silence of the furze.

In that airy quietness
  I would think as long as they;
Through the quiet sunniness
  I would stray away to brood
By a hidden beaten way
  In a sunny solitude.

I would think until I found
  Something I can never find,
Something lying on the ground,
  In the bottom of my mind.

THE MARKET

A man came to me at the fair
  And said, "If you've a poet's tongue
Tumble up and chant the air
  That the stars of morning sung.

"I'll pay you, if you sing it nice,
  A penny-piece." —I answered flat,
"Sixpence is the proper price
  For a ballad such as that."

But he stared and wagged his head,
  Growling as he passed along,
"Sixpence! well, I'll see you dead
  Before I pay that for a song."

I saw him buy three pints of stout
With the sixpence—dirty lout!

THE TWINS

Good and bad are in my heart,
    But I cannot tell to you
(For they never are apart)
    Which is stronger of the two.

I am this, I am the other,
And the devil is my brother.
But my father He is God,
And my mother is the sod;
Therefore, I am safe, you see,
Owing to my pedigree.

So I shelter love and hate
    Like twin brothers in a nest,
Lest I find when it's too late
    That the other was the best.

WASHED IN SILVER

Gleaming in silver are the hills,
    Blazing in silver is the sea,
And a silvery radiance spills
    Where the moon drives royally.
Clad in silver tissue I
March magnificently by.

THE VOICE OF GOD

I bent again unto the ground
And I heard the quiet sound

Which the grasses make when they
Come up laughing from the clay.

"We are the voice of God," they said:
Thereupon I bent my head
Down again that I might see
If they truly spoke to me.

But around me everywhere
Grass and tree and mountain were
Thundering in mighty glee,
"We are the voice of deity."

And I leapt from where I lay,
I danced upon the laughing clay,
And, to the rock that sang beside,
"We are the voice of God," I cried.

THE CENTAURS

Playing upon the hill three centaurs were!
They lifted each a hoof and stared at me,
And stamped upon the dust.

They stamped the dust, they snuffed upon the air,
And all their movements had the fierce glee
Of power and pride and lust.

Of power and pride and lust! then with a shout
They tossed their heads and wheeled and galloped round
In furious brotherhood.

In furious brotherhood, around, about,
They charged, they swerved, they leaped; then, bound on bound,
They raced into the wood.

THE LARK

There is a small bird cowering in the dark,
   His wing is broken, he will never sing;
He will not sing again, the little lark
   That has a broken wing.

The lark that cowers with a broken wing
   Is all alone; his mate has gone away;
To-morrow in the fields his mate will sing
   Her merry lay.

His mate will sing again her merry lay
   In the green fields; forgetting he is gone;
But he will never rouse a sunny day
   Again for any one.

He will not sing again for any one;
   The wing is broken of that little lark;
His song is broken, and his heart is gone
   There in the dark.

THE SNARE
To A. E.

I hear a sudden cry of pain!
   There is a rabbit in a snare:
Now I hear the cry again,
   But I cannot tell from where.

But I cannot tell from where
   He is calling out for aid;
Crying on the frightened air,
   Making everything afraid.

Making everything afraid,
　Wrinkling up his little face,
As he cries again for aid;
　And I cannot find the place!

And I cannot find the place
　Where his paw is in the snare:
Little one! Oh, little one!
　I am searching everywhere.

THE CAGE

It tried to get from out the cage;
　Here and there it ran, and tried
　At the edges and the side,
In a busy, timid rage.

Trying yet to find the key
　Into freedom, trying yet,
　In a timid rage, to get
To its old tranquillity.

It did not know, it did not see,
　It did not turn an eye, or care
　That a man was watching there
While it raged so timidly.

It ran without a sound, it tried,
　In a busy, timid rage,
　To escape from out the cage
By the edges and the side.

BLUE STARS AND GOLD

While walking through the trams and cars
I chanced to look up at the sky,
And saw that it was full of stars.

So starry-sown that you could not,
With any care, have stuck a pin
Through any single vacant spot.

And some were shining furiously,
And some were big and some were small,
But all were beautiful to see.

Blue stars and gold, a sky of grey,
The air between a velvet pall;
I could not take my eyes away.

And there I sang this little psalm
Most awkwardly, because I was
Standing between a car and tram.

THE FOUR OLD MEN

In the Café where I sit
  The four old men who look like bards
  Are playing at a game of cards;
And they are enjoying it.

They are so eager at their play,
  They shout together joyously,
They laugh with all their voices, they
  Are like the little boys you see
  Playing in your nursery.

But they'd be angry, they would rave
And swear and take it quite amiss,
If you walked across and gave
   Each a penny and a kiss.

THE ROAD

Because our lives are cowardly and sly,
   Because we do not dare to take or give,
Because we scowl and pass each other by,
   We do not live; we do not dare to live.

We dive, each man, into his secret house,
   And bolt the door, and listen in affright,
Each timid man beside a timid spouse,
   With timid children huddled out of sight.

Kissing in secret, fighting secretly!
   We crawl and hide like vermin in a hole,
Under the bravery of sun and sky
   We flash our meannesses of face and soul.

Let us go out and walk upon the road,
   And quit for evermore the brick-built den,
The lock and key, the hidden, shy abode
   That separates us from our fellow-men.

And by contagion of the sun we may
   Catch at a spark from that primeval fire,
And learn that we are better than our clay,
   And equal to the peaks of our desire.

from The Rocky Road to Dublin

The Adventures of Seumas Beg

IN THE ORCHARD

There was a giant by the Orchard Wall
  Peeping about on this side and on that,
And feeling in the trees: he was as tall
  As the big apple tree, and twice as fat:
His beard was long, and bristly-black, and there
Were leaves and bits of grass stuck in his hair.

He held a great big club in his right hand,
  And with the other felt in every tree
For something that he wanted. You could stand
  Beside him and not reach up to his knee
So mighty big he was—I feared he would
Turn round, and trample down to where I stood.

I tried to get away, but, as I slid
  Under a bush, he saw me, and he bent,
Far down and said, "Where is the Princess hid?"
  I pointed to a place, and off he went—
But while he searched I turned and simply flew
Round by the lilac bushes back to you.

A VISIT FROM ABROAD

A speck went blowing up against the sky
    As little as a leaf: then it drew near
And broadened.—"It's a bird," said I,
    And fetched my bow and arrows.
      It was queer!
It grew up from a speck into a blot,
    And squattered past a cloud; then it flew down
All crumply, and waggled such a lot
    I thought the thing would fall.—It was a brown
Old carpet where a man was sitting snug
    Who, when he reached the ground, began to sew
A big hole in the middle of the rug,
    And kept on peeping everywhere to know
Who might be coming—then he gave a twist
    And flew away. . . . I fired at him but missed.

MIDNIGHT

And then I wakened up in such a fright;
    I thought I heard a movement in the room
But did not dare to look; I snuggled right
    Down underneath the bedclothes—then the boom
Of a tremendous voice said, "*Sit up, lad,*
    And let me see your face." So up I sat,
Although I didn't want to. I was glad
    I did though, for it was an angel that
Had called me, and he said, he'd come to know
    Was I the boy who wouldn't say his prayers
Nor do his sums, and that I'd have to go
    Straight down to hell because of such affairs.
. . . I said I'd be converted and do good
If he would let me off—he said he would.

The Rocky Road to Dublin

THE FIFTEEN ACRES

I cling and swing
  On a branch, or sing
Through the cool, clear hush of morning, O:
  Or fling my wing
  On the air, and bring
To sleepier birds a warning, O;
    That the night's in flight,
    And the sun's in sight,
And the dew is the grass adorning, O:
    And the green leaves swing
    As I sing, sing, sing,
      Up by the river,
        Down the dell,
      To the little wee nest,
        Where the big tree fell,
      So early in the morning, O.

I flit and twit
  In the sun for a bit
When his light so bright is shining, O;
  Or sit and fit
  My plumes, or knit
Straw plaits for the nest's nice lining, O:
    And she with glee
    Shows unto me
Underneath her wings reclining, O:
    And I sing that Peg
    Has an egg, egg, egg,
      Up by the oat-field,

Round the mill,
Past the meadow,
Down the hill,
So early in the morning, O.

I stoop and swoop
On the air, or loop
Through the trees, and then go soaring, O:
To group with a troop
On the gusty poop
While the wind behind is roaring, O:
I skim and swim
By a cloud's red rim
And up to the azure flooring, O:
And my wide wings drip
As I slip, slip, slip
Down through the rain-drops,
Back where Peg
Broods in the nest
On the little white egg,
So early in the morning, O.

THE FUR COAT

I walked out in my Coat of Pride,
I looked about on every side,
And said the mountains should not be
Just where they were, and that the sea
Was badly placed, and that the beech
Should be an oak—and then from each
I turned in dignity as if
They were not there: I sniffed a sniff
And climbed upon my sunny shelf,
And sneezed a while, and scratched myself.

STEPHEN'S GREEN

The wind stood up and gave a shout;
  He whistled on his fingers, and
Kicked the withered leaves about
  And thumped the branches with his hand,
And said he'd kill, and kill, and kill,
And so he will, and so he will.

THE COLLEGE OF SURGEONS

As I stood at the door
  Sheltered out of the wind,
Something flew in
  Which I hardly could find.

In the dim, gloomy doorway
  I searched till I found
A dry, withered leaf
  Lying down on the ground.

With thin, pointed claws
  And a dry, dusty skin,—
Sure a hall is no place
  For a leaf to be in!

O where is your tree
  And your summer and all,
Poor dusty leaf
  Whistled into a hall?

THE DODDER BANK

When no flower is nigh, you might
Spy a week with deep delight;
So, when far from saints and bliss,
God might give a sin a kiss.

THE PAPS OF DANA

The mountains stand and stare around,
    They are far too proud to speak;
Altho' they're rooted in the ground
    Up they go, peak after peak,
Beyond the tallest tree, and still
    Soaring over house and hill
Until you'd think they'd never stop
    Going up, top over top,
Into the clouds—
                    Still I mark
    That a sparrow or a lark
Flying just as high can sing
    As if he'd not done anything.

I think the mountains ought to be
Taught a little modesty.

from Reincarnations

From the Note

. . . Some of the poems owe no more than a phrase, a line, half a line, to the Irish, and around these scraps I have blown a bubble of verse and made my poem. In other cases, where the matter of the poem is almost entirely taken from the Irish, I have yet followed my own instinct in the arrangement of it, and the result might be called new poems. . . .

In two of the poems which I tried to translate from Raftery I have completely failed. . . . This is Raftery's reply to the man who did not recognise him as he fiddled to a crowd, and asked "who is the musician?"

> I am Raftery the poet,
> Full of hope and love,
> My eyes without sight,
> My mind without torment,
>
> Going west on my journey
> By the light of my heart,
> Tired and weary
> To the end of the road.

Behold me now
With my back to a wall,
Playing music
To empty pockets.

. . . Dissimilar as these poets are from each other in time, education, and temperament, they are alike in that they were all poor men, so poor that there was often little difference between them and beggars. They all sing of their poverty: Keating as a fact to be recorded among other facts, O'Rahilly in a very stately and bitter complaint, and Raftery as in the quotation above; but O'Bruadair lets out of him an unending, rebellious bawl which would be the most desolating utterance ever made by man if it was not also the most gleeful.

GEOFFREY KEATING

O woman full of wiliness!
  Although for love of me you pine,
Withhold your hand adventurous,
  It holdeth nothing holding mine.

Look on my head, how it is grey!
  My body's weakness doth appear;
My blood is chill and thin; my day
  Is done, and there is nothing here.

Do not call me a foolish man,
  Nor lean your lovely cheek to mine:
O slender witch, our bodies can
  Not mingle now, nor any time.

So take your mouth from mine, your hand
  From mine, ah, take your lips away!

Lest heat to will should ripen, and
  All this be grave that had been gay.

It is this curl, a silken nest,
  And this grey eye bright as the dew,
And this round, lovely, snow-white breast
  That draws desire in search of you.

I would do all for you, meseems,
  But this, tho' this were happiness!
I shall not mingle in your dreams,
  O woman full of wiliness!

THE COOLUN

Come with me, under my coat,
  And we will drink our fill
Of the milk of the white goat,
  Or wine if it be thy will;
  And we will talk until
Talk is a trouble, too,
  Out on the side of the hill,
And nothing is left to do,
  But an eye to look into an eye
And a hand in a hand to slip,
  And a sigh to answer a sigh,
And a lip to find out a lip:
  What if the night be black
And the air on the mountain chill,
  Where the goat lies down in her track
And all but the fern is still!
  Stay with me, under my coat,
And we will drink our fill
  Of the milk of the white goat
Out on the side of the hill.

NANCY WALSH

I, without bite or sup,
  If thou wert fated for me,
I would up
  And would go after thee
Through mountains.

A thousand thanks for me
  To God have gone,
Because I have not lost my senses to thee,
Though it was hardly I escaped from thee,
  O ringleted one!

EGAN O'RAHILLY

Here in a distant place I hold my tongue;
I am O'Rahilly:
When I was young,
Who now am young no more,
I did not eat things picked up from the shore.

The periwinkle, and the tough dog-fish
At even-time have got into my dish!
The great, where are they now! the great had said—
This is not seemly, bring to him instead
That which serves his and serves our dignity—
And that was done.

I am O'Rahilly:
Here in a distant place I hold my tongue,
Who once said all his say, when he was young!

RIGHTEOUS ANGER

The lanky hank of a she in the inn over there
Nearly killed me for asking the loan of a glass of beer:
May the devil grip the whey-faced slut by the hair,
And beat bad manners out of her skin for a year.

That parboiled imp, with the hardest jaw you will see
On virtue's path, and a voice that would rasp the dead,
Came roaring and raging the minute she looked at me,
And threw me out of the house on the back of my head!

If I asked her master he'd give me a cask a day;
But she, with the beer at hand, not a gill would arrange!
May she marry a ghost and bear him a kitten, and may
The High King of Glory permit her to get the mange.

ODELL

My mind is sad and weary thinking how
    The griffins of the Gael went over the sea
From noble Eiré, and are fighting now
    In France and Flanders and in Germany.

If they, 'mid whom I sported without dread,
    Were home I would not mind what foe might do,
Or fear tax-man Odell would seize my bed
    To pay the hearth-rate that is overdue.

I pray to Him who, in the haughty hour
    Of Babel, threw confusion on each tongue,
That I may see our princes back in power,
    And see Odell, the tax-collector, hung.

THE GERALDINE'S CLOAK

I will not heed the message which you bring:
    That lovely lady gave her cloak to us,
And who'd believe she'd give away a thing
    And ask it back again?—'tis fabulous!

My parting from her gave me cause to grieve,
    For she, that I was poor, had misty eyes;
If some Archangel blew it I'd believe
    The message which you bring, not otherwise.

I do not say this just to make a joke,
    Nor would I rob her, but, 'tis verity,
So long as I could swagger in a cloak
    I never cared how bad my luck could be.

That lady, all perfection, knows the sting
    Of poverty was thrust deep into me:
I don't believe she'd do this kind of thing,
    Or treat a poet less than daintily.

SKIM-MILK

A small part only of my grief I write;
    And if I do not give you all the tale
It is because my gloom gets some respite
    By just a small bewailing: I bewail
That I with sly and stupid folk must bide
Who steal my food and ruin my inside.

Once I had books, each book beyond compare,
    But now no book at all is left to me,

And I am spied and peeped on everywhere,
    And my old head, stuffed with latinity,
And with the poet's load of grave and gay
Will not get me skim-milk for half a day.

Wild horse or quiet, not a horse have I,
    But to the forest every day I go
Bending beneath a load of wood, that high!
    Which raises on my back a sorry row
Of raw, red blisters; so I cry, alack,
The rider that rides me will break my back.

Ossian, when he was old and near his end,
    Met Patrick by good luck, and he was stayed;
I am a poet too and seek a friend,
    A prop, a staff, a comforter, an aid,
A Patrick who will lift me from despair,
In Cormac Uasal Mac Donagh of the golden hair.

BLUE BLOOD

We thought at first, this man is a king for sure,
Or the branch of a mighty and ancient and famous lineage—
That silly, sulky, illiterate, black-avised boor
Who was hatched by foreign vulgarity under a hedge.

The good men of Clare were drinking his health in a flood,
And gazing with me in awe at the princely lad,
And asking each other from what bluest blueness of blood
His daddy was squeezed, and the pa of the da of his dad?

We waited there, gaping and wondering, anxiously,
Until he'd stop eating and let the glad tidings out,
And the slack-jawed booby proved to the hilt that he
Was lout, son of a lout, by old lout, and was da to a lout!

O'BRUADAIR

I will sing no more songs: the pride of my country I sang
  Through forty long years of good rhyme, without any avail;
And no one cared even as much as the half of a hang
  For the song or the singer, so here is an end to the tale.

If a person should think I complain and have not got the cause,
  Let him bring his eyes here and take a good look at my hand,
Let him say if a goose-quill has calloused this poor pair of paws
  Or the spade that I grip on and dig with out there in the land?

When the great ones were safe and renowned and were rooted
    and tough,
  Though my mind went to them and took joy in the fortune of
    those,
And pride in their pride and their fame, they gave little enough,
  Not as much as two boots for my feet, or an old suit of clothes.

I ask of the Craftsman that fashioned the fly and the bird,
  Of the Champion whose passion will lift me from death in a
    time,
Of the Spirit that melts icy hearts with the wind of a word,
  That my people be worthy, and get, better singing than mine.

I had hope to live decent, when Ireland was quit of her care,
  As a bailiff or steward perhaps in a house of degree,
But my end of the tale is, old brogues and old britches to wear,
  So I'll sing no more songs for the men that care nothing for me.

from A Poetry Recital

ON A LONELY SPRAY

Under a lonely sky a lonely tree
Is beautiful. All that is loneliness
Is beautiful. A feather lost at sea;
A staring owl; a moth; a yellow tress
Of seaweed on a rock, is beautiful.

The night-lit moon, wide-wandering in sky;
A blue-bright spark, where ne'er a cloud is up;
A wing, where no wing is, it is so high;
A bee in winter, or a buttercup,
Late-blown, are lonely, and are beautiful.

She, whom you saw but once, and saw no more;
That he, who startled you, and went away;
The eye that watched you from a cottage door;
The first leaf, and the last; the break of day;
The mouse, the cuckoo, and the cloud, are beautiful.

For all that is, is lonely; all that may
Will be as lonely as is that you see;
The lonely heart sings on a lonely spray,

The lonely soul swings lonely in the sea,
And all that loneliness is beautiful.

All, all alone, and all without a part
Is beautiful, for beauty is all where;
Where is an eye is beauty, where an heart
Is beauty, brooding out, on empty air,
All that is lonely and is beautiful.

THE PIT OF BLISS

When I was young I dared to sing
Of everything and anything;
Of joy and woe and fate and God,
Of dreaming cloud and teeming sod,
Of hill that thrust an amber spear
Into the sunset, and the sheer
Precipice that shakes the soul
To its black gape—I sang the whole
Of God and man, nor sought to know
Man or God, or joy or woe:
And, though an older wight I be,
My Soul hath still such ecstasy
That, on a pulse, I sing and sing
Of everything and anything.

There is a light shines in the head;
It is not gold, it is not red;
But, as the lightning's blinding light,
It is a stare of silver white
That one surmise might fancy blue:
On that mind-blinding hue I gaze
An instant, and am in a maze
Of thinking—could one call it so?
It is no feeling that I know

—An hurricane of knowing, that
Could whelm the soul that was not pat
To flinch and lose the deadly thing,
And sing, and sing again, and sing
Of everything and anything.

An eagle, whirling up the sky,
Sunblind, dizzy, urging high,
And higher beating yet a wing,
Until he can no longer cling,
Or hold, or do a thing, but fall
And sink, and whirl, and cream through all
His dizzy, heaven-hell of pit,
In mile-a-minute flight from it
That he had dared—From height of height
So the poet takes his flight
And tumble in the pit of bliss,
And, in the roar of that abyss,
And falling, he will sing and sing
Of everything and anything.

What is knowing, 'tis to see:
What is feeling, 'tis to be:
What is love, but more and more
To see and be, to be a pour
And avalanche of being, till
The being ceases and is still
For very motion. What is joy
—Being, past all earthly cloy.
And intermixture: being spun
Of itself is being won:
—That is joy. And this is God
To be that in cloud and clod,
And in cloud and clod to sing
Of everything and anything.

from Collected Poems

LITTLE THINGS

Little things, that run, and quail,
And die, in silence and despair!

Little things, that fight, and fail,
And fall, on sea, and earth, and air!

All trapped and frightened little things,
The mouse, the coney, hear our prayer!

As we forgive those done to us,
—The lamb, the linnet, and the hare—

Forgive us all our trespasses,
Little creatures, everywhere!

from Strict Joy

SARASVATI

As bird to nest, when, moodily,
The storm-cloud murmurs nigh the tree,
Thus let him flee,
Who can to sing,
Here hath he calm, and sheltering.

As bee to hive, when, with the sun,
Long honey-gathering is done,
Who can to sing,
There let him flee,
This is his cell, his companie.

As child to mother running, where
The thunder shudders through the air,
Thus let him flee,
Who can to sing,
Here hath he ward, and cherishing.

Fly to thy talent! To thy charm!
Thy nest, thine hive, thy sheltering arm!
Who can to sing,
There let him flee,
This is, naught else is, certainty.

458

CADENCE

See the lightning
Leaping in the sky
How fleet he goes:

See the rose
Leaping to the eye
How neat she blows:

See the mother
Running to her child
How sweet she goes!

STRICT CARE, STRICT JOY
To W. T. H. Howe

1

To-day I felt as poor O'Brien did
When, turning from all else that was not his,
He took himself to that which was his own
—He took him to his verse—for other all
He had not, and (tho' man will crave and seek)
Another all than this he did not need.

So, pen in hand, he tried to tell the whole
Tale of his woe in rhyming; lodge the full
Weight of his grief in versing: and so did:
Then—when his poem had been conned and cared,
And all put in that should not be left out—
Did he not find, and with astonishment,

That grief had been translated, or was come
Other and better than it first looked to be:
And that this happed, because all things transfer
From what they seem to that they truly are
When they are innocently brooded on
—And, so, the poet makes grief beautiful.

2

"Behold me now, with my back to the wall,
Playing music to empty pockets!"
So, Raftery, tuning a blind man's plight,
Could sing the cark of misery away:
And know, in blindness and in poverty,·
That woe was not of him, nor kin to him.

And Egan Rahilly begins a verse—
"My heart is broken, and my mind is sad . . ."
'Twas surely true when he began his song,
And was less true when he had finished it:
—Be sure, his heart was buoyant, and his grief
Drummed and trumpeted as grief was sung!

For, as he meditated misery
And cared it into song—strict care, strict joy!
Caring for grief he cared his grief away:
And those sad songs, tho' woe be all the theme,
Do not make us to grieve who read them now
—Because the poet makes grief beautiful.

3

And I, myself, conning a lonely heart
—Full lonely 'twas, and 'tis as lonely now—
Turned me, by proper, to my natural,

And, now too long her vagrant, wooed my Muse!
Then to her—Let us look more close to these,
And, seeing, know; and, knowing, be at ease.

Seeing the sky o'ercast, and that the rain
Had plashed the window, and would plash again:
Seeing the summer lost, and winter nigh:
Seeing inapt, and sad, and fallen from good:
Seeing how will was weak, and wish o'erbearing:
Seeing inconstant, seeing timidity:

Seeing too small, too poor in this and yon:
Seeing life, daily, grow more difficult:
Seeing all that moves away—moving away
 . . . And that all seeing is a blind-man's treat,
And that all getting is a beggar's dole,
And that all having is a bankruptcy . . .

4

All these, sad all! I told to my good friend,
Told Raftery, O'Brien, Rahilly,
Told rain, and frosted blossom, and the summer gone,
Told poets dead, and captains dead, and kings!
—And we cared naught that these were mournful things,
For, caring them, we made them beautiful.

from Kings and the Moon

FOR THE LION OF JUDAH

Tell what now is happening
On the sole Arabian Tree:
There is no song in anything,
No tale of glee,

Since Phoenix and the Dove did part
Love loves no more, no more is kind:
—What is happening in the heart,
What has happened to the mind?

Mind that late did never cease
To hark, to hasten, and to aid,
Bringing comfort, bringing peace
To everything that was afraid!

And the heart, that could espy
All that mind can fail to see,
Saying—where naught is am I,
Be not lone, I stay with thee!

*

Here the anthem doth commence,
Here the Swan shall sing the threne,
Pity, Love and Innocence
He remembers to have seen.

—Mind does mind no more, nor care:
Minding is no more its will:
To murder is its main affair,
Treachery its main of skill!

And the heart, that said to love
—Thou and I—says that no more,
Phoenix and the Turtle-Dove
Show each other to the door.

Only now the third, the wise,
On the sole Arabian Tree,
Who singeth only as he dies,
Sings the final ecstasy.

OR WHERE GUILE FIND

There is a nothing, is a vacancy:
There is a no, not, non, null, never, naught!

'Tis not that this is not—this is: and this
Thou art: and this the earth is: and the sun
Is this: and God, all these, is this—and can!

Who I? What may I? Or by what of guile?
Or where guile find? Or how that what apply?
Or in what problem? Or to what an end?

Not by, not round, not under, not above!
Not by a means! Nay, even, not by grace!

For, see! This all-not is! This cannot can!
Is, is its secret! Is, is its name!
Can, is its nature! Can, is what it can!
And this thou art! And can do! And dost do!

Index to First Lines and Titles of Poems